CW01090616

Victorian Telescope Makers

Thomas Grubb (1800–1878)

VICTORIAN TELESCOPE MAKERS

The Lives and Letters of Thomas and Howard Grubb

by

I S Glass

South African Astronomical Observatory

With a foreword by Patrick Moore

Institute of Physics Publishing
Bristol and Philadelphia

British Library Cataloguing-in-Publication Data

A catalogue record for this book is available from the British Library.

ISBN 0 7503 0454 5

Library of Congress Cataloging-in-Publication Data are available

Published by Institute of Physics Publishing, wholly owned by The Institute of Physics, London

Institute of Physics Publishing, Dirac House, Temple Back, Bristol BS1 6BE, UK

US Editorial Office: Institute of Physics Publishing, The Public Ledger Building, Suite 1035, Independence Square, Philadelphia, PA 19106, USA

Typeset in TEX using the IOP Bookmaker macros
Printed in the UK by J W Arrowsmith, Bristol

Contents

Preface

The idea for this book originated when I discovered some quite literally mouldy volumes of correspondence between Sir David Gill and Howard Grubb in the archives of the Royal Observatory (now South African Astronomical Observatory) in Cape Town. Having grown up in Dublin, quite close to where the Grubbs lived and had their factories, I was surprised how little was generally known about them. Later I found that a number of other astronomical libraries also possessed quite extensive collections of Grubb letters. As it turned out, the Cape Town records are especially interesting because Gill and Grubb were lifelong friends and their correspondence was not confined to business matters, but contained a great deal of material on telescope design as well as giving an occasional glimpse into family affairs.

Rather than writing a straightforward biography of the Grubbs, I have tried to let them speak for themselves through their letters. This primary material has been augmented by information derived from secondary, published, sources in order to make it coherent. The introduction is intended to give the reader a brief orientation about the Grubbs, their times and their achievements before he or she plunges into the details contained within the body of the work.

The chapters are on the whole chronologically arranged except for some that are devoted to particular projects which stretched over long periods of time. There is thus some overlap. Part of the material about early photography at the Cape and the construction of the Astrographic telescopes has been published before (Glass 1989, 1991).

During the gestation of this project Professor Patrick Wayman, formerly of Dunsink Observatory, and I found that we were each interested in the Grubbs. Although we made sporadic attempts to prepare a joint book, the physical distance between us and the differences in our approach made this too difficult in the end. Each of us has seen a good deal of the others' material and will inevitably owe some of his ideas to the other.

Ian S Glass

Acknowledgments

The following are thanked for their help, great and small, in the preparation of this volume:

Alan C Aimone, Special Collections Div., US Military Academy, West Point
Barbara J Becker, Irvine, CA
John W Briggs, Chicago
G Bromage, University of Central Lancashire
C John Butler, Armagh Observatory
David Clarke, University of Glasgow
Brenda Corbin, US Naval Observatory
The late Jon Darius, Science Museum, London
A Daroff, Philadelphia
Mart de Groot, Armagh Observatory
David H DeVorkin, Natl Air and Space Museum, Washington DC
D W Dewhirst, The Observatories, Cambridge
Ian Elliott, Dunsink Observatory
M G Firneis, Vienna University
S C B Gascoigne, Canberra, Australia
David N Glass, Dublin
The late R Brian Grubb, Calne, Wiltshire
R C Hambleton, Springfield, VA
J Hart, Mt Stromlo Observatory
J Hearnshaw, University of Canterbury, New Zealand
The late Francis J Heyden, SJ, Manila Observatory
P D Hingley, Royal Astronomical Society
Timothy Hobbs, Trinity College Library, Cambridge
Derek Howse, Sevenoaks, Kent
F Kerschbaum, University of Vienna
G Klare, Landessternwarte Heidelberg-Königstuhl
J Drummond Laing, South African Astronomical Observatory
Ethleen Lastovica, South African Astronomical Observatory
Shona McEachern, Royal Observatory, Edinburgh
R Charles Mollan, formerly of Royal Dublin Society

K Moore, Royal Society, London
Alison Morrison-Low, Natl Museums of Scotland
E B Nagelgast, Africana Museum, Johannesburg
W Orchiston, Carter Observatory, Wellington
D E Osterbrock, Lick Observatory
A J Perkins, Cambridge University Library
R A J Potts, Tyne & Wear Archives
Dorothy Schaumberg, Mary Lea Shane Archives, University of California, Santa Cruz
A V Simcock, Museum of the History of Science, Oxford
Mary Shackleton, Religious Society of Friends, Dublin
George Sisson, Hexham, Northumberland
A Vagiswari, Indian Institute of Astrophysics, Bangalore
Janie van Zyl, CSIR Archives, Pretoria
Deborah Warner, Natl Museum of American History, Washington DC
Patrick A Wayman, Wicklow, Co. Wicklow
Maurice J Wigham, Carrigeen, Waterford
Cambridge University Observatory Archives
Johannesburg Public Library
Natal Society, Pietermaritzburg
National Library of Ireland, Dublin
Patent Office, London
The Director of the Royal Greenwich Observatory
Royal Society, London
SA Naval Museum, Simonstown
The Syndics of Cambridge University Library
Trinity College Dublin Library (MS Dept)
University of Cape Town Library

Foreword

Among telescope makers of the 18th and 19th centuries, Thomas and Howard Grubb rank very high. The firm founded by Thomas Grubb and continued by his son was responsible for some of the world's finest telescopes, including some which are still in full operation.

The history of the firm is a fascinating one, and to the best of my knowledge has never before been documented in full detail. It may be said that the Grubbs have been somewhat neglected by scientific historians, so this new work by Ian Glass will fill a notable gap in the literature. It is excellent in all respects; the author has made extensive use of the surviving correspondence and letters, so that for much of the time the Grubbs are telling their own story. There are some misadventures: the first major telescope, the Great Melbourne Reflector, was a failure, but through no fault of Grubb's (he was given quite the wrong brief by the Royal Society Committee, who preferred a metal mirror to a silver-on-glass), and there was some later acid correspondence between Howard Grubb and David Gill at the Cape Observatory. But most of the Grubb telescopes were the equal of any, and I can speak with some experience here, because during my spell as a lunar cartographer in the pre-Apollo period I used several—including the Innes refractor at Johannesburg, which is superb both optically and mechanically.

It is sad that the original Grubb firm came to an end in 1924, when money ran out and it was put into liquidation; the government of the day made no attempt to rescue what was a major national asset. (Governmental attitudes never seem to change.) It is also sad that the successor, the firm of Grubb–Parsons, has now ceased to make astronomical equipment, leaving us without a major optical works. But at least we can look back with pride at what the Grubbs achieved, and this book should remain the standard both for casual readers and for serious students of scientific history.

Patrick Moore

Introduction

A Nineteenth-Century Technological Enterprise

The telescope-making firm of Thomas and Howard Grubb, father and son, was unique as a technologically advanced enterprise in nineteenth-century Ireland. The manufacture of telescopes is highly specialized and requires optical accuracies at the sub-micron level over large areas as well as mechanical accuracies in the drive components with a precision of a few microns. Techniques for achieving such extreme precision were developed by the Grubbs and involved the construction of many unusual machines. Their staff included vocationally trained personnel such as engineers and engineering draughtsmen, instrument makers, pattern makers, glass grinders and opticians. The Grubb 'Optical and Mechanical Works' in Rathmines, constructed in the 1870s, included specialised offices and workshops for these functions as well as an assembly area for completed instruments, often of a considerable size.

Thomas Grubb, the founder, was a highly original and inventive person, whose awkwardly written and frequently polemical prose suggests that he was largely self-educated. Nevertheless, he had a sophisticated analytical approach to problem solving, exemplified by his pioneering use of ray-tracing to design lenses and his use of Babbage's 'mechanical notation' to describe the complicated machinery that he invented for banknote printing. In contrast, his son Howard seems to have been a less profound thinker, with a practical rather than a theoretical outlook, and a tendency to solve problems by experimentation rather than by theoretical analysis.

The time of Thomas Grubb's entry into manufacturing, around 1830, was one of great change in Ireland and the United Kingdom as a whole. Politically, it saw the reform of Parliament, which was starting to acquire its present democratic basis. With the advent of canals, the early railways and organized long-distance carriage services, people of all classes, not merely the rich, began to be able to travel with relative ease. Newspapers became cheap and ideas flowed much more freely than before. Technology was on the rise, and machinery was becoming universal in manufacturing industry. The British machine tool industry was experiencing its most inventive period and its products were spreading far and wide.

The eastern regions of Ireland benefited from rapid economic advancement because of the free trade encouraged by the creation of the United Kingdom of Great Britain and Ireland in 1801. The Grubb family through their Quaker background were relatively well-educated and enjoyed a modest prosperity based on their farming and trading activities, mainly in the provincial towns of the southeast which formed part of the 'first world' at that period.

Although we know nothing of his upbringing, Thomas Grubb may have had experience of working in one of the pioneering British machine tool factories such as that of Boulton and Watt. This seems possible in view of his first business enterprise as a cast-iron billiard table manufacturer, with a factory near Charlemont Bridge. Later, he developed an engraving machine, as well as printing equipment and glass-working machinery, all of which suggest he possessed the kind of skills a background in the machine-tool industry might have provided. During his youth, engineering was not yet taught at universities, so that technological education was necessarily of a practical nature.

Telescope construction contracts were few and far between in the mid-19th century and it is thus not surprising that they represented only one part of Thomas Grubb's activity. His interest in this field almost certainly started as a hobby, but his obvious intelligence and skill soon attracted the attention of serious amateurs and the small professional astronomical community. Paramount amongst his promoters was Romney Robinson, a Dubliner who spent most of his life as director of Armagh Observatory. Robinson was well-educated and widely known in scientific and social circles. He seems to have boosted both Thomas Grubb and his son, Howard, whenever contracts for the construction of instruments were in the offing.

Probably through Robinson, Grubb made contact also with Lord Oxmantown (later Lord Rosse) who was at that time constructing larger and larger reflecting telescopes supported on relatively crude mounts. They clearly exchanged many ideas. Oxmantown adopted Grubb's method for mounting large mirrors on equilibrated levers and later Grubb made use of the other's technology for casting large speculum-metal blanks. Grubb also shared an interest in photography with the Countess of Rosse and it is likely that they had some contact in this area, since its early practioners were few and enthusiastic.

Although one of Thomas Grubb's earliest telescopes, that at Markree, had the largest aperture in the world at the time, it was not very actively used, perhaps because of the poor weather in the west of Ireland where it was installed. Consequently, he did not immediately receive the acclaim which his innovations deserved. More important for him, perhaps, was the construction, a few years later, of an equatorial mount for the Sheepshanks telescope. This was commissioned by the Astronomer Royal, G.B. Airy, for the Royal Greenwich Observatory. Airy was a demanding customer as well as a highly influential one, and his evident approval of the instrument must have been a powerful advertisement. Unfortunately, the market for large telescopes was a tiny one at mid-century, since observatories were usually more interested in measuring and cataloguing the positions of bright stars using small instruments, such as meridian circles, on precision mounts. The study of fainter and more distant objects was almost the monopoly of John Herschel, who made use of reflecting telescopes constructed by his father, Sir William Herschel, mounted on crude altazimuth stands.

Thomas Grubb's main income for a good part of his working life probably came from his appointment as 'Engineer to the Bank of Ireland'. His interest in photography led to the development of a relatively cheap camera lens which he patented. This lens, made by him in large numbers, may also have brought in a good income.

Howard Grubb, on the other hand, had a conventional high school education and entered university with the intent of becoming a graduate engineer. However, before he graduated, his father secured the contract for the Great Melbourne Telescope and the telescope business was established as a separate entity with the purchase of new premises in Rathmines. The founding of this enterprise was well-timed and coincided with a rise of interest in astrophysics and a great increase in the numbers of observatories being built in the United Kingdom and its colonies, as well as in many other countries. The former student Howard took over the Melbourne project and soon became manager of the whole company.

After the retirement of his father around 1870, Howard developed the business with rapidity. Early on, he obtained the contract for the world's largest refractor, to be erected in Vienna, and the publicity surrounding this work made his name. For about twenty years he was highly innovative, turning out telescope objective lenses of excellent quality, as well as equatorial mountings and clock drives having the necessary precision for the new science of astronomical photography.

Howard Grubb's innovations were largely driven by the requirements of his more demanding customers, particularly David Gill who worked for Lord Lindsay's private observatory at Dun Echt in Scotland and later became famous as Her Majesty's Astronomer at the Cape of Good Hope. Gill pointed the way to many improvements in Grubb's designs, particularly in the field of refining telescope controls to permit photography with long exposures. Advice on difficult optical questions was provided by a leading physicist, G.G. Stokes of Cambridge University, who was a son-in-law of Romney Robinson.

By about 1890, real innovation in the telescope-construction industry, represented by ever-increasing lens diameters, had passed to the United States. Grubb tried hard to enter this market by bidding for the huge Lick Observatory contract but, by this time, American industry had almost caught up with that in the United Kingdom and the work was to be done within the United States. Grubb tirelessly continued to propagandize for the construction of larger telescopes within the British Empire but none of his large schemes ever came to fruition.

Around 1900, Grubb turned his attention to military optics as the large number of patents he took out thereafter shows. His main activity seems to have been the construction of periscopes for submarines, then undergoing rapid development. Although contracts were placed for several moderately large telescopes just before the Great War of 1914–1918, these were not completed until long after it ended. Sadly, Howard Grubb's largest telescope, the one-metre reflector at Simeis in the Crimea, was destroyed during the Second World War.

Towards the end of the Great War, the Grubb factory was moved to St Albans in England for security reasons, and the company ceased to be a purely Irish one. Following the end of the War, Howard Grubb never succeeded in adapting to the new conditions and the concern slid into bankrupcy. It came to an end in 1925 and was purchased by Sir Charles Parsons, youngest son of Lord Rosse, who re-incorporated it as Grubb Parsons. This firm carried on until 1985.

The work of both Grubbs came to be widely acknowledged. Both men were made fellows of the Royal Society (FRS), London, and Howard was knighted in 1886. They were very much part of the scientific establishment in Dublin and took active parts in the Royal Irish Academy and the Royal Dublin Society. Howard Grubb gave public lectures at the Royal Institution in London about his work and his optical techniques. Many of his biggest projects were described at length in the engineering journals and excited considerable contemporary interest.

The Grubb Contribution to Telescope Technology

Prior to Thomas Grubb's work, the peak of telescope technology was the Great Dorpat Refractor of 1824 from Fraunhofer's works in Munich. This famous instrument was mounted on a reinforced wooden stand and was equipped with a driving clock and fine motions. Nevertheless, it must have been very flimsy and subject to severe vibrational instability.

Grubb's earliest telescopes, the Armagh reflector, the Markree refractor and the Sheepshanks refractor for Greenwich, showed a marked improvement in stability compared to anything that had gone before. The support was made of masonry to which was bolted a heavy iron baseplate carrying a massive polar axis which rotated in strong bearings. The drive clock was a substantial unit placed inside the masonry pier. The final gear was a worm which drove a long and massive sector attached to the telescope by a cumbersome clutch system. The speed of the clock was regulated by a governor which increased the frictional drag if it went too quickly and decreased it if it went too slowly. The sector had to be rewound at frequent intervals.

The movement of heavy parts in a smooth manner was by no means an easy matter before the invention of ball bearings. Many clever devices were used by the Grubbs to relieve the friction between moving parts without losing the positional stability of the telescope axes.

For the Armagh telescope, the 'equilibrated lever' system of mirror mounting, a Grubb invention, was employed for the first time. This enabled a large mirror to keep its shape independently of position with respect to the vertical. The same scheme was adopted by Lord Oxmantown (later Rosse) for his mirrors, the largest made at that time.

The next Grubb telescope mounting, that for West Point, relied more heavily on cast iron for supporting the polar axis and resembled many later instruments produced by the company. It still, however, retained the cumbersome clutch system for disconnecting the slow motion drives. The screw arrangements for slow motion control were very coarse and suffered greatly from backlash.

Although Thomas Grubb's mountings were progressively refined, they were awkward to use by later standards. His last design, the Great Melbourne Telescope, was the first really large and heavy instrument to have an equatorial mount. Whereas the main mirror of the telescope was not really an advance on Lord Rosse's work, the rest of the mounting was highly innovative. This telescope required frequent and sophisticated maintenance to keep it in prime condition but the required infrastructure was lacking in Melbourne. It came to be regarded as a failure and set back the development of large reflectors for several decades.

Howard's improvements also related mainly to controls. He early on refined the action of the slow motions used for centering stars in the field of view and devised new clamps that did not disturb the position of the telescope as they were applied.

David Gill and Lord Lindsay sought to control the drive *rate* of the Dun Echt telescope relative to an observatory master clock by linking the control of the governor to a pendulum clock. Their system, while an improvement on a free-running clock, was not reliable because of its dependence on frictional components which wore out and altered their characteristics with ambient conditions. With the rise of celestial photography, Grubb was pressured by his clients to provide drives capable of tracking a star for tens of minutes. He turned his talents to the improvement of the Gill-Lindsay scheme and succeeded in developing a system where the telescope *position* was adjusted by reference to a pendulum clock. He arrived at the conditions necessary for stable operation of the system by trial and error. This innovation may be the first example of what is termed today a 'phase-locked loop'.

The generation of telescopes built by Grubb for celestial photography, mainly those built for the *Carte du Ciel* international programme, incorporated many refinements as to stability and precision, as well as plate holders of a design by Gill which allowed precise adjustments of focus and rotation. After this point, few design changes were made until about 1910, when Grubb employed another engineer, Cyril Young.

Grubb's interest in the 36-inch Lick contract drove him to consider new methods for controlling massive telescopes and, in particular, he designed a rising floor and electrical controls which would make such a large instrument more user-friendly. To his chagrin, the contracts did not come his way, although he was given some compensation for his efforts, as certain of his ideas were incorporated in the final design.

Several large refractors, of around 25 inches diameter, were however made in the 1890s and 1900s. Their designs were scaled-up from earlier ones. The sector method of driving the telescopes was regarded as awkward by many clients, who did not like having to stop operations for rewinding every few hours. The sectors were also subject to uneven wear in use. Gill and others advocated complete worm wheels to overcome these problems, but Grubb claimed that his method gave better stability and accuracy within a compact design. The first mounting to incorporate a full wormwheel was that delivered to Heidelberg around 1900 for their Bruce lenses.

Grubb's simple methods of optical design came unstuck when he was working on the lenses for the *Carte du Ciel* telescopes. It took him much time and wasted effort to realise that he would be unable to beat the work of the French opticians, the Henry brothers, and that indeed he would be lucky to be able to do as well as them. In fact, he had reached the limit of simple two-component lens design so far as simultaneous size of field, uniformity of focus and colour correction were concerned. Large-angle telescopes took another direction with the invention of the 'Cooke Triplet' by H.D. Taylor in the early 1890s. In fact, Taylor's interest was probably stimulated by his employment as a consultant on this very problem by Grubb.

The latter part of Howard Grubb's working life was largely devoted to submarine periscope manufacture. He developed close connections with Vickers, Sons and Maxim, the builders of most of the submarines for the Royal Navy. Telescope design work seems to have been carried out by Cyril Young. After a period of coolness around 1900, due to arguments over a contract, Gill continued to place work with Grubb. After retirement, Gill acted as an agent for overseas observatories in supervising work at British firms. In this capacity he continued to press for improvements in telescope design. The later, Young-designed, telescopes formed the pattern on which Grubb Parsons (the successor company) instruments were built, and his continued employment in the new company ensured continuity of design.

The Grubb Company

Telescope building was only a small part of Thomas Grubb's activities. The only large contract that he had was for the provision of the Great Melbourne Telescope at a cost of £4600. By this time, in fact, most of the work was being done by Howard. In 1869, the firm was called 'Messrs Grubb and Son (Formerly Thomas Grubb)', and by 1873 it was 'Howard Grubb (late Grubb and Son)'. It remained under this name, prefixed by 'Sir' from 1887, until the end of the First World War, when it became 'Sir Howard Grubb and Sons'.

Table 1: Messrs Howard Grubbs' turnover

Quinquennium	turnover ($£$)
1870–1874	8320
1875–1879	17350
1880–1884	6430
1885–1889	12930
1890–1894	22625
1895–1899	8230
1900–1904	17200
1905–1909	1450
1910–1914	930
1915–1919	0
1920–1925	17490

Note: Based on total prices of telescopes and domes completed during each quinquennium. The 1920–1925 period reflects orders placed before the World War, but the prices given are pre-war. Difficulties with inflation made these prices impossible to maintain and essentially led to the demise of the firm.

The estimated turnover of the firm is shown in table 1. This information was obtained by combining the list of Grubb telescopes and domes given in Appendix C with price information from the 1888 and 1903 catalogues. Prices appear to have been fairly stable from 1870 until the end of the Great War in 1918. The apparent turnover fluctuated wildly from year to year, but was smoothed out in reality by Grubb's usual requirement that one third of the price of a large contract had to be paid with the order, one third after substantial progress had been made and one third on completion.

The figures given in the table do not include small telescopes (5 inches or below), accessories, such as micrometers, chronographs etc, alteration or repair work. However, these items are likely to have been worth 10% or less of the total.

Telescope business dropped off after 1905 and was replaced by periscope work for the Royal Navy and possibly other military contracts. The turnover from these sources is unknown, but probably more than compensated for the loss of other business. The total turnover during the working life Howard Grubb (55 years) thus probably approached £150,000.

The number of employees during busy periods around 1888 was 35 to 40. The weekly wages bill in May, 1882, was £70. Such expenditure clearly cannot have been usual. Some especially useful employees were probably kept on permanently and one, at least, was even welcomed back after working elsewhere. The wages of individual employees were rarely mentioned. Some reletively skilled workmen, sent out to help with erecting telescopes, were charged for at about 8–12 shillings per day (around £0.5). Grubb's profits cannot have been very great, but were nevertheless sufficient for him to have considered buying out the French glassmaker Feil in 1884 for £4000. Only during the early 20th century does he seem to have lived in a really large house, signifying actual affluence.

Grubb's business of making large telescopes depended on a very small number of customers and much of his marketing effort involved buttering up these individuals. He made frequent visits to the London, where he was a fellow of both the Royal Society and the Royal Astronomical Society. Personal referral from satisfied customers was clearly the main source of new business, although he showed his instruments from time to time at international exhibitions. He set out his standard prices in his catalogues, at least six editions of which were printed. Very frequently he offered the inducement of a small price reduction, usually accompanied with an expression of his admiration for the work of the astronomer concerned.

Grubb was quick enough to adopt aids to running his business. The map of his works of 1877 shows 'telegraph' lines running between buildings, presumably a form of ennunciator or intercom. He first mentions a telephone number in 1883. By 1892 official letters were typed. Drawings were traced by hand until around 1895, after which they were blueprinted.

Customers who received telescopes seem to have been expected to arrange for their assembly on site themselves, except in a few cases where Grubb supervised their erection in person. Presumably he hired millwrights locally or relied on whatever technical help was available in the client's workshop.

Chapter 1

Thomas Grubb

1.1 Origin of the Grubb Family

The telescope-making Grubbs were members of a large family which can be traced back with certainty to John Grubbe (1620–1696), a Cromwellian settler in the southeast of Ireland (Grubb 1972). Although it is believed that he came from Ravensthorpe in Northamptonshire, England, his history before being granted land in Ireland is uncertain. Whatever his origins, John Grubb, his wife, Mary, and five children arrived in Waterford in 1656 and eventually took possession of Annaghs Castle and 1000 acres of land on the banks of the river Barrow in County Kilkenny, some four miles from the town of New Ross. The original owners of the property were probably amongst those banished to the west of the river Shannon. In 1676 the Grubb family was converted to Quakerism by a wandering preacher named John Exham and were thus amongst the earliest Irish members of the Society of Friends. To be a Quaker involved considerable sacrifice as in those days, in addition to the discrimination in official appointments and education applied to all those who were not members of the Church of Ireland (the established protestant episcopalian church), the Quakers were not prepared to take oaths—a great hindrance to them in business and legal matters.

John Grubb Jr (1682–1731) was the youngest of four sons of the John Grubb mentioned above and was the only child of his second marriage in 1681 to one Elizabeth (maiden surname unknown). He married Anne Willan of Co Wexford in 1707, living at first at Meyler's Park, also near New Ross. They moved to Co Tipperary about 1719. John was spectacularly unsuccessful in his business affairs and was at one stage jailed for default in the American colony of New Jersey. On his return to Ireland he had to obtain financial help from his fellow Quakers of the province of Munster in order to survive. Nevertheless, after his death, his wife Anne saw to it that their children were well taken care of. Around the time of John Grubb Jr's death they were living at Rathronan in Co. Tipperary. The four sons of the family all became prosperous in and around Clonmel: Joseph, the oldest, was a miller in Clonmel, John, the next oldest, was a draper and Benjamin, the youngest, was a grocer.

William Grubb (1719–1774) was the third son of this family and he became a farmer. He married Margaret Boles, daughter of John Boles, a former landlord of his father's, of Woodhouse, Fethard, Co Tipperary. They had six sons and eight daughters of whom seven died young.

Their third son, also a William Grubb (?–1831) and a farmer, married twice. His first wife, Elizabeth Taylor, died in 1787. Thomas, the first of the telescope makers, was born by his second wife Eleanor Fayle of Dublin, whom he married in 1791. There were three children from each of these marriages. An older full brother of Thomas, Joshua, was killed while young in an accident. Their full sister, Charlotte, never married and lived until 1862.

1.2   Early Career of Thomas Grubb

Thomas Grubb, according to Quaker records, was born in Waterford on 4th August, 1800. Although his birth was registered with the Society of Friends, his marriage and the birth of his son Howard were not, so it is probable that he did not remain an active member. His early years were quite obscure. He married Sarah Palmer (1798–1883) in Kilkenny in 1826. Their family commenced with three daughters: Annabella (1827) who never married, Ellen (1829), who died young and Mary Anne (1831), who married Romney Rambaut[1].

Until sometime before 1832 he was 'a clerk in a Dublin house' (Doberck, 1884) but 'early abandoned mercantile pursuits' (DNB 1890). He had somehow taken up optics as a hobby and had constructed a small observatory with a 9-inch reflector (FitzGerald 1896). This observatory and his engineering business where he produced specialized machinery and instruments was situated near Charlemont bridge, the place where one crossed the Grand Canal on the way out from Dublin towards Ranelagh. His products included small machine tools, telescopes and other astronomical instruments as well as the unlikely sideline of cast iron beds for billiard tables! (Manville 1971). In fact, his name first appeared in Wilson's Dublin Directory for 1833, referring of course to the state of affairs in 1832, as 'Metal billiard table manufacturer'. Members of the public were admitted to his private observatory on payment of a fee.

The Charlemont Bridge Works remained in the hands of the Grubb concern until some time after the end of the First World War. The building no longer exists.

---

[1]Romney Rambaut (1829–1884), a nephew of Romney Robinson (see next section).

1.3   Influence of Romney Robinson

It is very likely that Grubb's interest in astronomy was stimulated through an acquaintance with Rev Thomas Romney Robinson (1792–1882) who was Director of Armagh Observatory from 1823 until his death and a very active figure in British astronomy. Robinson, a Doctor of Divinity, was actually a mathematical physicist with a strong practical bent and had been a Scholar of Trinity College (1808) and a Fellow (1814). He was the author of a textbook *System of Natural Philosophy for Students* (Dublin 1820). Amongst his early interests was the improvement of optical glass. In 1818 he applied to the excise authorities for permission to construct a small glass furnace for experimental purposes but was informed that this was impossible to give. This unreasonable decision he later felt to have been an example of the foolish way in which the law was being administered (Robinson 1862).

As we shall see, he became a close friend and supporter of Thomas and later Howard Grubb, although how their acquaintance began is unknown. Dreyer (1882)[2], a later director of Armagh Observatory, in an appeal for funds for a 'Robinson Memorial Telescope' to be located at Armagh, stated '... it was to a very great extent owing to his encouragement and ever ready counsel, that the late Mr. Grubb was enabled to found the establishment which has done so much credit to Irish industrial enterprise'.

Romney Robinson was the son of the Belfast artist, Thomas Robinson, and a godson of George Romney (1734–1802), the famous portrait painter. The Grubbs used the Christian name 'Romney' for their children for several generations and this is indicative of the close relations between the two families. Robinson's first wife was Elizabeth Rambaut[3], a member of a family that later produced more than one astronomer[4]. His second wife was Lucy Jane Edgeworth, of the cultivated family which included Richard Lovell Edgeworth (1744–1817), a pioneering engineer and economist[5], and his daughter Maria Edgeworth (1767–1849) the novelist. He could thus be said to have been 'well-connected'. They had two sons, Thomas and William, as well as a daughter (Mary) who married G.G. Stokes, the famous Cambridge physicist who later provided much help and theoretical advice to the Grubbs.

Robinson was acquainted in turn with William Parsons (1800–1867), then Lord Oxmantown and later third Earl of Rosse, who had since 1828 been publishing the results of his work on the improvement of telescope mirrors of speculum metal[6]. This had involved experiments on the composition of the

---

[2]Dreyer is remembered today as the compiler of the *New General Catalogue of Nebulae and Clusters of Stars* or NGC (1888) and the *Index Catalogues* or ICs of 1895 and 1905.

[3]Elizabeth Rambaut was the daughter of Jean Rambaut (1738–1810) who arrived from Bordeaux in 1754 at the age of 14 and later became a sugar refiner in Dublin.

[4]Rev W.H. Rambaut FRS (1822–1893), astronomer at Lord Rosse's telescope in Parsonstown and Arthur Rambaut (1859–1923), astronomer at Dunsink 1892–97 and later at the Radcliffe Observatory in Oxford.

[5]Inventor of the cup anemometer, later developed by Robinson.

[6]The use of glass for telescope mirrors only became possible around 1856 following the

Figure 1.1: Four people who played large parts in the life of Thomas Grubb: *Top left:* Romney Robinson, Director of Armagh Observatory (From Larmor 1907), *Top right:* Prof George Gabriel Stokes, Cambridge University (SAAO collection), *Bottom left:* William Parsons, Third Earl of Rosse, (SAAO collection), *Bottom right:* Sir George Biddell Airy, Astronomer Royal (SAAO collection).

copper/tin alloy and its annealing. By 1840, he had constructed a 36-inch telescope and by about 1845 his famous 72-inch, the 'Leviathan of Parsonstown', was in use.

1.4 Markree Observatory

Thomas Grubb's first big contract was for the construction of an equatorial mounting for the 13.3-inch lens of Markree Observatory.

Edward Joshua Cooper FRS (1798–1863) was a landowner in Co. Sligo in the west of Ireland. As a young man he travelled extensively, indulging in Egyptology and other fashionable 'scientific' activities. At first possessing only portable instruments, on the death of his father in 1830 he decided to found a regular observatory on his estate, Markree. He probably saw the announcement in *Astronomische Nachrichten* (Cauchoix, 1831) that R.A. Cauchoix (1776–1845), a leading Paris optician, had, in March 1831, completed an objective of about 13.3 inches aperture and 25 feet 3 inches focal length. He at once purchased it. At first, his telescope was mounted on a crude alt-azimuth stand (illustrated in King 1955, p181).

The word gradually spread that an unknown amateur had constructed the largest telescope then in existence, in a remote corner of Ireland. Romney Robinson started to correspond with Cooper and soon became friendly with him. His practical experience proved invaluable and he pointed out that the apparently poor performance of the lens was due to improper centring and that the alt-azimuth stand was limiting the accuracy of the work which Cooper had undertaken on double stars. The unfortunate dispute between Sir James South (1785–1867) and the instrument maker Edward Troughton (1753–1835) over the mounting for another Cauchoix lens, of 11.75 inches diameter, was then in progress but Robinson nevertheless succeeded in persuading Cooper to order, 'though not without some misgiving' an equatorial mounting from Grubb.

By December 1832 the declination axis and circles were finished and the polar axis was being cast. The maker did not fail to ensure their stability, Dr Robinson declaring 'all were jolly-looking affairs, with an appearance of strength that seemed to set unsteadiness at defiance'. The solidity of the mounting represented a 'great leap forward', one which can readily be appreciated when a comparison is made with that of 'The Great Dorpat Refractor' —Fraunhofer's[7] masterpiece with an object glass of 9.5 inches diameter—the largest and most sophisticated instrument previously built (Struve 1826). The

---

development of a suitable silvering process by the chemist Justus von Liebig (1803–1873) and the physicist J.B.L. Foucault (1819–1868).

[7] J. von Fraunhofer (1787–1826) of Bavaria was a pioneering lens designer, glass technologist and physicist. His is noted for the re-discovery, following W.H. Wollaston (1766–1828), and mapping of spectral lines in sunlight as well as for the development of optical glasses. His design of the Dorpat refractor was a marked improvement over all contemporary telescopes, both in its optics and its mounting.

Figure 1.2: The Markree telescope as mounted by Thomas Grubb in 1834 (Reproduced by permission of the Master and Fellows of Trinity College Cambridge. Ref R.6.14 [31][3].)

new telescope was erected in April, 1834 on a triangular pier made of black marble blocks (Anon 1834). The axes were solid castings of considerable diameter, the polar being tapered from the bottom, or thrust, end to the top which carried the declination bearing. The driving clock engaged a gearwheel at the lower end as did Fraunhofer's: later Thomas Grubb mounts were driven at the top. There was no dome—the instrument was exposed to the sky with only the object glass covered when not in use. Circular walls 16 feet high protected the observer from the wind

> "which, however, is free to act with full force on the upper half of the telescope; the yard in which it is placed is very damp. The driving-clock, though crude in comparison to modern instruments, deserved to be looked upon as a masterpiece at the time of its erection.
>
> While in Dublin, the object-glass narrowly escaped a fatal accident, a couple of splinters being knocked out of its edge; the places were filled with pitch, which still remains; there are also some fine scratches on it and a few veins, but the amount of light lost is imperceptible, and such trifling defects are met with in even the best modern glasses." (Doberck 1884).

The subsequent history of this early giant instrument shows that Cooper soon tired of it. It was used for example for sketching the 1835 appearance of Halley's comet and for the solar eclipse of May 15 1836, but it does not seem to have been central to any major programme. In 1835–6 Cooper travelled the Continent with his assistant Mr Andrew Graham and took the telescope along, mounting it again on an alt-azimuth stand for cometary observations.

The observatory acquired a meridian circle by Ertel of Munich about 1839 and collimators were made for it by Grubb. This instrument was mostly used by Graham. The most important publication of the Markree Observatory was the 'Catalogue of stars near the ecliptic observed at Markree', containing over 60,000 stars.

> "The heyday of Markree Observatory ended with the resignation of Graham in 1860 and the death of Cooper in 1863. It enjoyed a minor revival after 1874, when Doberck, Albert Marth and Frederick Henkel were successively appointed directors, but fell into disuse on the death of the then owner, E.H. Cooper, in 1902. The Grubb refractor was then sold to the Jesuit seminary at Aberdeen, Hong Kong, in or about 1928, and was erected there during the 1930s. The structure was damaged by aerial bombardment in 1941 and the telescope was dispatched to the Manila Observatory in the Phillipines in 1947 or thereabouts, where it is believed still to be." (Hoskin 1982).

The late Francis J. Heyden SJ (private communication, 1989) stated that the lens is still at Manila Observatory, where it forms part of a solar Littrow spectrograph.

Figure 1.3: The Markree telescope as re-erected in Hong Kong during the 1930s (photo supplied by the late F.J. Heyden SJ).

1.5 Armagh—the First Grubb Reflector

When Romney Robinson took over Armagh Observatory in 1823 he found that the instruments were totally antiquated, being essentially those ordered for the original installation in 1790 (Moore 1967, Bennett 1990). Armagh is the religious capital of Ireland and its observatory was set up by Primate (head of the protestant episcopal Church of Ireland) Richard Robinson (Lord Rokeby). Fortunately, however, the Primate of Romney Robinson's time, Lord John George Beresford, was very favourably disposed to the Observatory and offered to provide new instruments as well as to finance needed repairs to the buildings. Although the Observatory possessed a small reflecting telescope of 9 inches aperture made by Sir William Herschel[8], Robinson asked Grubb to provide him with a duplicate of the Markree mounting for a 10-inch mirror but the instrument ended up in 1835 as a 15-inch instead, with a speculum metal mirror by Grubb. A driving clock was also provided. It was erected in the east tower of the observatory building where the Herschel telescope had been.

It appears from a letter (STC1, supplement) from Robinson to Col E. Sabine[9] of 8 July 1853 in connection with what was to become the Great Melbourne Telescope (see Chapter 2) that this mounting actually antedated Cooper's. In discussing the undesirability of using small wheels alone to support the polar axis of a telescope (instead of using counterpoises in conjunction with simple bearings as was the later Grubb practice), Robinson remarked

> ".... my 15-inch Cassegrain, which was constructed by Mr. Grubb as an experimental model of Mr. Cooper's, [suffered from 'floating motion'] till the friction-wheels were removed, Y's substituted, and counterpoise levers supplied."

This instrument is of considerable historical importance because it was the first sizeable reflector to have been given a proper equatorial mount. Until then, and indeed for a long time afterwards, the fact that mirrors were only a tiny fraction of the price of objective lenses tended to encourage their purchasers to have them mounted on the cheap. The Armagh mirror cell was also the first to be provided with the system of 'equilibrated levers' for supporting the primary mirror (Robinson and Grubb 1869). Before this, mirror supports were very crude and must have severely degraded their optical performance.

Possibly Robinson obtained this mounting at a knock-down price having seen it standing unused in Grubb's shops. Accounts for modifications carried

---

[8]Sir William Herschel (1738–1822). Born in Hanover, he was originally a composer and musician. Later he became a telescope maker and indefatigable observer. He was favoured by King George III. He was the discoverer of the planet Uranus and also first detected infrared radiation. His son, John Herschel, was also a famous astronomer and was involved with the Southern Telescope Committee (see Chapter 2)

[9]Sir Edward Sabine, (1788–1883) noted scientific administrator and pioneer of geomagnetic observations.

Figure 1.4: Cell of Armagh Reflector. This was Grubb's first use of the 'Equilibrated Lever' system of mirror support (Author's photograph).

Figure 1.5: Remains of the clock drive of the Armagh Reflector. The governor, which would have resembled that of the West Point mounting, is missing. The very short worm is seen in front (author's photograph).

out at various times over the next few years still exist at Armagh[10] and these rather suggest that improvements were carried out piecemeal. In 1837, a new clock, radial bars and sector were supplied, in addition to new slides for carrying mirrors, a new eyepiece and an illuminated position micrometer. In 1842–43, parts for a mirror-making machine and a cast iron grinding tool were delivered, amongst other items. An account dated December 1873, from Howard Grubb, shows that a new speculum was supplied rough-ground and with a central hole.

This instrument did not play a very active part in the observing programmes of the observatory which were mainly of an astrometric nature and it was largely ignored by Robinson's successors. The mount and drive were 'cannibalized' around 1919 for use with a 6.25-inch refractor made by Rev W.F.A. Ellison (1864–1936), who was himself a noted amateur telescope maker and Director at Armagh from 1918 until his death.

In *ca* 1968 the mounting found its way across the road to the Royal School, Armagh, with the intention of its being used to carry another telescope. However, it remained unused and forgotten until re-discovered in the School's basement in 1988. The cell of the speculum mirror still exists (Dr John Butler 1988, private communication) as well as a polishing tool. The remaining parts of the mounting are again at the Observatory. The pier still stands in the east tower of the Observatory.

1.6   Life of Thomas Grubb, continued

In 1833, the Thomas Grubbs' first male child was born. This was Henry Thomas Grubb who, in 1862, obtained a Licentiate in Engineering from Trinity College Dublin. He did not enter the family firm but eventually took over his father's post as 'Engineer to the Bank of Ireland'. He lived until 1902. Another son, Alfred, was born in 1836 but died in 1843. A daughter, Emily, was born in 1838 but she also lived a rather brief life, surviving only until 1859.

About 1835, Thomas began to move a good deal in scientific circles. He became a member of the British Association for the Advancement of Science, which met in Dublin that year. He was then living at Parnel Place, a group of terraced houses forming part of the present-day Parnell Road beside the Grand Canal, in the district of Harold's Cross. One of the events of that meeting was the knighting of the mathematical physicist William Rowan Hamilton (1805–1865) at the early age of 30. Hamilton was made Andrews Professor of Astronomy, as a sinecure, at the University of Dublin in 1827 and was officially in charge of Dunsink Observatory. Unfortunately for astronomy, though not for science in general, he devoted his efforts to mathematical and physical theory, subjects much better suited to his talents than observing.

---

[10]See Armagh (1837) in Bibliography

On March 11 1836, Grubb read before the Royal Astronomical Society 'A short account of the results of some experiments made with the view of ascertaining how far the Gregorian and Cassegrain forms of the reflecting telescope are suited to micrometrical purposes; with a description of a simple and effective mode of illuminating the wires of all kinds of telescopes, &c.' This paper describes how, in the case of reflectors, a small amount of field illumination can be introduced by having a hole in the centre of the secondary mirror, behind which is a diagonal reflector of a lamp placed at the side of the telescope.

Grubb also did some work on a specialized instrument for James McCullagh[11]. At a meeting of the Royal Irish Academy in 1838 'Prof. McCullagh exhibited and described a new optical instrument, intended chiefly for the purpose of making experiments on the light reflected by metals ... The instrument is beautifully executed by Mr Grubb, who himself contrived the subordinate mechanism.'

On 14 Jan 1839 he was made a member of the Royal Irish Academy. Not being an academic, this was a considerable honour.   .

Magnetic instruments were probably a major interest at this time. Humphrey Lloyd (1800–1881), Professor of Natural Philosophy in Trinity College, Dublin, and a noted experimenter, was a leading spirit in a movement which led to the establishment of some forty identical British magnetic stations around the World. Grubb supplied the equipment for these. Amongst the equipment installed in the Magnetic Observatory of Trinity College were a declinometer, unifilar and bifilar magnetometers and an induction inclinometer made by Grubb (Lloyd 1842).

1.7   The Sheepshanks Refractor

In 1837 Rev R. Sheepshanks (1794–1855), the Secretary of the Royal Astronomical Society, presented to the Royal Greenwich Observatory a 6.75 inch object glass by Cauchoix. Thomas Grubb was given the order for the mounting. That he was considered fit to supply the national observatory under its exacting Director G.B. Airy[12] indicates the degree of acceptance that Grubb had achieved. In the beginning of June 1838, Airy (1838) reported to the Board of Visitors that 'I had been led to expect the mounting from Mr. Grubb in the present week'. In the end 'the Sheepshanks Telescope was received late in the last summer from Mr. Grubb, and, though inconvenient, appears to answer very well. Some trifling matters in the mounting, suggesting them-

---

[11]McCullagh (1809–1848) was professor of mathematics in Trinity College and a noted theoretical physicist who contributed to the wave theory of light. According to Poggendorff (1863) 'Nahm sich aus Melancholie das Leben' (He took his own life from melancholy).

[12]George Biddell Airy (1801–1892) was Astronomer Royal from 1836 to 1881. He was a mathematician by background and made contributions to the theory of optics. He was famous for the introduction of mass-production techniques to the acquisition of astronomical data.

selves experimentally, step by step, are hardly completed at the present time [June 1, 1839]. The power and general goodness of this telescope make it a most valuable addition to the instruments of the Observatory. It was used last autumn in the observations of Encke's Comet' (Airy 1839). In the following year, it was fittted with a 'double-image-micrometer', manufacturer not stated (Airy 1840).

Its mounting was lugubriously described in the precise language of a mathematician by Airy himself (1847).

This telescope was used over the years for a great variety of tasks. It was adapted for photography in 1888. It was reconditioned in 1952 and is still at the old Royal Observatory in Greenwich, though at present in storage.

1.8 Engineer to the Bank of Ireland: the 1840s

About 1840 Thomas Grubb became 'Engineer to the Bank of Ireland' where he was responsible for some ingenious machinery used for engraving, printing and numbering banknotes (Grubb 1865). The printing of banknotes at that time was from copper-plate engravings, a process which was very labour-intensive. The plates had to be inked evenly all over, the ink had then to be wiped off carefully so that it remained only in the engraved grooves and the plates had to be pressed heavily onto the paper for the actual printing. Grubb devised a cam-operated machine which took care of all these processes and involved a minimum of human intervention. He explained the operations involved by means of the 'Mechanical Notation' that had been introduced by Charles Babbage (1791–1871) as a device to simplify the design of his pioneering digital computers.

The softness of the copper plates used for the printing ensured that they wore out after only a few thousand copies had been made. Grubb also devised a process whereby a hardened steel master plate was forced against copper in order to make additional printing plates all of which were identical.

Although the work at the Bank of Ireland must have occupied most of his time, it appears that Grubb's telescope-making activities continued.

Romney Robinson (Robinson 1840), in an 1840 paper (at the Royal Irish Academy about Lord Oxmantown's 36-inch telescope) makes reference to Grubb's ability to cast speculum mirrors of up to 15 inches diameter, saying that even the London opticians did not dare to proceed beyond 9 inches. 'But even with all his distinguished mechanical talent, [Grubb] is believed to be doubtful of the possibility of more than doubling this last magnitude in pure speculum metal'. A mirror-polishing machine of Grubb's is also mentioned. In a paper to the Royal Society at about the same period, Lord Oxmantown (1840) discusses his means of supporting mirrors in the telescope. His smaller mirrors were supported

> "in their box on three strong iron plates, each plate being one-third part of a circular area, the same size as the speculum, and

a sector of it; the plates rest at their centres of gravity on points fixed at the bottom of the box of the speculum, and therefore no flexure of the box can affect the speculum".

He then rather condescendingly continues

"Although the same simple means would probably be effectual for specula of the largest size, in supporting specula of three feet diameter I have availed myself of the suggestion of a clever Dublin artist, Mr. Grubb, and, at the expense of a little more complication, have substituted nine plates for the three, resting on points supported by levers, which rest on three original points; and if flexure is thus more effectually prevented, which I think it ought to be, the additional workmanship is of no importance."

1.9   Birth of Howard Grubb

Thomas Grubb's family increased during the 1840s. Two boys, John H. (born 1840) and Romney Rambaut (born 1842 and named after Romney Robinson and his wife) died young. However, his last child, Howard, who was to become even better known as a telescope maker than his father, was born in 1844.

We know of little astronomical activity on the part of Grubb during this period. The records of Armagh Observatory show that he was asked to make a number of small modifications to their instruments.

1.10   West Point Refractor

In 1840 William H.C. Bartlett (1804–1893), Professor of Natural and Experimental Philosophy at the the United States Military Academy, West Point, from 1836 to 1871, obtained permission to make a trip to Europe in order to visit observatories and instrument makers (Holden 1911). His extensive manuscript report includes a description of a visit to Dublin. After visiting Dunsink Observatory, he saw the Magnetic Observatory of Trinity College, some of whose instruments had been built by Thomas Grubb. He then went on to Grubb's Charlemont Bridge works, writing (Bartlett 1841):

"Mr Grubb with great liberality and kindness took me through his work shop & gave me much explanation in regard to the use and objects of many things that appeared new & highly interesting. Among other instruments I found there a fine equatorial mounting carrying Cassegrainian Telescope of fifteen inches aperture, both the Telescope & mounting by Mr Grubb, the latter appeared to me well conceived and if possible better executed. In its general features it resembles the Dorpat mounting already referred to, though it differs from it in many particulars which appeared to me improvements. Its heliostatic [sic] motion is regulated by the centrifugal governor constructed in a particular way—One of the principal difficulties experienced in the application of the governor to the purpose in question consisted in so adjusting its different parts that the angular retarding force should increase gradually and the law of the increase be such as soon to make this force equal to the accelerating force and keep it so. Mr Grubb has given a practical solution of this difficulty in his mounting.

The polar axis is enveloped by an iron cylinder, which when the instrument is mounted, is fastened by a strong flange and bolted to a large stone having the face of contact parallel to the equator of the place. The instrument is thus suited to any latitude. The bottom of the polar axis rests in a socket of bell metal with adjusting screws, the socket being supported by a strong iron stirrup fastened to the under surfaces of the cylinder. The upper end of the axis is embraced by a collar at the top of the cylinder above which the crossbeam which carries the Telescope and declination circle with it. The diameter of the declination circle has recently been altered. It is now fifteen inches, that of the hour circle being twelve and a half. Both circles are graduated upon silver belts let into their outer rims or cylindrical surfaces. The divisions are to ten minutes the subdivisions being made to one second by micrometer microscopes [?] of which each circle has two. Motion in right ascension is communicated by means of a circular section whose vertex is cut away. The positioning of this section is such that its plane is perpendicular to the polar axis, its vertex is in that line, and they are connected with an endless screw [today called a worm] by means of deep and very accurately cut teeth, the screw being turned by clockwork regulated as before described. The sector carries at the end next the vertex a clamping arrangement which embraces the axis, and the habitual state of the clamp is such as to cause the axis to obey the motion of the clock when unobstructed, at the same time that it permits the axis to move in either direction when a small force is applied to the [?] end of the Telescope which may thus be moved from one body to another while the sector is carried forward by the screw. The clamps and sector are so united by a tangent screw device that their relative positioning may be altered, which furnishes the means of making the finer adjustments. When the sector which is about twenty two degrees or an hour and a half is exhausted, the screw may be thrown out of gear by a very simple device, and the sector restored to its primitive position by turning the screw in an opposite direction. The micrometers and illuminating apparatus are very beautiful. By a small lamp connected with the tail piece of

the telescope, the wires may be illuminated <u>on both sides,</u> and the
field made perfectly dark, or the reverse, <u>according</u> to the wants
of the observer. I have been very particular in referring to this
mounting, as I thought it advisable, on my return from Germany,
to purchase it for our eight foot refractor, which has heretofore
been in a great measure useless for want of suitable means to use
it."

The instrument was described in considerable detail, accompanied by copperplate engravings, in *Transactions of the American Philosophical Society*
(Bartlett 1846). The telescope proper was a refractor of six inches diameter
and eight feet focal length by J.N. Lerebours (1761–1840) of Paris. The same
article describes some observations of the Great Comet of 1843.

This telescope left its mark on astronomical history when it was used to
make the first known quantitative astronomical measurement by photography.
On 26 May 1854 Bartlett observed a partial solar eclipse. The size of the solar
images was $\frac{7}{8}$ inches diameter. Nineteen images were taken and the distances
separating the cusps were later measured. The results were published in the
Astronomical Journal for 10 November 1854. (Bartlett 1854)

According to André and Angot (1877), it was replaced in 1856 by a 9.75-
inch refractor due to the U.S. manufacturer, Henry Fitz (1808–1863), and
costing $5000. The old mounting at least later found its way into the hands
of Fitz and was erected in the open air at Fitz's estate in Peconic, Long Island,
New York. There it bore a 9-inch lens of Fitz's manufacture. The polar axis
was no longer encased in its casting but rested instead on an inclined plane
like the Markree refractor. It is not clear whether there was a drive clock. It
remained with the family until it passed from Fitz's great-grand-daughter to
the minister of her parish. Around 1980, it was acquired by Mr Alan Daroff
(private communication from A. Daroff, May 14, 1990) of Philadelphia. It was
sold by him to its present owner, R.C. Hambleton of Springfield, Virginia, in
1990. Many of the original parts are still recognizable, although others are
heavily corroded (private communication from R.C. Hambleton, Oct 20 1991).

1.11   Engraving Machines

According to an article in *Engineering* (Anon 1888), there was an engraving
machine, constructed by Thomas Grubb, still in use in the Optical Works in
Rathmines at that time:

"This is one of the earliest pantographic copying machines,
and it was constructed in 1847 by the late Mr. Thomas Grubb for
engraving registration numbers on gun barrels. The circumstances
which called this machine into existence are curious. About the
date mentioned a scare had arisen respecting a rebellion in Ireland,
and a short Act of Parliament was passed enforcing the registration

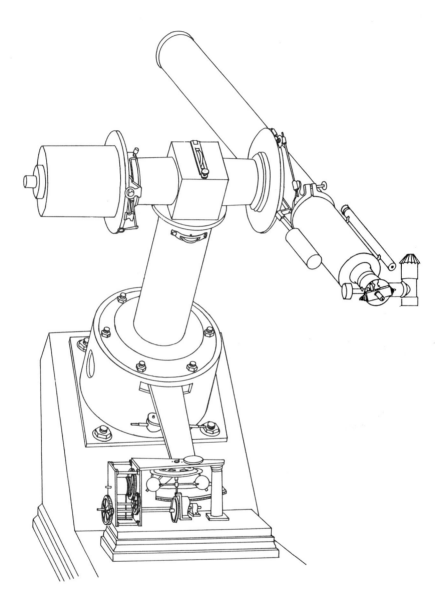

Figure 1.6: West Point Refractor. The mounting was by Thomas Grubb (Traced by the author from Bartlett 1846).

of all firearms in the island and enacting that each arm should have its registration number engraved upon it. But our legislators in framing this Act had utterly ignored the fact that the engraving which they thus stipulated to satisfy the provisions of the Act

amounted to a quantity which it was utterly beyond the power of
all available engravers to accomplish within a reasonable time, and
thus there seemed every chance of the Act becoming a dead letter.
To meet this difficulty the late Mr. Thomas Grubb devised the
machine noticed above. Thirty of these machines (each worked by
a treadle motion) were made, and members of the constabulary
were instructed in their use, the result being that the provisions
of the Act were carried out without difficulty. The tool at Sir
Howard Grubb's factory is one of the original machines so made,
and it still does excellent work."

1.12   Glasgow Reflector, Polishing Techniques

During this period Grubb re-worked a reflecting telescope of 22 inches aperture
belonging to the Horsethistle Observatory of Glasgow University. This was
constructed originally by John Ramage (1784–1835) of Aberdeen and had a
focal length of 16.5m! (Gavine 1982)

Robinson, in an article on 'Specula' in J.P. Nichol's[13] *Cyclopaedia of the
Physical Sciences*, mentions (1857) a Newtonian of 20 inches aperture and
15 feet focal length belonging to Glasgow Observatory that was figured by
Grubb. Apparently, the Ramage mirror had been sent to Grubb around 1847
to have its focal length reduced to 4.25 m and was not returned until 1851,
when its figure was found to be unsatisfactory. After further work by Grubb,
it was finally accepted. According to André and Rayet (1874), this instrument
was installed in 1855 and was used by Nichol and the Marquis of Breadalbane
for taking a series of Lunar photographs which were, at that time, 'beaucoup
remarquées'. In the article on Specula in Nichol's *Cyclopaedia* Robinson also
discusses the polishing machines and techniques of Rosse, Lassell[14] and De la
Rue[15] as well as of Grubb. Grubb's machine comes in for particular praise
for the variety of movements it could impart to the polishing tool (although
it must have been a very difficult machine to use!).

> "Mr Grubb decidedly prefers the Rossean action for grinding
> but thinks the other (Lassell's) less likely to fail in the polishing
> with unpractised hands, and uses it himself. He begins with a
> large eccentricity and gradually diminishes it, which can be done
> without stopping the machine. His polisher is also of wood, but
> made with peculiar care. It is formed by six layers of mahogany,
> each $\frac{5}{16}$ of an inch thick, and not continuous, but built up of pieces
> three inches square. These are only glued where they cross, being,

---

[13] (1804–1859), Professor of Astronomy at Glasgow.

[14] William Lassell (1799–1880) brewer turned amateur astronomer.

[15] Warren de la Rue (1815–1889) was heir to the famous stationery and banknote printing
firm as well as an amateur telescope maker. He learned how to make speculum mirrors
from Nasmyth.

Figure 1.7: Early Grubb polishing machine. The mirror being worked on was mounted above shaft g. The sub-table B could be made to oscillate on slides, so that many complicated motions could be given to the polisher, which was driven by shaft m (From Nichol 1857).

at least in the interior, not in close contact at their edges, and the direction of their grain varied as much as possible. The disc when turned true, is plugged at the edges, varnished, and coated with tin foil, at the edge and back. It is the same diameter as the speculum. He uses pitch alone; rolls it like Lord Rosse, cuts it into squares of $\frac{3}{4}$ inch, and attaches them to the surface, warming it by a spirit lamp. This machine measures about three feet every way, and can work a two feet speculum; but the largest on which it has been tried is the Newtonian of the Glasgow Observatory."

The article continues by discussing a proposal to make, using this machine, a Herschelian telescope, i.e. one with an off-axis paraboloidal primary and no secondary (Such a telescope would have been much more efficient than a conventional type using two mirrors on account of the low reflectivity of speculum metal).

Many years later, writing to Capt. Floyd, secretary to the Trustees of Lick Observatory, on 10 Aug. 1877, Howard Grubb mentions: 'At Glasgow I believe there is a very old Reflector of my Fathers. I never saw it but it must be quite out of date.' Again, in a letter to Gill dated 21 Mar 1894, Grubb says: 'By the way, I was looking at the instrument at Glasgow which my father made so many years ago and it is almost identical with the Potsdam [astrographic] instrument, or rather the Potsdam instrument is identical with it.' However, Gavine (1982) says that Randolph and Elliot, the builders of its dome, had put forward plans for mounting it, so uncertainty remains as to who actually built the mount. A micrometer, similar to that built for Lord Rosse, was supplied by Grubb.

A report in 1912 (Anon 1912a) indicates that this telescope was then still usable.

1.13   Southern Telescope Committee

This period also saw the beginning of interest in erecting a large southern telescope. However, a detailed discussion of this project is deferred until the next chapter. The project did not reach fruition until the 1860s.

The correspondence concerning this instrument was printed for private circulation by the Royal Society and in it can be found information about some of Grubb's other activities during this period. We find out, for example, that Grubb and Robinson had been interested in the question of how best to mount a large reflector in the late 1840s from the following letter [Robinson to Lord Rosse 28 December 1852, STC1-13]:

> "I enclose you a tracing (which return when you have looked
> at it) of two schemes which were discussed by Grubb and myself
> in reference to the southern reflector some years since. In that
> marked R, I proposed to make the speculum box itself the decli-
> nation axis, providing it with journals and a circle, and to have
> a short and massive polar axis. The tube above the box was to
> be merely an open skeleton, framed so as to be stiff enough to
> support the ocular part and small mirror. This would bring the
> centre of gravity very near the speculum. Grubb did not like this
> and suggested another marked G. The polar axis here has its up-
> per bearing about 6 feet diameter, but is cut at the top so as to let
> the tube pass in for reaching the pole. This would weaken the axis

there, but from its greater diameter the strength would be abundant.. It would also interfere with the motion of the instrument at more than five hours from the meridian".

The Grubb scheme sounds like a precursor of the 'yoke' type of mounting employed for the Palomar 200-inch reflector.

1.14 The South Refractor at Dunsink

In December 1852 Robinson also mentioned in his letter to the Earl of Rosse that

> "Grubb is getting ready two equatorials for the Dublin Exhibition; one a model of that noticed above [i.e. the Palomar-like mounting], with a 15-inch reflector, the other an improvement of Mr. Cooper's, with an 8-inch achromatic of his own grinding."

However, later, in April 1853, he remarks in a letter to Mr Bell [STC 1–24]

> "Grubb is grinding a 12-inch achromatic for the Dublin Exhibition; but I scarcely think he will be ready with it. The equatorial for it, however, is ready and I think no doubt will exist as to its efficiency when it is seen. He grinds the lenses by a new and very simple machine, which acts without forming rings on the glass (Andrew Ross's[16] great difficulty) and if it does as well for specula, will be an advance. I shall be curious to see how this object-glass acts; if it succeeds, there is some probability that he will try even larger sizes. But the two glass discs alone for a 24-inch would cost £1000."

Robinson, in a footnote to his article in Nichol's *Cyclopaedia* (1857), is probably referring to the same lens and machine when he says:

> "Mr Grubb has since contrived another machine of remarkable simplicity, which seems to possess the powers of all those described ... with some peculiar to it. It is not described here because it has not yet been tried on specula. Its chief performance as yet has been the lenses of an object-glass of twelve inches aperture, which it has wrought with singular facility, varying the curves at pleasure, by changing the adjustments, so as to make slight change of the corrections".

The mounting was in fact exhibited at the Dublin Exhibition of 1853 on the Leinster Lawn premises of the Royal Dublin Society. However, it

---

[16] A British optician who later built a solar telescope for de la Rue.

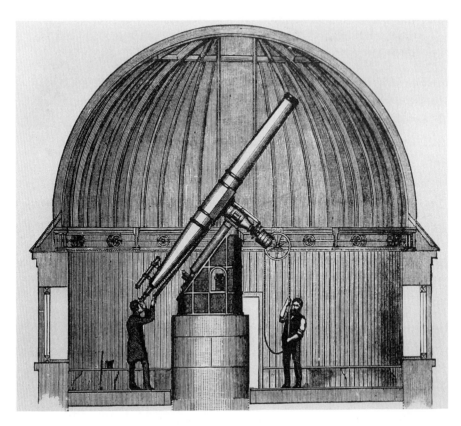

Figure 1.8: The South Telescope at Dunsink Observatory, Dublin. The Grubb-built dome rides on a 'live ring', which rotates at half the speed of the dome itself. (From Ball 1892.)

remained with Grubb and was available for the London exhibition of 1862. Robinson (1862) gives a description of this mounting as it appeared in London. It incorporated the first example of the system for relief of bearing friction which was to become an important feature of all large Grubb telescopes. He mentions that the weight of moving parts amounts to 1000 lbs and goes on:

> "... if this weight acted uniformly, and in a constant direction on the surfaces which support it, it would be an easy matter to manage it. The most obvious way is to make all the bearings friction wheels; but though these give extreme freedom of motion, the motion has a character fatal to our object—an unsteadiness like that of a suspended body. The bearing wheels must therefore be fixed, and the friction wheels must leave a certain part of the weight to press on them."

He shows how this is done for the straightforward case of the right ascension axis, where the forces do not change direction as the telescope moves about the sky. More subtle is the mechanism which is located inside the polar axis and compensates for the variable forces along the declination axis and perpendicular to to it. 'A force of one pound applied at the eyepiece moves the telescope easily and smoothly in any direction'.

The mount as it exists today is otherwise of an intermediate type: the clockwork is contained inside a cast iron pillar which forms the top portion of the pier in the place of the older style where the pier was made of stone right up to the level of the tilted base-plate for the polar axis. The clock includes provision for pendulum control of the drive rate, although this was not featured in Robinson's description. However, the position circles have singularly inaccessible verniers' (Wayman 1988), although Robinson indicates that the intention had been to install a special microscope to enable them to be read from the ground. Later models certainly had such devices.

What became of the 12-inch object glass that Grubb was preparing for this telescope in not clear. Robinson wrote that it was to be a cemented doublet. However, a letter from G.G. Stokes on 20 October 1870 (Larmor 1907a) to W.V. Vernon Harcourt[17], contains the following:

> "Grubb had been commissioned to make a 12-inch object-glass, but before the work was complete the order was withdrawn, in consequence, I think, of an object-glass having been bequeathed to the party ordering, compensation I presume being made to Grubb in some way or other. He still has this glass in his hands".

Stokes mentions further that Grubb had had trouble correcting the lens for spherical aberration, having used a test object that was too close by to give realistic results. In a letter to Grubb dated 5 April 1871, Stokes (Larmor 1907b) advocated what might now be called an auto-collimation method for the testing of objective lenses: a plane, or very nearly so, speculum should be placed behind the lens to be tested and object and image should be at twice the focal distance. However, this system was only adopted much later by Howard Grubb.

As to the object glass that this mount eventually carried: the list of 'Benefactors of Trinity College' (Anon. 1912b) contains the following entry:

> "1863 February 17. Given by Sir James South, on the occasion of the Installation of the Right Hon. the Earl of Rosse, as Chancellor of the University, a valuable collection of Astronomical Instruments, including his celebrated twelve-inch achromatic object-glass."

---

[17]William Venables Vernon Harcourt (1789–1871), inventor engaged from time to time in making experimental optical glasses and inventor of a standard lamp fuelled by pentane.

Sir James South, as mentioned in the section on Markree, was the amateur who had purchased the 11.75-inch lens, made by Cauchoix in 1829, for his private observatory in Kensington. Troughton and Simms had been asked to mount it. The resulting instrument was found to be unsteady but South was uncooperative over the makers' attempts to remedy its defects. Troughton eventually had to go to court to obtain payment for his work and South's rage at losing the case led him to smash the mount to pieces. He later offered the scrap for sale in a scurrilous poster designed to embarrass Troughton and Simms. (King 1955)

The proposal to purchase the mounting for the Dunsink Observatory of Trinity College was probably initiated by Romney Robinson after the receipt of South's gift. Robinson would have seen the need for a new instrument following the long tenure of Sir William Rowan Hamilton of the Andrews' Professorship of Astronomy. The telescope was installed when F.F. Brunnow (1821–1891) became Professor.

This instrument is still in use at Dunsink, where it is demonstrated on Visitors' Nights etc. It was overhauled in 1987 and found to be in remarkably good condition. 'Examination of Grubb's work always shows how carefully the designs were worked out. Items such as weight-driven clock drives were scaled up or down according to the size of telescope, with minor modifications, as required. The distinctive style of Grubb was imposed on every major item produced. Generally speaking, massiveness in the major components, elegant finish to brasswork, and proper provision of devices for mechanical adjustment were the hallmark of the designs. If there was a characteristic fault in the Grubb designs it arose from the hand-made nature of the products, so that screws might not be interchangeable because they are of different lengths or clearances. Parts were always dot-marked or numbered, and in certain cases the order in which parts have to be dismantled could be an inconvenience.' (Wayman 1988)

1.15   1852–1862: A Frustrating Ten Years

The British Association met again in Dublin in 1857 and Grubb (1857) presented a 'Report on the Improvement of Telescope and Equatorial Mountings'. He was clearly itching to be at work on a large instrument once again but was disappointed at the lack of opportunity. After pointing out the success of the Earl of Rosse's giant reflectors he says

> "Meanwhile the achromatic objective has received but small increment of dimension, and is now probably for ever distanced, in this respect, by its competitor the reflector. The spirited exertions of the Messrs. Chance[18] in Birmingham have indeed produced a

[18]The Chance brothers were the first outsiders to acquire the secrets of making large optical glass pieces—this knowledge had previously been the property of the Guinand family.

pair of discs suited to the formation of an object-glass of about 29 inches diameter, but these exertions have not been seconded by a corresponding spirit in Great Britain, either public or private. A few years since, the possible acquisition of an achromatic telescope, of corresponding gigantic size, was looked forward to as a national triumph, if ever accomplished; but our Government, retaining its character of proverbial supineness (if not apathy) in such matters, has allowed these splendid discs to be transmitted to a more congenial kingdom; yet even there the work seems to progress but slowly, and I apprehend that their formation into an object glass is still a work for the future. Four years have now passed since the production of these discs, and nearly three years since, on being applied to by Messrs. Chance, I offered to form them into an object-glass."

(According to Robinson (1862) Secrétan[19], in Paris, was attempting to construct a 27-inch from Chance discs[20].)

Grubb went on to point out that the increasing lens thicknesses necessary in refractors of increased diameter will decrease the transmission so much that reflectors, in spite of the poor reflectivity of the speculum metal then in use, will ultimately prove more efficient. He had developed a backsilvered, or rather quicksilvered, secondary with an achromatic glass support:

"the image appears both brighter and whiter than when using the ordinary small speculum; the image also appears perfectly free from chromatic dispersion. When the quicksilver shall have been replaced by a surface of pure silver, the increase of light will of course be equivalent to the proportionably higher reflective power of the latter, which, in the absence of good photometric observations, may be estimated at the least as a fourth".

Finally he discusses the form of equatorial mounting which should be employed for a large reflector:

"I modify the German type ... by placing the declination axis within instead of beyond the larger end of the polar, and I invert the whole. Thus the previous steadiness is rather increased; the bearings of the polar axis may both be of minimum size, and the centre of gravity of the whole instrument is brought as close to the ground-level as can be desired, instead of being considerably aloft; also the settings and readings of the largest instrument are

---

[19]Mark François Secrétan (1804–1867), successor to Lerebours.
[20]Tobin (1987) mentions that the Chance discs were first exibited at the *Exposition Universelle* of 1855 in Paris. In fact, it was Foucault who started work on the 27-inch lens. As late as 1880, his former pupil Adolf Martin was still attempting to complete this task. It was never finished.

rendered most convenient, and the observer is generally close to
the ground, and never more than a few feet from it."

This is practically a description of the plan Grubb had prepared for the
Southern Telescope which in some ways was the precursor of all the large
Grubb–Parsons (successor company to the Grubbs) reflectors until the mid–
1950s.

1.16   Ray Tracing and Other Interests

A series of papers in the Proceedings of the Royal Irish Academy and the
Journal of the Royal Dublin Society show that Grubb was at this period
broadening his optical interests.

For example, the Reports of Scientific Meetings of the Royal Dublin Society mention Mr Grubb's 'Exhibition of his oxy-hydrogen microscope and
polariscope' in 1849 and 'Contrast of illuminating powers of the Electric and
Drummond lights' in 1853 (Anon, 1855).

A paper entitled 'Determination of Spherical Aberration in the Microscope' (Grubb 1854) is particularly interesting because that it shows that
Grubb was an early practitioner, perhaps the first, of ray-tracing:

> "The methods hitherto at our option for investigating the spher-
> ical aberrations of a system of lenses, having spherical surfaces,
> are—firstly, the purely mathematical, involving (where the thick-
> ness of the lenses is required to be included, and more especially
> where the angle of aperture is considerable) such intricacy in the
> calculations as renders the process nearly useless to practical per-
> sons; and, secondly, the more practical method of constructing
> diagrams of large size, in which two or more rays, at different dis-
> tances from the axis of the compound, are geometrically traced,
> according to the laws of optics.
>
> Much of my leisure time has, for several years, been devoted to
> inquiries including, necessarily, the construction of such diagrams;
> and I cannot speak too highly of their value in giving to the ex-
> perimenter in optics a thorough practical insight into the effects
> of the various forms and combinations which will be suggested ...
>
> It may be desirable here to state, that these diagrams were
> usually drawn on a scale ten times that intended for use ... the
> measurement of the sines [were] taken with a scale of fiftieths of
> an inch, using a magnifier, and estimating to tenths of divisions,
> or say 1 500th of an inch."

He went on to explain how he could mix the mathematical and practical
approaches to work out the aberrations surface by surface and add them to
predict the overall behaviour of the lens under investigation. According to von

Rohr (1904) in his book on image formation in optical instruments, Grubb was the first to have properly appreciated the field properties of camera lenses. These investigations led to the invention of a wide-angle achromatic portrait lens which he patented (Lummer 1900) and about which he read a paper to the Royal Dublin Society in 1858 (Grubb, 1860). Several hundred of these were manufactured (Manville 1971). Very similar meniscus lenses were employed later in cheap box cameras.

In 1855 he had a few words to say on 'Decimal Systems of Money' (Grubb 1858). This was probably in response to the interest created by the appointment in 1853 of a select committee of the House of Commons to consider the question. The introduction of the florin of two shillings in 1849 (later the 10p piece) had been a first step in this direction.

1.17   Microscopes

Grubb also contributed to the development of microscopes. His first paper on the subject was 'Illumination of Objects in the Microscope' (Grubb 1853). This was followed in 1854 by the article on spherical aberration in the microscope, already referred to in connection with ray-tracing.

In 'On a new Table Microscope' (Grubb 1862a), read by Grubb to the Royal Dublin Society in 1858, a microscope with a highly elaborate illuminating system was described. This was basically a development of his earlier paper of 1853. The underlying idea was that the microscopist should easily be able to alter the angle of illumination of the specimen whilst looking through the instrument. The construction was made particularly solid, so that the specimen would not be disturbed as the illuminating components were moved about. The operator could note the exact positions of the adjustments from scales, so that the precise set-up could be repeated if necessary. Other features of the instrument were an improved adjustment for fine focussing, an improved safety tube for the object glass and a means of tilting the whole instrument for the comfort of the observer.

Only one Grubb microscope is known to have survived, namely that at the Museum of the History of Science in Oxford. This instrument is similar in appearance to that illustrated in the 1862 article except for its tube, which is bent for convenience, and the extra objectives on a turntable.

Grubb concludes his 1858 article with the following:

> "Perhaps I may be permitted to conclude this imperfect description by mentioning what one, who is well qualified to judge of the merits of the instrument, has communicated respecting it. He quaintly says, 'I find but one fault in your microscope; and that is, that it puts me out of conceit with the using of any other".

Figure 1.9: Microscope by Thomas Grubb, now in the Museum of the History of Science, Oxford. It featured solid construction, a versatile system of illumination and several other improvements. Reproduced by permission of the Museum of the History of Science, Oxford.

1.18 Photography

Thomas Grubb was highly interested in photography and was a frequent contributor to *Journal of the Photographic Society* (London) from 1856 onwards for a few years. His letters to the journal were usually in the form of sarcastic corrections to other peoples' misconceptions. They also contained descriptions of various inventions and suggested improvements of his own. He was, for example, critical of people who were too casual in the way that they specified lens characteristics.

He was honorary treasurer of the Dublin Photographic Society in 1857.

Reports of the meetings of the Dublin society were carried in the London *Journal*. During 1856 he showed his prints from waxed-paper negatives (some of Grubb's negatives still exist). He made stereoscopic and ordinary views of the Earl of Rosse's great telescope 'taken under very adverse conditions of light and weather'. His papers read at meetings of the Society included 'On Lunar Photography' and 'On the Use of Rock Crystals (in lieu of glass) in the formation of View Lenses. He showed his ideas for improvements in the support of 'large-sized portable cameras'. He also advocated a clock-driven slide for counteracting the lunar motion in long-exposure photography at the focus of a telescope.

At one point in 1858, there appeared an article 'Mr Grubb's New Lens', in the form of a letter to the Editor. This described the newly invented achromatic meniscus lens mentioned in the last section. A certain Thomas Slater of Euston Rd in London wrote in claiming that the invention was not a new one. However, the editor came to Grubb's defence: 'We are inclined to think the law will hold Mr Grubb as the real inventor, he having been the first to disclose his invention to the public. But for Mr Grubb, the lens would have lain dormant, and in all probability for some time to come would not have been heard of . . .'.

In 1862 Grubb (1862b) indulged in a typically polemical correspondence in the *British Journal of Photography* about the angular field covered by lenses. He points out the importance of the focus of the lateral pencils as opposed to merely measuring the total solid angle accepted, irrespective of quality. Minimal pincushion distortion should also be considered in judging a good lens.

In a strange footnote to one of his 1862 articles, he made the claim 'I am not professionally *an optician* . . .'. This may have meant that he regarded his work with the bank as his main occupation at that time.

In 1864, Grubb's originality was recognized by his being made a Fellow of the Royal Society (FRS).

Chapter 2

The Great Melbourne Telescope

2.1   The First Proposal

The telescope-building efforts of Lord Rosse and his discoveries relating to the nature of nebulae, together with John F.W. Herschel's[1] epic effort in cataloging the southern nebulae from the Cape in 1835–38, appealed to the imagination of the mid-19th century scientific world and led to the suggestion that a large telescope should be installed in the southern hemisphere.

Concrete steps to this end seem to have originated with Sir Edward Sabine (1788–1883) in the late 1840s (Warner 1982). Sabine was noted principally for his researches into geomagnetism and had travelled extensively in the southern hemisphere. He was a leading member of both the Royal and Royal Astronomical Societies. Romney Robinson took up the idea with enthusiasm and, in September 1849, induced the Council of the British Association to make an official recommendation 'that an application be made to Her Majesty's government to establish a Reflector not less than 3 feet in diameter, at the Observatory at the Cape of Good Hope ...'. However, Thomas Maclear[2], the Astronomer at the Cape, was too busy with conventional positional work and geodesy and could raise no enthusiasm for the proposal. As a result, the project became a more general one and the Cape ceased to be singled out in later correspondence. The Royal Society, older and likely to carry more weight with the government, then took up the idea and Robinson, together with its President, who happened to be Lord Rosse, drafted a proposal or 'Memorial' to be sent to the Prime Minister, Lord John Russell. Unfortunately this document was intercepted by G.C. Lewis, Secretary of the Treasury, who sought the opinion of the Astronomer Royal, G.B. Airy. The latter was luke-warm;

---

[1] Herschel, Sir John Frederick William, Bart, 1792–1871
[2] 1794–1879

he may even have been piqued at not having been consulted during the preparation of the proposal and clearly regarded the observation of nebulæ as a passing fad. Besides, he was notoriously conservative in his views. He did, however, point out that the management of a large reflector required the services of a very special kind of astronomer. The net result of all this was a refusal originating from the Treasury Secretary: '[There is] so much difficulty attending on the arrangements that [the Lords Commissioners of the Treasury] are not prepared to take any steps without much further consideration'.

It became pretty evident what had happened when Sir David Brewster[3], as President of the British Association, on speaking to the Prime Minister, found out that the latter had heard nothing of the proposal. Brewster afterwards wrote to the Assistant Secretary of the Royal Society 'If another application is made to the Government, which, of course, it will be, I trust the Committee will take care that it is made by persons whose hearts are really in the cause, and that they will take care to meet any underhand opposition that will be made to it'. (STC 1–5)

By 1852 even Airy saw the merit of the proposal and, at the suggestion of the British Association, the Royal Society set up the Southern Telescope Committee which included the main professional astronomers such as Airy, Robinson and Adams[4] and leading amateurs such as Rosse, Nasmyth, Lassell, Cooper of Markree fame and Herschel. James Nasmyth (1808–1890) was one of the great pioneers of the machine-tool industry and was known to astronomers for the 20-inch altazimuth telescope of his own design which boasted the eponymous Nasmyth focus. William Lassell (1789–1880), a wealthy brewer, had learned telescope-making from Rosse and Nasmyth, had developed his own polishing machine and, with his 24-inch telescope, had become famous by discovering Triton, a satellite of Neptune. In fact, the committee constituted an expert body of large telescope makers, many of its members having had experience of casting and polishing speculum metal mirrors. Interesting suggestions were received concerning the form such a telescope should take from Nasmyth, Airy and Charles Piazzi Smyth[5], as well as from Thomas Grubb who communicated through Romney Robinson. It was generally agreed that an equatorial mounting was desirable although never before attempted on such a large scale. Also, it was to be in the open air. Smyth and Nasmyth both advocated Newtonians with the observer placed high above the ground in what Herschel referred to as an 'aerial chamber'.

Robinson encouraged the Committee to go for a reflector as follows: (STC 1–24) '.... I must express my belief that the opinion expressed by several members of the Committee as to the difficulty of making a 4-feet reflector is exag-

---

[3]1781–1868

[4]John Couch Adams 1819–1892, Lowndean Prof of Astronomy and Geometry at Cambridge. He predicted the existence of Neptune, but lost the credit for this to the French astronomer, Urbain Jean Joseph Le Verrier (1811–1877), thanks to his own diffidence and a lack of interest on the part of Sir G.B. Airy

[5]1819–1900, Astronomer Royal for Scotland and formerly First Assistant at the Cape

Figure 2.1: Four leading amateur telescope makers involved with the Great Melbourne Telescope: *Top left:* William Lassell, *Top right:* James Nasmyth, *Bottom left:* Warren de la Rue and *Bottom right:* Sir John Herschel. All had experience with speculum-metal mirrors (SAAO collection).

gerated. I have seen so much of Lord Rosse's operations, that I feel authorized to say this, <u>absolutely</u> for a 3-feet reflector; with high probability for one of four. And were the difficulty and the uncertainty even as great as those gentlemen suppose, <u>that is the strongest reason for pursuing this our purpose.</u> It is only by the reflecting telescope that we shall reach the remotest parts of the visible universe. There is no likelihood that an achromatic of 3 feet (the equivalent of a 4-feet reflector) will be made in the next century; if made it must be of enormously greater cost [It was, see chapter on the Lick telescope], and will be embarrassed by the evils of flexure and the polarizing action caused by pressure. It is therefore specially desirable that the reflector shall be made as perfect as possible; and never was a better opportunity offered than now, when we shall be authorized to experiment under the guidance of Lord Rosse, Sir J. Herschel, Mr. Lassell and Mr. Nasmyth'. Robinson pointed out the advantages of a Cassegrain as compared to a Newtonian: e.g. its more compact size and its convenience to the observer. He also mentioned the greater reflectivity of the speculum at near perpendicular incidence and that the zonal errors of the large mirror might be corrected by local figuring of the secondary.

As to the suggestion that the observer should be appointed first, made by Airy, Robinson says scathingly 'Nothing is gained by this except delay. The Committee must fix the nature of the work to be performed; they are the proper persons to fix also the means of doing it ...Let us provide the telescope, choose the site, and an observer will not be wanting. <u>If Britain cannot furnish a qualified person,</u> let us carry out free trade and seek him at Berlin or Poulkova'(STC 1–33).

To this letter Rosse subjoined '...I should be most happy to afford the gentleman engaged in constructing the instrument all the assistance in my power in the shape of information, and also by lending him any apparatus I might have suitable for his purpose ...'

On 30 June 1853 Robinson put in a strong plea—and a quotation—from Thomas Grubb (STC 1–36):

> "Dear Col. Sabine,
> I have communicated with Mr. Grubb as to his undertaking the construction of a 4-feet Reflector, and after discussing with him the whole matter, I think that he will be quite able to do it. With the exception of Mr. Nasmyth, who at present is too deeply engaged to wish to attend to such a task, I know of none at all so likely to succeed in this work as Mr. Grubb, especially if assisted by Lord Rosse's counsel and presence at the casting of the speculum. His premises are large enough to permit the instrument to be mounted on them, and he has a lathe of sufficient power to form the 4-feet tools and the axis of the equatorial. He would make this after that modification of the German plan which has been tried by Mr. Cooper on one of his own, of which he will have a model ready when Lord Rosse comes to Dublin. In casting the

specula he would leave a small aperture in the centre to try them as Cassegrains, which will not interfere with their employment as Newtonians, but which can be enlarged to give the full field if the former construction be preferred. In that case he would make the small mirror spherical, as more easily repolished if made of silver, and correct the larger one to it. As to costs, he <u>thinks</u> the instrument, two specula, a polishing machine, and one horse-power steam engine, could be furnished for £5000. As however several things must be experimental, I think it would be safer to ask for Lord Rosse's figure of £6000, with the understanding that the expenditure should be kept as low as possible. He thinks also, that with Lord Rosse to refer to in case of difficulties, the work ought to be completed in a twelvemonth from its commencement; the chief doubt being the loss of a month's annealing in case the first casting fails. Of this, from my acquaintance with Lord Rosse's process, I have little fear.

I would urge strongly on the committee the propriety of making this offer of Mr. Grubb the base of their application to the Government: if he be placed under the supervision of a small committee of practical men, with Lord Rosse as Chairman and Treasurer, I am confident he will do the work in a way that will prove satisfactory. If Mr. De la Rue would consent to be joined in this Committee, he could also give valuable aid; and if the Committee think that I can be useful, I shall be quite ready to assist.

While the telescope is in progress, the inquiries suggested by Mr. Airy and others as to Photography and elevation of site may be instituted, and when it is completed it can be tried by the Members of the Committee so fully, that we may be sure of its being a perfect working tool before it leaves the kingdom. All this presents no real difficulty, and the subsequent arrangements can be easily settled.

Yours ever ... "

[Note: The form of Cassegrain which makes use of a spherically-formed secondary and a primary which corrects for the consequent aberration is now referred to as a Dall-Kirkham. Without appropriate field-correcting lenses its images are only satisfactory on-axis and, as a consequence, this design is nowadays confined to instruments where low price is the primary consideration]

"At a Meeting of the Committee on the Southern Telescope, at the Royal Society, on July 5, 1853, The Earl of Rosse, P.R.S. [President of the Royal Society], in the Chair, it was Resolved:-

1. That the Committee approve the proposition made by Mr. Grubb, contained in Dr. Robinson's letter of the 30th of June.

2. That application be made to H.M. Government for the necessary funds.

3. That the Presidents of the Royal Society and of the British Association, accompanied by Dr. Robinson, who was associated with the Earl of Rosse in the former application, and Mr. Hopkins, President Elect of the British Association, be a Deputation to communicate with Government respecting the two preceding resolutions.

4. That the Earl of Rosse, Dr. Robinson, Mr. De la Rue and Mr. Lassell be a Sub-Committee for the purpose of superintending the progress of Mr. Grubb's undertaking." (STC 1–45)

Unfortunately, although representations were made in due course to the government, the outbreak of the Crimean War in effect caused the project to lose its urgency and get put aside. It was to remain dormant for nine years.

2.2   The Renewed Proposal

The proposal was renewed in 1862 by the Board of Visitors of the Melbourne Observatory, at the instigation of Prof W.P. Wilson[6], Professor of Mathematics at the newly founded University of Melbourne, who knew of the previous attempt. The Observatory had been established in 1853 for meteorological and meridian work and Wilson's idea was to make a name for the new institution by observations of nebulae. 'The attention of the Board was drawn to the following circumstances ... That the geographical position and clear atmosphere of Melbourne render it particularly suitable for this work, and that the arrangements already made for the establishment of an Astronomical Observatory on a permanent footing offer great facilities for carrying it on ...' (STC 2–6). The Governor of the relatively prosperous Colony of Victoria was induced to approach the Royal Society for advice on a suitable telescope. This renewal of interest may not have been quite as spontaneous as it seemed. Wilson had previously been a Professor at Queen's University, Belfast (see Perdrix 1992) and was acquainted with Romney Robinson, who had assisted him in setting up a small observatory there. Robinson had also been a member of the selection committee for Wilson's chair in Melbourne.

Lassell had by then built his 48-inch fork-mounted Newtonian reflector and he put forward reasons why the Committee should copy it. Robinson strongly opposed this proposal and continued to favour Grubb's design, pointing out the many drawbacks of Lassell's—excessive friction and lack of precision in the bearings, inability to observe within 35° of the Pole and danger to the observer from falling.

However, Herschel believed that a Cassegrain design would cause the observer to become excessively fatigued compared with the Newtonian or 'front-

---

[6]William Parkinson Wilson (1826–1874)

Figure 2.2: Romney Robinson, probably in his sixties (SAAO collection).

view' Herschelian[7] with which he was familiar. He advocated his own system of alt-azimuth mounting: '...there must be no <u>daring experiment</u> in-

---

[7]The Herschelian front-view telescope used a tilted primary which directly focussed on the eyepiece through which the observer looked, with his head at the front of the telescope tube. The extremely high f-ratios of Herschel's reflectors ensured that the distortion introduced by the off-axis arrangement was insignificant

curring <u>risk of failure'</u> (STC 2–21). Once again Robinson pooh-poohed the objections (STC 2–22). After all, Lassell had shown the practicality of an equatorial mounting. How could the observer be more fatigued when using a Cassegrain if he did not have to keep going up and down lofty ladders? 'Let us not raise up difficulties. It is undoubtably true that in Sir J. Herschel's hands the 20-foot reflector has wrought wonders; but there are few indeed like him, and even he must excuse me for thinking that he would have done still more with it, had its mounting been equatorial' (STC 2–22)

2.3   Speculum Metal or Silver-on-Glass?

The Committee were united in advocating the use of speculum metal mirrors instead of the newly-developed silver-on-glass reflectors of J.B.L. Foucault (1819–1868). As this decision appears today to have been a near-fatal one so far as the telescope's long-term success was concerned, it is interesting to examine why it went the way it did. Silver-on-glass mirrors have the desirable property that their reflecting surfaces can be renewed by a relatively simple process of chemical deposition while speculum metal ones have to be heavily re-polished with every likelihood of destroying their optical perfection. Further, a single silver surface in good condition reflects about 92% of visible light whereas a speculum reflects only 65%. In a two-mirror telescope such as a Newtonian or Cassegrain, the advantage in light output is thus almost 2:1 in favour of silver-on-glass optics.

Many of the Committee had cast, ground and polished their own specula and probably discounted the skills that they had had to acquire—for example, Lassell: 'It is therefore by no means necessary to repolish frequently, though there is no reason for hesitation on the ground of risk; for with the usual amount of care in the operation, a good and efficient surface, at least, may be always depended on. The process when resorted to consumes a day, and the operation of taking out one speculum and putting in another a like period' (STC 2–9).

Robinson was aware of Foucault's work, since the latter (Foucault 1857) had spoken on 'A Telescope Speculum of Silvered Glass' when the British Association met in Dublin in 1857. The telescope he described had an aperture of 10 cm diameter and a focal length of 50 cm. Thomas Grubb (1857) spoke in the same session, which concerned Light and Optical Instruments. In fact Foucault's reputation was already so well established that he was given the honorary degree of Doctor of Laws by Trinity College during the meeting, on September 2nd (Anon 1912b).

By 1862, Foucault's 80-cm reflector had been completed (Tobin, 1987), but Robinson remained sceptical. 'The application of silver surfaces to form specula which has been made by M. Foucault, seems very promising, but has not yet been sufficiently tested by experience for me to recommend its trial ... Nor have we sufficient knowledge whether the process which availed to figure a glass disc of 33 inches would be equally successful for one of 48 inches; or whether such a disc might not be more affected in its curvatures by changes of temperature than one of better conducting power. The Foucault system could easily be adapted to the small mirror; or in the Cassegrain (as has been tried successfully) this might be an achromatic combination silvered at its posterior surface. But as to the great speculum, I think the usual material is safest at present.' (STC 2–11). Herschel was in agreement (STC 2–13).

Rosse had perhaps a more realistic appreciation of the average astronomer's optical skills and wrote: 'I think it essential that some one should accompany the telescope as a mechanical assistant—he having been the principal operator in grinding and polishing the specula. Some intelligent optical glass-grinder who was sufficiently educated to read and understand all that had been written on the construction of reflecting telescopes, would probably answer' (STC 2–14). Robinson concurred '... but perhaps it might be better if the Australian observer himself were to come over, and while the process was going on, make himself familiar with all the details. The polishing [of] large specula is 'skilled work' of the highest order, and I do not think it can be effectually supervised by a mere mechanic' (STC 2–17).

The President and Council of the Royal Society duly recommended to the Melbourne authorities that the mirror should be of speculum and that the future observer should witness the construction of the instrument. De la Rue, who had been out of England, advised, on seeing the recommendation '... let the observer use the telescope, and not trouble himself about acquiring the art of figuring mirrors—I defy him to acquire the art in less than from four to five years. The possession of a polishing machine will be at first of about the same advantage as the possession of a complicated turning lathe would be to a gentleman desiring to become an amateur turner. Each must buy his experience by trial and failure. The finest figure may be spoiled in half an hour, and without the necessary knowledge will not be readily regained. Even for the most experienced the difficulties of producing critically fine figures are very great ... I have had a little experience with a silvered glass mirror of small size by Steinheil[8]. It was placed in my observatory, and care taken of it, but in less than two years the silvering underwent a molecular change, and broke up into minute scales. I think that glass mirrors should only be used by persons capable of resilvering them ... '(STC 2–33).

2.4   Grubb's Quotation

Grubb's quotation or estimate was contained in a letter to Robinson dated Dec 3, 1862 (STC 2–23):

"My Dear Dr. Robinson,

---

[8]Karl August von Steinheil 1801–1870, Munich optician

The plans and estimates which about nine years ago I transmitted for the consideration of the Committee, at that time formed to report on the erecting of a powerful telescope in the Southern Hemisphere, having had the honour of being approved of by that Committee (although the design was never carried into effect on account of the British Government declining to supply the requisite funds), it seems desirable, now that the same Committee are reconsidering the matter at the request of some of the spirited inhabitants of Melbourne, that I should, as the successful projector on the former occasion, prepare for laying before the present Committee such data as circumstances occurring during the interval suggest.

I would then first state that nothing has presented itself to induce me to alter even in details the original design, much less to disturb my faith in its entire effectiveness ...

Estimate—The residents of Melbourne having sometime since desired to have an estimate including one large speculum (only), and exclusive of polishing machinery, I have estimated for either such, or with the additional large speculum (ad libitum). With respect to the prices named, I desire to make a few observations. I should think it imprudent on my part to name a sum which would only pay provided everything went smoothly, and no such thing happened as a failure in the casting, or breakage in the completion, of the specula; and I should think it very indiscreet to name a sum which would curb me in executing the entire in a manner creditable and satisfactory to all concerned, including myself. The recent strides in the manufacture of steel would induce me to see how far this substance might be advantageously substituted (of course not without adding to the expense) in several parts where I had originally intended to use either cast or wrought iron—for example, the declination axis, and the telescope-tube. Another observation I desire to make is, that without wishing in any way to detract from the merits and excellence of Mr. Lassell's large equatorial, of which indeed I have only seen a lithographic drawing, and therefore could not pretend to form an opinion—I say without expressing any opinion as to the workmanship, I think that any one at all conversant in such matters may see that the two constructions (viz. his and mine) are so entirely different in character that it would be quite impossible to judge of what one could be made for by knowing what the other cost ...

My original estimate was £4500. There are some things now added, and my present estimate will be £3800 for one speculum only and no polishing machinery, or £4600 for everything as before with the present additions. The difference between these two sums, of £800, would scarcely more than cover the actual cost of the items to be furnished for it; but it is not unlikely that in any case I should find it desirable to cast a second large speculum, and I place the advantage of taking the second speculum with the customer.

Faithfully yours,

Thomas Grubb."

In spite of an eleventh hour offer from Lassell to present his telescope outright, Grubb got the order. A 'Committee on the Melbourne Telescope', consisting of Rosse, Robinson and De la Rue, was appointed to supervise the construction.

2.5 Enter Howard Grubb

When the order for the telescope finally arrived in February 1866, Howard Grubb was 21 years old and a student of Engineering at Trinity College . He had first registered as a 'pensioner', or ordinary fee-paying student, of the 'English Church' on 13 October 1863 at the age of 18. His previous schoolmaster, according to College records, was Mr North, whose establishment was at the Grand Canal end of Rathmines Road, not far from the Grubb workshops and home. Much later in life he related to an interviewer (FitzGerald 1896) that his father had given him the choice of entering the Royal Engineers or joining him at his optical work.

Because Grubb senior was fully occupied with his work for the Bank of Ireland, Howard was withdrawn from College before completing his degree, to be effectively placed in charge of the Melbourne work. In his 1896 interview he recollected '... this Melbourne Telescope practically brought our optical works into being; for the moment the order was given, my father bought a piece of land at Rathmines and erected temporary workshops, machinery, and furnaces, suitable for casting the 4ft. speculum mirror.'

2.6 Building the Telescope

We are fortunate in having a detailed account of the telescope and its construction written by Robinson and T. Grubb (1869). The speculum was composed of four equivalents copper to one of tin, the combination found by Rosse to have the greatest resistance to tarnishing. The casting process itself was also based on Rosse's experience. The mould was of a special construction. Its base was made of iron hoops clamped tightly together side by side, i.e. on edge, and turned smooth after assembly. This was to allow the escape of gases as the bottom of the casting was found to remain molten much longer than the top and cavities were likely to form. This base had to be pre-heated to prevent premature solidification of the metal and bolted when hot to the rest of the mould. A special underfloor mechanism was devised to tilt the mould

Figure 2.3: Howard Grubb, probably aged about 35 (Mary Lea Shane Archives, Lick Observatory).

for the start of the pouring and lower it as it became full—this was found necessary to obtain a homogeneous disc. Once the metal had solidified, the base was released and the hot mirror was winched into the annealing furnace where it was cooled very slowly.

Howard Grubb well remembered those fateful days which he knew would make or break his name as a telescope maker. Later, as Sir Howard, the famous telescope-maker, he recollected the dramatic proceedings of 1866 (Fitz-Gerald 1896):

'First of all, we bought two tons of fine copper and one of tin. When this metal was mixed, the two small furnaces were removed and a very large one built, capable of containing a cast-iron pot weighing one and a half tons and holding two tons of metal.

The first actual casting took place on the 3rd July, 1866, but for three weeks previously the annealing oven had to be kept fired night and day with a mixture of coke and compressed peat. At last the whole mass of brickwork, and 12 tons of sand on top, were well heated, so we lifted the great pot by its crane and placed it in position on its cast-iron cushion. The furnace was then loosely filled with turf, and lit at the top at 1 p.m.

Everything went on grandly till evening, and we thought to put the first charge in the pot at three o'clock the following morning. Knowing that next day would be a little trying, I went to bed early, leaving word that I was to be called at 3 a.m. At 12.30 a messenger rushed into the house with the cheerful news that the works were in flames; the almost red-hot chimney had set fire to the roof. I rose quicker than usual, and was presently playing on the blazing timbers with a garden-hose. This was no good, so I just sawed away the beams from around the shaft, and then let the roof flare away. I felt like Nero, rather; only more so, considering the outlook for our big mirror.

After this we charged the pot with the first 2 cwt [100kg] of metal, which behaved well; but at ten o'clock the same morning, troubles began. The chimney's roar decreased, and the furnace became dull, as though tired of the whole process already. No wonder; it was fairly choked with the ashes of that awful peat we used. We had to begin stoking, only it was killing work. You see, we had to get on top of the furnace and the molten metal to do it. We all took spells, and when each man gave up, he dashed out, panting, into the open air. Then the metal began to solidify, and things looked desperate. We expected to be ready to pour at 5 or 6 p.m., and had therefore asked a few scientific friends round to see the operation; so you can imagine how we were placed. The heat had to be got up somehow, so we resolved to make the chimney higher. There were lots of bricks about, and in twenty minutes the shaft had grown 6ft.—no easy job, I can tell you, with a great flame mounting high into the air out of it.

At this point the men grew listless and exhausted, so my father

and I set to work ourselves, with the best results. We mixed coke
with the peat and the furnace revived; so did the men. At 11 p.m.
all was ready for pouring; but so excited were the men by this time
that we had to call them into another room and warn them about
the serious and dangerous operation they were about to conduct.

The bed of hoop was placed in position by the crane, and the
ring of loam [used to form the side of the mould] put round it. The
pot stirrups were placed on the crane, and every man was at his
place. I leaped onto the annealing oven and ordered the furnace
cover to be removed. Great flames immediately leaped from the
furnace. The four men at the crane hauled on, and out came the
mighty red-hot pot, with its mass of molten metal; the cushion
came too—stuck to the bottom. I skimmed the pot myself; but
here I want to give you a notion of the awful, withering heat of
the place. The room was small. Besides the monstrous red-hot
pot and its glowing contents, there were the melting furnace, the
open furnace for heating the hoop bed, and, lastly, the fifty tons
of red-hot brickwork that formed the annealing oven. I'm a strong
man, but the moment I did reach the open air I fainted away.

The metal was poured in about six seconds. Every man wore
a large apron and gauntlets of thick felt, with an uncanny-looking
calico hood, soaked in alum, drawn completely over his head. This
hood was provided with large, glistening talc eyes. These weird
figures flitted about in the ghastly light of the intense soda-flame
that leaped from the great furnace, and the windows were filled
with the eager faces of fascinated spectators.

There was another hitch: the solidified speculum would not
come off its bed, in spite of the efforts of six ghostly individuals
winching the chain leading through the annealing oven to the casting. If the temperature had decreased too far, the casting would
have become useless. Some metal had got into the interstices of
the hoops and formed solid pins. At last someone jumped on the
chain and the pins gave way. Within seconds, the casting was in
the oven. All apertures of the oven were then sealed. A thermo-
couple, connected to a galvanometer, was sealed in to monitor the
temperature just above the mirror.

At 1 a.m. on the 4th. July I got home, having laboured continuously in that frightful place for twenty-four hours.'

This first casting was unsuccessful but served to show how the procedures
could be improved. 'The men were drilled every day for a fortnight before the
second and third castings, which were conducted in perfect silence.' The first
satisfactory speculum, known as 'A' was cast on September 22, 1866, and the
second, 'B', on November 24. Annealing took 23 days.

The grinding and polishing machine is shown in fig. 2.5. It is much simpler

Figure 2.4: The casting of a speculum for the Great Melbourne Telescope. The crucible of molten speculum metal is seeing being moved to the tipping frame, from which it will be poured into the circular mould. After that, the mirror and the upper part of the mould was hauled into the annealing furnace in the background. The lower part of the mould was removed by the step in front of the annealing oven (FitzGerald 1896).

than that previously described and, in fact, is very similar in design to modern ones. The speculum itself was rotated slowly while the tool was driven by the adjustable cranks HH. Thus circular or elliptical motion of the tool was possible. To lighten the action of the tool, the rod K reached up to the ceiling where it was pulled upwards by a lever and weights. A sort of inverted set of mirror support levers made sure that the weight of the tool was evenly relieved. A geared sector at the side of the machine was used to tilt it so that the mirror could easily be tested optically without dismounting it.

The first operation was to cut out the central hole in the primary which was partly, but not completely, formed during the casting. This was done 'with a crown saw and sand'. The front was then ground roughly to the approximate curve, the back ground flat, and the edge trued. The speculum was then placed on its 'equilibrated lever' supports and the front completed. The grinder was a convex disc of cast iron, the same size as the mirror. Its surface was divided into 3-inch squares with half-inch spaces. Rough work was done using sand and water while the fine grinding utilised very fine emery and water. [These were the standard grinding materials before about 1890, when the much harder substance, carborundum, became available.]

"The pressure in grinding was, on an average, 112 lbs, [50 kg], and the number of strokes of the machine 32 in a minute, and of considerable extent. The speculum revolves once for 14 strokes. The rough grinding occupied 650 hours and the fine grinding 520 hours.

The polisher is built up of a great number of slips of fine deal laid in layers and crossed, each layer being firmly glued and nailed to the next. The face was turned to the requisite curvature, and strongly varnished. This is coated with pitch, adjusted to the requisite hardness by Mr. Nasmyth's test; this material was rolled into slips of uniform thickness, and cut by pressure into $\frac{7}{8}$ inch squares, while still soft, and these were applied to the surface of the polisher, by softening one side of them over a gas- or spirit-flame; the intervals between the squares were $\frac{5}{8}$ inch. It is needless to go into the details of polishing, which have been fully described by Lord Rosse and Mr. Lassell, beyond remarking that both the pressure and the lengths of the strokes are about $\frac{1}{5}$ of what are used in grinding."

Three secondaries were supplied, two of speculum with slightly differing compositions, and the other an achromatized, back-silvered, glass one. The long focal length of the primary, 366 inches, (f-ratio 7.6) ensured that the aspherization of the mirrors was somewhat less critical than it would be for a modern design. We know almost nothing about the kinds of optical tests that were performed. It is quite possible that Grubb employed the Foucault test by this time, since it had been published in 1859 (Foucault 1859; Tobin 1987) but this would only have been of use for the primary. Some later papers of Howard Grubb and a letter of G.G. Stokes, who began to furnish advice on optical matters to the Grubbs about this time, suggest that preliminary testing was done with the aid of relatively local light sources and diaphragms, allowing particular zones to be tested independently. The final touches depended on the examination and interpretation of stellar images (see later chapters).

The mirror back support system was a particularly compact form of the system of equilibrated levers first utilized for the Armagh reflector. This was supplemented for edge support by a closely, but not tightly, fitting band of L cross-section, which itself was held in place by a closely fitting fixed band of similar section. Thus at the expense of a little variation in the position of the primary, it was supported similarly in all orientations. This system was viewed sceptically by old-timers such as Herschel who supported his mirror from slipping downwards when tilted by means of a horizontal bar fixed to its rear surface. Herschel's mirrors thus were only suited to alt-azimuth mounts because they could not be rotated.

The mounting was very massive to give stability, but counterbalanced by Grubb's usual arrangement of levers so that no very great weight rested on

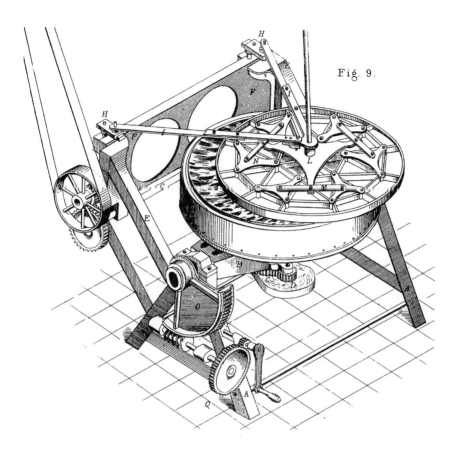

Fig. 9.

Figure 2.5: The polishing machine supplied with the Great Melbourne Telescope. It was driven by a steam engine (Robinson and Grubb 1869).

the bearings which defined the exact positions of the axes. For the right ascension axis, a torque of 5 lbs at 20 feet radius was required, while for the declination axis, $12\frac{1}{2}$ lbs at 20 feet were needed. 'Still one man can raise the telescope from the horizon to the zenith in 20 seconds. In reversing it from one side of the pier to the other, two men are necessary for quick work, as it must be moved in [declination] as well as [right ascension]. They do it in 45 seconds.' The position circles could be read by means of verniers to 1 second of time and 10 seconds of arc. A large and powerful governor-regulated clock of Grubb's usual design provided the R.A. drive. It could be adjusted to give special speeds for following planets and a special set of gears gave a lunar rate. The final right ascension drive was through a sector. 'Extraordinary precautions were taken in cutting the teeth of this sector, which are believed to be as exact as many dividing engines.'

Figure 2.6: The Great Melbourne Telescope assembled in Grubb's yard in Dublin. The houses in the background are on Rathmines Road. The well-known engraving by André and Rayet (1874) is a romanticized version of this picture (Mansell Collection).

Eyepieces giving powers from 220 to 1000 were furnished. These had to be specially designed on account of the large focal-plane scale. A micrometer was also provided. A plate holder and shutter were available to be used at the prime focus instead of the secondary. Finally, a spectroscope could be attached at the Cassegrain focus.

> "The weight of the moving parts of this huge telescope is 18,170 lbs., of which the great speculum and its box and support are 3500."

The final inspection by the Melbourne Telescope Committee took place at Grubb's works on February 17, 1868. By this time William Parsons, 3rd Earl of Rosse had died and his son, Laurence, had succeeded as 4th Earl. The Committee reported to the Council of the Royal Society on March 19: (STC 3–9)

> "...The Committee, after minutely and carefully studying the mechanical details of the equatorial, have come unanimously to the conclusion that it is a masterpiece of engineering. Its movements are surprisingly smooth and steady ...The clock is smooth and equable in its action ...The Committee found that the light even of large [sic] stars was collected into small, hard, and perfectly circular disks, free from rays ...The 5th and 6th stars of the Trapezium of Orion were not only plainly seen, but were very bright ...the companion of gamma Andromedae was clearly divided with the powers of 350 and 450, and the different tints of the components were evident ...With respect to the Nebulae, it is needless to say more than that Lord Rosse considers its performance in bringing out the details of the Orion Nebula, 1 M. (the Crab), and 51 M. (the Great Spiral), quite satisfactory ...
>
> The Committee conclude by stating that they have no hesitation in declaring that the instrument is perfectly fit for the work for which it was designed. They therefore consider that Mr. Grubb has fulfilled his contract, and have directed him to lose no time in preparing the necessary cases and packing it for Melbourne ...
>
> The Committee feel bound to say that Mr. Grubb has put a most liberal construction on the terms of his contract; and after their minute examination of the excellence of the Telescope, and the amount and perfection of the machinery connected with it and its manufacture, they are convinced that Mr. Grubb has been more influenced by the desire of producing a perfect instrument than by any prospect of pecuniary advantage, and can scarcely realize the possibility of giving so much for the sum named in the contract, especially when it is considered that special works had to be erected for the purpose of constructing the telescope.'
>
> Rosse,
T.R. Robinson, D.D.,
Warren De La Rue.

Lassell, though not a member of the Committee, added a report of his own:

> "...I freely express my opinion that the entire instrument is a great triumph of mechanical engineering and optical skill; and, with the advantages of efficient working and a fine atmosphere, I trust it will add something to our knowledge of the heavenly bodies." (STC 3–13)

Figure 2.7: Group of workmen at the base of the Great Melbourne Telescope during assembly in Dublin. The special mirror-handling trolley is seen beneath the instrument (Royal Astronomical Society).

The dismantling of the telescope for shipment started at the end of April 1868. To protect the specula they were coated with varnish on the advice of Lassell. Le Sueur, who had been appointed Assistant at Melbourne on Stokes's recommendation and who had participated in the polishing operations, personally supervised their stowage on board a steam tug specially chartered for the trip from Dublin to Liverpool and their transshipment for the voyage to Australia. The trip took from July to November 1868 (Hyde 1987).

2.7 The Fate of the Great Melbourne Telescope

The telescope was to be housed in Melbourne in an 80-foot long building orientated N–S. The northern 40 feet had a sliding roof of corrugated iron and the remainder housed the polishing machine, its engine and other facilities. Regular observing commenced in mid-August 1869.

Trouble had been encountered in the attempt to remove the varnish layer from speculum A. Brush-marks remained visible, and the surface had 'an unpleasant mealy appearance'. Nevertheless, mounted like this, 'the views given of the brighter nebulae were grand in the extreme, and left nothing to be desired' (Le Sueur 1870). However, the surface tarnished and became yellow very rapidly. Worse still, the stellar images were like an imperfect cross 'somewhat resembling the ace of clubs' (Wilson *et al* 1870). The second mirror (B) was successfully cleaned, although pocked by two patches 2 inches square caused by droppings of the acid flux used when the mirror was being sealed up in a tin box for shipment. However, the performance with mirror B was more satisfactory. As reports reached Grubb and Robinson of the apparently poor performance that was being experienced, they naturally became upset and felt they had to defend themselves. Robinson (STC 3–27) commented on the deterioration of mirror A. The centre piece that had been cut out of the speculum to form the centre hole was still in Dublin. It was experimentally varnished and cleaned without problems arising. Robinson and Grubb were soon led to the conclusion that the problems had arisen from the use of methylated spirits instead of alcohol to remove the lac, some of whose constituents were waxy. This process had been followed by mopping with water 'which was quite improper' and known to accelerate tarnishing. Since re-polishing seemed inevitable, it was decided to send out a scaled-down model set of mirrors, complete with mounting, to practise on. This cost a further £165.

Further aspects of the instrument were attacked in Ellery's Report to the Board of Visitors of the Melbourne Observatory on 31 March 1870. The drawings sent for construction of the piers had allegedly been incorrect for the latitude of Melbourne and, if they had been followed as they were, the movement of the telescope would have been limited unnecessarily. [Grubb later retorted that the proper drawing had been sent but a much earlier one intended only as a guide to laying the foundations for the piers had been followed. (Grubb 1870)] The lengths of the drive shafts from the clock had not been corrected for the revised latitude and had had to be changed. Various other small parts had also to be altered. The secondary mirror associated with speculum A had been successfully re-polished. Perhaps too much had been expected:

> "The experience which can only be obtained by years observing
> with large reflectors is the only safe guide in forming an opinion
> of the comparative merits of a telescope of this kind, and that it

> is an experience which no one outside of Great Britain possesses;
> it is more than probable, therefore, that the want of it has led
> ourselves and others to expect more from optical science, than we
> had any right to, and that we looked for as comparatively a perfect
> telescope as is sometimes obtained with smaller apertures."

These reports, particularly about the tarnishing of speculum A and the cruciform images, disturbed Thomas Grubb so much that he printed a pamphlet (Grubb 1870) in his own defence, attributing the problems to improper techniques having been used at Melbourne.

Matters in Melbourne were not helped by local carpers who went so far as to question the wisdom of the whole project. A lengthy and ill-informed debate took place at the Royal Society of Victoria which was printed in *The Illustrated Australian News* and later in the *Astronomical Register* (Anon 1870) in London. This criticism, lacking a reasonable basis, was easily dealt with. More seriously for the project, Le Sueur decided to resign his post in 1870 and thus first-hand experience of figuring and polishing techniques was lost to the Observatory. However, mirror A was repolished together with the secondaries before his departure and was shortly afterwards put back in the telescope. The 'ace of clubs' images were found to have been the result of some pinching of the speculum and did not reappear.

The telescope was used mainly for visual observations of nebulae. Some photography was undertaken in the early 1870s, but this promising work was not followed up. Part of the reason appears to have been wind-shaking, caused by the lack of a dome to shield the instrument. A volume of *Observations of the Southern Nebulae made with the Great Melbourne Telescope* was published, with difficulty, in 1885 (Ellery 1885).

Whatever the reason, Ellery did not give the telescope the attention it deserved and it gradually fell into disuse. It may be presumed that Ellery's interests were those of a positional astronomer rather than of an astrophysicist. It is a rather remarkable feature of the period that the professionals largely ignored astrophysics and left the great discoveries to amateurs. It is easy, of course, to see in retrospect that the reflector could have been used for photography or spectroscopy, both of which were to become rapidly advancing fields within a decade. Ellery saw no reason to exert himself in these areas and he consequently lacked the incentive to maintain and observe with the Great Melbourne Telescope. The staff of the Melbourne Observatory was too small, like many others of those times, and could not cope with the observing opportunities presented by a large telescope, let alone its maintenance requirements. Published observations made with the instrument were few and far between and it came to be regarded as a failure.

A recent evaluation of the Great Melbourne Telescope by Gascoigne (1995) suggests that it was really unsuited for almost all the types of astronomical work being pursued at the end of the 19th century. Mainly, its Cassegrain f-ratio (41) was far too high. Both photography and the examination of nebulae by eye, the two fields for which it was supposedly built, require that the light should be concentrated as far as possible. Attempts to obtain photographs at the prime focus (f7.6) were made, but the problems involved were very great.

G.W. Ritchey's widely quoted comment of 1904 can now be seen to be unfair, or at least to have implicitly laid the blame in the wrong place: 'I consider the failure of the Melbourne Instrument to have been one of the greatest calamities in the history of instrumental astronomy; for by destroying confidence in the usefulness of great reflecting telescopes, it has hindered the development of this type of instrument, so wonderfully efficient in photographic and spectroscopic work, for nearly a third of a century'. The instrument as such was not the reason for failure. It was the organization of its users and their inability to produce spectacular discoveries that was lacking. Ritchey had the benefit of building his successful 60-inch for George Ellery Hale, an astronomer possessing an abundance of organizational ability who saw to it that his telescopes were properly staffed and used. Other giant telescopes built in the meantime, such as Common's[9] silver-on-glass 60-inch, were also rather unsuccessful.

The Melbourne Observatory's funds were whittled away by the Victoria Government and it was finally closed in 1945 (Hogg, 1958). The 48-inch was removed to Mt Stromlo where it was reconstructed almost completely during the 1950s, using a 50-inch glass mirror. Few of the original parts remain in use. It is now, at last, housed in a dome. Although the reconstruction had been done with the idea of using it for infrared work, in fact it has provided the base for the MACHO gravitational lensing project and has at last, in this guise, made a major contribution to astronomy (Hart 1996).

---

[9] Andrew Ainslie Common (1841–1903). See section 5.2

Chapter 3

The 1870s—David Gill

3.1 Changes in the Firm

The construction of the Great Melbourne Telescope marked not only the establishment of the Grubbs' new Optical Works as a serious concern, but also made them internationally famous. From now on, everyone interested in the construction of large telescopes flocked to see them and at least sought their advice before embarking on new projects.

Although it is often stated that Howard Grubb took over the firm in 1868 on the retirement of his father (see for example Young 1931), it seems that this date marks the commencement of a partnership between them, for much of the correspondence was still signed by Thomas. An advertisement in *The British Journal Photographic Almanac and Photographer's Daily Companion* for 1869 gives the name of the firm as 'Messrs Grubb & Son (Formerly Thomas Grubb)'. They were 'Manufacturers of Patent and Other Photographic Lenses, Reflecting and Refracting Telescopes, Equatorial and Other mountings for Ditto, Machinery & Apparatus for Revolving Domes, Spectroscopic Apparatus, &c., &c.'

The 'Other' photographic lenses probably did not constitute a large part of the business. The Royal Dublin Society has however a Grubb lens marked 'Grubb Dublin 3712' which is not of the 'patent' type. Instead, it has three elements and a removable stop. By 1873 the firm was called 'Howard Grubb (Late Grubb & Son)' (Burnett and Morrison-Low 1989).

Thomas Grubb's original workshop, the Charlemont Bridge Works, was probably leased out, since Thom's *Dublin Directory* for 1870 lists their occupant as David Harris, billiard table maker and mechanical engineer. However, during World War I it was again occupied by Grubb for war production.

3.2   Theoretical Advice from G.G. Stokes

Theoretical backing in optics for the Grubb telescope concern was provided
by George Gabriel Stokes (1819–1903), Lucasian Professor of Mathematics in
Cambridge University. Stokes, although educated mostly in England, was a
member of a well-known Irish family. One of his ancestors, Gabriel Stokes
(1682–1768), had been an instrument maker in Dublin. George Gabriel had
married a daughter of Romney Robinson and was consequently a frequent
visitor to Armagh Observatory.

His interest in the Grubbs probably arose around 1869, when he was asked
to help in evaluating a 12-inch cemented doublet telescope objective. He
examined the performance of several zones with the aid of an object only 150
feet away. The cement was found to have caused severe distortion (Stokes
G473). He also interacted with them as Secretary of the Royal Society, from
which he had sought their help (Stokes G475) in testing the experimental
glasses being produced in a sort of national research programme by Vernon
Harcourt.

Later, he had occasion to make further contact in connection with the telescope that the Royal Society was providing for Huggins (see below). Asking
Stokes for advice had to be done with caution as Sir Joseph Larmor (1907c),
who edited Stokes's collected correspondence after his death, found out when
he wrote to Howard Grubb to enquire whether he had any material to con-
tribute:

> "After such a long lapse of time I am afraid that any letters
> of Prof. Stokes' I could get together would be of very little use,
> as many I fear have been lost amongst the mass of correspon-
> dence which accumulated in so many years; they are for the most
> part disconnected and disjointed, he having written in his spare
> moments, sometimes in railway trains, sometimes at the Royal
> Society, and sometimes at home, and it would be very difficult in-
> deed to find anything that would be really useful for publication.
> He was wonderfully painstaking in answering my queries, so much
> so that I sometimes hesitated to ask him even a simple question,
> fearing it would encroach upon his time, for he went so deeply and
> minutely into every aspect of the question that in some cases I
> had as many as 5 postcards or letters from him in 24 hours, each
> describing some new view of the particular subject I had enquired
> about."

Stokes saw the Grubbs as much more scientific in their work than other
contemporary lens makers. In a letter of 1870 to Vernon Harcourt (Larmor
1907d), discussing the methods for correcting spherical aberration in lenses
he says 'As to the first requirement [accurate calculation of the radii of cur-
vature], few I imagine, if any, of our English practical opticians possess the
requisite mathematical knowledge ... [They] correct for the residual spherical

aberration by polishing the glass in zones by trial. This a bungling process compared with that which Grubb employs—less scientific and incomparably more difficult[1]'. Again, from a letter to Joseph Lockyer about a faulty lens in a solar telescope: '...it would not cost much to get a proper [lens]. I should think Grubb would do it for 3 or 4 pounds or less. Why go to Paris for a bad article when we can get a good one in Dublin?' (Larmor 1907e).

3.3 Huggins

During the 1860s astrophysics began to take off. The Grubbs, now established successfully as astronomical instrument makers, made many of the new instruments that were required. The great pioneer of spectroscopy was William Huggins (1824–1910) who worked at his private observatory at 90 Upper Tulse Hill, London, with his friend the spectroscopist W.A. Miller. The main telescope they used had an 8-inch lens supplied by Alvan Clark of Cambridge, Massachusetts on an equatorial by Cooke of York. Clark and his sons were to be the suppliers of a large fraction of the lenses for the world's refracting telescopes including the three largest and were, of course, rivals of Grubb. The Royal Society felt the need to promote the new field in England, the President (Sir Edward Sabine 1869) observing that 'Celestial spectroscopy has indeed attained such importance, that it requires for its successful prosecution the undivided attention of the astronomer who devotes himself to it, as well as an observatory specially designed for it.' Referring to the one-sidedness of the official astronomical community he went on 'our greatest national observatories cannot supply this want, for they have their own specific destination; and the high optical power which is required, if we wish to make further progress, is scarcely within the reach of amateurs'. It was suggested that the Royal Society should 'provide a telescope of the highest power that is conveniently available for spectroscopy and kindred inquiries. The instrument ...will be intrusted to such persons, as in their opinion, are the most likely to use it to the best advantage for the extension of this branch of science; and, in the first instance, there can be but one opinion that the person so selected should be Mr. Huggins.'

Proposals were solicited from the chief optical companies. G.G. Stokes seems to have been in charge of arrangements from the Royal Society's side. On 19 January 1869, Thomas Grubb wrote [Stokes G648]:

"With respect to the proposed object glass—of course I guarantee its excellence, for the accomplishment of which my previous success including that in reflecting Instruments should entitle me to confidence."

---

[1]Before Howard Grubb started manufacturing refractors, the most noted British telescope maker was Thomas Cooke of York (1807–1868). According to Smiles (1884), Cooke was self-taught.

Figure 3.1: *Left:* William Huggins, pioneer astrophysicist *Right:* Charles Pritchard, Professor of Astronomy at Oxford (SAAO collection).

The formal quotation was sent only on 1 March 1869 and was accepted in April. The Grubbs were to provide an achromatic refractor of 15 inches aperture and not more than 15 feet focus. The circles were to be readable from the floor, at the suggestion of Mr de la Rue. A reflecting telescope of 18 inches aperture with a mirror of speculum metal was also to be provided in order to be able to study the infrared. This was to be interchangeable with the refractor. Completion was expected in December 1869.

Grubb seems to have been very confident about getting the contract for, as early as the 23rd of March [Stokes G662], he mentions that he had already got the blanks from Chance Brothers and was busy determining their optical characteristics:

> "We have got the pair of 15 in discs safely and they are being fascetted[2] preparatory to taking the indices.
>
> An ordinary theodolite you will see is not adapted to such work and I think you will approve of what I have constructed. It consists of two sectors of about 9 inches radius and 30° of readings— divided to 5′ of arc & reading by verniers to 5″—each sector carries

---

[2]Small flat surfaces were made on the sides of the rough blanks so that they could be placed like prisms in a spectrograph for measurement of their optical constants.

in its arm a telescope of 14 inches focus & $1\frac{3}{4}$ aperture.

The sectors are mounted on a frame so as to be capable of being placed at any required distance asunder (in the case before me at about 17 inches) — and the disc to be examined is placed upon a stage at the proper height and not disturbed during the examinations. The telescopes being first collimated the measures for minimum deviation are obtained by moving both telescopes through equal or nearly equal arcs. The limit of error will probably [be] the accuracy of the surfaces of the facets."

There was a good deal of trouble with the Chance discs for the 15-inch refractor (Stokes G674), and the lens took almost a year to figure. We learn that the cricket field (Leinster Cricket Club) behind the Rathmines works was used for testing [T. Grubb to Stokes, 21 June 1869; Stokes G685]:

"It happens with us that the ground on which alone it would be of any use to erect the proposed apparatus [for testing the lens] is for the most part a cricket field and I can scarcely suppose any thing safe if left out."

When the telescope was at last ready Grubb told Stokes:

"Mr Huggins defers coming over until after the 1st Proximo. He seems to think hardly [?] of coming over but whether it is the sea voyage or the Fenians which deter him seems doubtful."

These telescopes were mounted under a drum-shaped roof on top of Huggins' London house, in the southern suburb of Tulse Hill.

During 1879 Huggins told Gill [SAAO, 26 July 1879] that he was thinking of using his own money to purchase a 3-foot reflector from Grubb, usable in either his own observatory or at the Cape. He suggested that the Royal Society would be willing to send the existing twin telescope to the Cape, as Gill had been looking for something better than existed there and was considering the possibility of borrowing Newall's 25-inch telescope, a somewhat old-fashioned one. In fact, the reflector was never ordered.

In 1882, the mounting of Huggins' telescope was modified by Grubb so that both reflector and refractor could be made use of simultaneously.

3.4 Marriage of Howard Grubb

On 5 September 1871 Howard Grubb married Mary Hester Walker in St Peter's Church (Church of Ireland). His bride was born in 1854 in New Orleans, of Irish parents. Her father, George Hamilton Walker, had been born in Kells, Co Meath. Their first home was at 17 Leinster Square, Rathmines, close by the Optical Works.

Figure 3.2: Mary Hester Grubb, wife of Howard Grubb. Date unknown (Photo: Mr R.B. Grubb).

The children of this marriage were Ethel (1872), Howard Thomas (1875), George Rudolph (1878), Romney Robinson (1879), Herman (1882) and Mary (1889).

3.5 Edinburgh Reflector

In July 1871 Howard Grubb visited Edinburgh for discussions with Charles Piazzi Smyth, the eccentric Royal Astronomer for Scotland, about the provision of a 24-inch reflector for his observatory, then on Calton Hill. Smyth had an idea in the back of his mind that the telescope should be transportable and the mounting was consequently designed to be rather lighter than was usual. The result was an unstable instrument that never did much good work.

According to Smyth's biographers, (Brück and Brück, 1988) 'The terms of the contract were extraordinarily simple, saying essentially no more than that the telescope with subsidiary apparatus, a 15-foot revolving dome and observing chair at a total cost of £2350 should "work well to the satisfaction of the Astronomer Royal for Scotland" '. The contract was signed on 14 October 1871 and it provided for delivery within 14 months, a penalty of £10 per week being payable in the event of a delay.

The 24-inch reflector gave the Grubbs some trouble in silvering, as they reported to Stokes [Stokes G485]. In fact, it was their first silver-on-glass primary, and it is not surprising that the coating required some experimentation to perfect.

By 19 December 1872, the telescope was almost complete. Smyth was at first quite pleased and advised G. Russell, the Secretary of the Office of Works (ROE), that Grubb should be paid:

> "In all main essentials his work is not only performed, but admirably performed; so that the large Edinburgh Equatorial so long looked forward to by the scientific public here, is now at last a reality, is mounted in its place and is nearly ready to begin a useful course of observation ... Mr Grubb however intends leaving his men here for some days longer to wait for better weather ... I would beg therefore to recommend that the balance of the contract be forthwith paid over to Mr Grubb as being deservedly due to him. Indeed, considering the size and difficulty of the work, including both an iron revolving Dome and a reflecting Equatorial of larger aperture than at present contained in any other public Observatory in this country, Mr Grubb's performance has been truly a marvel of despatch, punctuality, economy and success almost without a parallel in the history of large telescopes ... "

At this point, something seems to have happened which soured Smyth's attitude. He suddenly became very truculent. Although Lambert was sent over from Rathmines to clear up small remaining matters, Smyth kept wanting

more and more things done and Grubb had to put in a claim for money still
owing [ROE, Grubb to Smyth, 19 February 1873]. Relations deteriorated,
and we find this cautionary letter from Thomas Grubb to Howard, written 1
September 1873 [ROE]:

> "I consider you ought to be very careful how you enter upon an
> arbitration with such a man as Professor Smyth has proved himself
> to be, more especially when some matters which have cropped out
> are kept in view. You will recollect the sudden apparent change
> in Prof Smyth's actions which occurred at the time of his being
> refused the Government Grant in connexion with the Instrument—
> from which time he appeared to me not only indifferent about its
> completion but rather inclined to retard it, perhaps in order to
> afford an excuse for not working it efficiently ..."

Writing to Captain Floyd, Secretary to the Trustees of Lick Observatory,
on 10 August 1876 [Shane], in order to prepare him for a visit to Scotland,
Grubb explained how he had seen the matter:

> "In Edinburgh there is a 2 foot silver on glass Reflector I put
> up a few years since but it is in a very unfortunate condition. I
> think I mentioned it to you but I may as well speak of it again
> in case you hear anything about it. The Astronomer Royal there
> Prof Piazzi Smyth is a very curious crotchety individual but I kept
> on good terms with him until on coming to put up the telescope I
> found the Pier (which he himself superintended) so unstable that
> I could rock it with my finger a quantity that could easily be seen
> by a person standing in a room below the observatory & thru'
> which the Pier passed. He asked me not to speak of this & I did
> not do so until I found he began to find fault with every part of
> the Telescope, even parts he had before praised in order to com-
> pel me to take the telescope down & give him an opportunity of
> remedying his Rickety Pier. I then informed the Government of
> the state of the case & ever since that he has annoyed me with
> every possible petty annoyance. He refused to pass the Telescope
> so that I could get my money & issued report after report with
> Series of complaints every one of which proved in the end to be
> utterly groundless; at last after a couple of years of such work I
> told the Government they should appoint an arbitrator & they sent
> up the 1st Assistant in Greenwich & when he sent in his report the
> Government wrote me a letter complimenting me on the success
> & efficiency of the whole affair including all those parts so much
> abused by Prof Smyth, so since that time I have heard nothing
> of him ... If you pay us a visit again here I must show you the
> most complimentary letter I received from the Government. I am

happy to say that Prof Smyth is the only person for whom I ever
did work whom I could not satisfy ... "

Smyth's eccentricity was quite well-known and this unfortunate episode
does not seem to have affected the general esteem in which the Grubbs' work
was held.

3.6   Meeting with David Gill

The following year (1872) Howard Grubb made the acquaintance of David Gill
(1843–1914) who was to become his lifelong friend and the source of many
ideas for technical improvements in telescope construction (Forbes 1916). Gill
was only a year older than Grubb. He was born in Aberdeen where he studied
under James Clerk Maxwell[3]. He learned the trade of watchmaker in England
and Switzerland, eventually succeeding to his father's watchmaking business.
However, astronomy was his real interest. Early on he had made a mounting
and driving clock for a 12-inch reflector and had determined the time for
Aberdeen by observing transits. When in 1872 he was invited to work at Dun
Echt, the newly-founded private observatory of Lord Lindsay[4], he jumped at
the opportunity in spite of the considerable drop in income involved.

Part of Gill's job at Dun Echt was to supervise the instruments being
built for the new establishment and this gave him the opportunity to tour the
main European Observatories and instrument-making concerns. A heliometer
had been ordered from Repsold of Hamburg, an 8-inch equatorial from Cooke
of York, an 8-inch transit circle from Troughton and Simms and a 15-inch
equatorial from Grubb of Dublin. Gill was able to observe their merits and
failings, storing information in his mind which turned out useful when he
himself became an observatory director.

The fact that Grubb had been asked to build the 15-inch refractor naturally meant that Gill had to visit Dublin on several occasions to discuss and
monitor the work. According to Gill's biographer, Forbes (1916), he found in
Grubb a 'kindred spirit'. Their friendship was to last, with some vicissitudes,
until Gill's death.

Cooke was building a 6-inch refractor which Gill was also monitoring. Gill
later recollected (Gill, 1912) that he had persuaded the two manufacturers to

"introduce many improvements, some of which were due to the
makers, some to my limited experience. So far as I am aware, the
Dun Echt 15-inch and 6-inch equatorials were the first instruments
of the kind in which the declination circle was mounted on the

---

[3]James Clerk Maxwell (1831–1879) is remembered for his formulation of classical elec-
trodynamics as well as work on the kinetic theory of gases and many other physical
investigations

[4]James Ludovic Lindsay (1847–1913), after 1880 Earl of Crawford

same end of the declination axis as the telescope so that it could
be read, or the instrument be set in declination from the eye-end."

A letter from H. Grubb to Gill on 26 September 1872 [ROE] shows that
Grubb provided at least one dome for Dun Echt, for he offers to send over
'two good hands' to help its erection. Their ordinary pay was 8/2^5 to 8/6
per day, with 2/6 extra for being away from home. Outdoor work normally
meant double pay.

By 16 June 1873 Grubb thought the new 15-inch lens for Dun Echt was
finished [Stokes G488]:

> "You will be glad to hear we have finished a second 15″ obj.
> (intended for Lord Lindsay) & it has been mostly highly approved
> of. I had to make a slight correction [presumably he means he
> had to use a slightly altered design for the new lens] on curves
> of Dr Huggins Obj owing to flint being slightly lower refraction
> & dispersion power & the focus consequently turned out about 4
> inches longer ... "

However, he had reckoned without the careful checking that Gill always
was to apply to his work. On 3 July 1873 Grubb wrote (ROE) in a report
'the object glass is still in its mercury trough.' Presumably, some re-touching
had been required. This letter is also interesting in showing that Grubb was
using mercury flotation to avoid uneven pressure from the supports of the lens
while it was on the polishing machine.

On 7 October 1873 Gill reported on the first use of the telescope to Grubb
(ROE):

> "The light of the OG is very great and I c^d not perceive any
> flexure - tho I c^d not use a high power to say very definitely.
> I sent Lord Lindsay the following telegram—'Night & Telescope
> splendid—lamp damnable'. I did not exaggerate—the lamp made
> me use very unwontedly forcible language. The slightest puff of
> wind put it out—and I had to light it six times on one occasion
> before I c^d set to the Dec^l of an object—it was always blown out
> before I c^d point the telescope. You must consider this matter and
> quickly too."

3.7   Gill's Drive-Correcting Mechanism

An important innovation due to Gill (Lindsay and Gill 1873) was to use an
independent pendulum to control the driving clock by electrical means. This
was necessary to keep an image perfectly steady for long periods during the

---

^{5}8 shillings and 2 pence. There were 20 shillings to one pound and 12 pence to one
shilling.

Figure 3.3: David Gill observing with a spectroscope attached to the Dun Echt 15-inch telescope (SAAO collection).

micrometric observations that Gill was planning to do. Previous attempts to improve the uniformity of drives had produced uneven results in that the clock ran fast between beats and was restrained on the beat so that the stellar image oscillated slightly back and forth. In Gill's scheme, the accumulation of even .01 seconds of error caused the governor to be be altered to produce a speed correction. This was achieved by generating precisely spaced pulses of electricity one second apart by passing a current through a pendulum every time a point on its bob touched a globule of mercury. The pulses then passed through a special contactor mounted on a shaft of the drive clock. If the clock was fast, a relay increased the friction applied to the governor; if slow, friction was decreased. Although the scheme worked under Gill's expert care, it had a serious weakness in that the frictional elements were bound to be somewhat unpredictable. Feedback theory was non-existent at the time, and the stability of this type of system was a hit-or-miss affair, requiring intuition rather than knowledge to ensure success. Grubb was later, during the 1880s, to take some elements of Gill's design and make it much more tractable.

During his period of working for Lindsay, Gill's reputation increased and he became accepted as an accomplished observer, particularly with the heliometer, an instrument which, though now obsolete, was the most accurate means in pre-photographic astronomy for measuring very small angles between celestial objects. A 4-inch heliometer had been taken by Lindsay and Gill to Mauritius for the Transit of Venus which took place at the end of 1874. This kindled his interest in the determination of the 'Astronomical Unit'—the distance from the earth to the sun—which was to be an important preoccupation later on.

Gill's association with Dun Echt lasted only until 1875 after which time he lived off his own funds in London for a few years until appointed H.M. Astronomer at the Cape of Good Hope. Forbes (1916) mentions that during this period Grubb and Gill seriously considered going into partnership and went at least as far as discussing terms. However, he was able to raise funds to pursue his heliometer work from the Royal Astronomical Society and private subscribers. His expedition to Ascension Island for further work on the astronomical unit[6] was a resounding success.

3.8   Gill's Opinion of Grubb

Increasing fame led to Gill being consulted on many instrumental issues and in the following letter to Simon Newcomb[7], astronomical head of the United States Naval Observatory and one of that country's leading astronomers, he summarized his views on the strengths and weaknesses of some contemporary European manufacturers. Newcomb was then acting on behalf of the Lick Trustees as a scout for a suitable builder for the proposed Lick 36-inch telescope in California (Newcomb 1875).

> Alexandria
> 21st Feb 1875

> My dear Newcomb
>   I am here in Egypt on my way home from Mauritius, and amongst my letters find one from Grubb of Dublin which is the immediate cause of my writing to you. He tells me that you have been making the rounds of the European Optical workshops in quest of a maker for the great Telescope of the new Californian Observatory. He asks me to write you and tell you my opinion of himself as a mechanic and an optician and my opinion as to whether he could be entrusted with such a work as the construction of a telescope of one metre aperture. Now I dont suppose you will be much influenced by my opinion one way or the other, and I certainly should never have thought of intruding it had I not been asked to do so—but as I have given you the history of the matter you can do just as you think best—and take this letter for just what it is worth—my opinion is at least an honest one.

---

[6]The distance from the earth to the sun.
[7]1835–1909

In the erection of Lord Lindsay's Observatory at Dun Echt
I have had to deal more or less with all the principal European
Opticians—and my opinion of them may be summed up thus:

For a carefully constructed divided instrument—of small size—
& the most carefully adapted in the finished details for use by the
Astronomer I believe Repsold is the man—Instance our Heliometer
which did not require a screw touched & has hardly had a screw
touched in all the many uses to which I have put it. The best
Micrometer Screws, Microscopes and divided circles are Troughton
& Simms—but I do not think much of them as engineers. For
a small equatorial, very complete, and of very great beauty of
workmanship both optical and mechanical Cookes of York are the
first — in fact in pure mechanical workmanship at least of the
larger parts of an equatorial I believe them (for workmanship)
the best as yet in the world—their circle dividing is defective.
Grubb's workmanship tho very sound is not so perfectly beautiful
as Cookes but as a designer, as a man of Science, as a man of
internal resources energy & skill Grubb is unapproached.

In all necessary parts such as the cutting of the driving screw
and arc I find a higher accuracy in Grubbs than Cookes work. I
find in his designs more of practical adaptability to the wants of the
astronomer. The Object Glass he made for us is a very beautiful
one and I daresay you have tested Dr Huggins' Obj by Grubb &
can judge for yourself—and from the ease and certainty with which
I have found Grubb make the minute final corrections in the figure
of large lenses I should believe him capable of constructing lenses
of any Size that he will undertake, and for which he can procure
the glass.

In all great matters I have never found Grubb to fail. But
he is more of an artist than a merchant—and when he has done
the great things you will find it necessary to keep him up to the
mark in the small. For example in illumination, microscope fittings
and so on he will design them very perfectly but is impatient of
working over them and you will have probably to spend some time
& trouble on details yourself as we have had to do on Grubb's work.

On the whole however I should say that if Grubb says 'I will'—
take him at his word & you will not be disappointed.

So much for these matters.

The Transit is over ...

I am staying here for some time to measure a base line and
commence the triangulation of Egypt for the Khedive. They wish
a determination of an arc of meridian —and the best in the world.
It will be hard to beat yr [?] survey but Egypt is small & we shall
try!

Drop me a line to care of British Consul Cairo. I hope I shall
meet you at Leiden.

Always sincerely yours
David Gill

Grubb writes me that not got the official order but he is told
that he is to make the great 27 inch Telescope for Vienna".

3.9   Charles Pritchard

Another individual who was to play an important role in the development
of Grubb's work was Charles Pritchard, Professor of Astronomy at Oxford.
Pritchard's astronomical career (Pritchard 1897) was an extraordinary one—
he had been a teacher and a theologian and had become Professor at an
age when most people would have been thinking of retiring. However, his
tenure of the Professorship was marked by energy and innovation, such as the
use of photography for determining stellar parallaxes and the publication of
his *Uranometria Oxoniensis,* a catalogue of visual stellar photometry made
with the aid of a wedge photometer. He was evidently a plump and jolly
sort of person from whom people expected humorous remarks. Finding no
instruments with which to observe when he entered his new job, he applied
successfully to the University for funds to provide a telescope for the study
of 'astronomical physics'. A 12-inch refractor was felt to be appropriate, with
the position circles readable from the eye end so that there was no necessity to
run up and down ladders with a lantern in the hand 'like a lamplighter'. The
spectre of the portly professor running up and down ladders was found highly
amusing by the fellows of the Royal Astronomical Society as they listened
to Pritchard expounding his plans on 14 December, 1874. (Pritchard 1874).
He told them 'As to the time of the probable completion of the telescope
and building, Mr. Grubb offered to complete his part of the work by the
1st of April next. We naturally declined this particular date (laughter), and
accepted the 2nd of that month.'

3.10   The Great Paris Reflector

A project in which Grubb took a lot of interest was the 47-inch silver-on-
glass reflector then being constructed for the Paris Observatory. While the
mounting had been completed successfully by Eichens around 1869, the figuring of the mirror by the devious Martin was a failure (Tobin 1987). Probably
well aware of the mistake it had been to go for a speculum mirror for the
Melbourne reflector, Grubb rather revelled in its lack of success. In a letter
marked 'private' to Capt. Floyd on 30 June, 1876, [Shane] he wrote:

> "In a former letter I mentioned that I knew now something
> more about the Paris Telescope than I did when I last saw you.

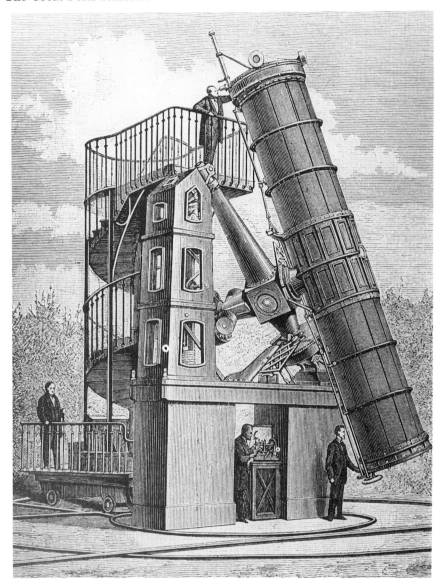

Figure 3.4: The unsuccessful Paris 47-inch reflector which Grubb believed was based on the designs of the Great Melbourne Telescope (Ambronn 1899).

As however the communication was from a private source I did not like to communicate it to you: by enclosed [illegible] which I have today extracted from 'Nature'[8] (an English Scientific Paper) I see that the affair has leaked out. In plain words the Paris Reflector is a failure as I long since predicted (since Prof Newcomb told me how

---

[8] *Nature*, **14**, 200, 1876.

they were working it)—but this does not at all modify my views concerning the practicability of making large Reflectors perfect. From the way they worked that mirror it would have been perfectly hopeless to expect any good result. Since this failure the present condition of the art in France may be thus expressed viz. That there is not a man now living in France who can point to any large Telescope either Refracting or Reflecting & say that 'There is a great Telescope of my manufacture working satisfactorily' ...

I have had a very polite private message from Mr Leverrier asking me to call upon him & if the French can only get over the shock to their self dignity I may perhaps have the Paris mirror over here to touch up but this of course is 'entre nous'."

Again, on 8 July:

"I am curious to know your opinion of the Great Reflector in Paris. You will recognise from the photos that with exception of such modifications as were required to make the Telescope suitable for use as a Newtonian (viz supporting tube near its centre & higher piers) the Paris Equatorial is an almost exact copy of the Melbourne Reflector. The story I told you of sending over the designs to my Fenian[9] Foreman in Paris explains this."

Many years afterwards, some light was shed on this episode by T.H. Mason, a well-known Dublin instrument maker (Mason, 1944). He tells the following story:

"Sir Howard's foreman for many years was Michael Lambert, who was mixed up in the Fenian activities of the last century; he made the key that opened the prison door of James Stephens [on 25 November 1865]. Detectives came to arrest him at Grubb's works, but he was warned in time and escaped by the back as the detectives approached. He fled to Paris, where he worked for some years in an optician's workshop, eventually returning to take up his old position in the Rathmines works ... "

In July 1876 Grubb submitted a quotation for working a 29-inch objective for France at a cost of £3600. [Shane: Grubb to Floyd 24 July]. This was probably the project referred to in Section 1.15, which Secrétan never completed.

On 25 Sept 1876 he wrote to Floyd [Shane]

---

[9]The Fenians were a revolutionary movement which existed in Ireland and the USA, aiming for the establishment of an Irish Republic. James Stephens was the leader of the Irish part, known as the IRB (Irish Republican Brotherhood). It appealed mainly to the urban Catholic working classes. It had over 100,000 members in Ireland. Stephens was captured during a more-or-less successful attempt to suppress the movement in 1865. Even though he escaped, the movement never again recovered its earlier strength.

"I saw a short notice in Nature stating that the Paris Observatory had determined to manufacture the Objective by steam power & machinery and had entrusted it to the maker of the French lighthouses. Feil says it is only the rough shaping that is alluded to."

Chapter 4

The Great Vienna Telescope

4.1 An Enquiry from Vienna

In 1873 Karl Ludwig von Littrow (1811–1877), director of the National Observatory in Vienna, induced the Minister of Public Construction, R. von Stromayer, to move the Observatory from its old site in the University to a new one on elevated ground five kilometres from the centre of the city. A huge new building was to be erected in the shape of a cross with small domes on top of each of the arms and a large one of 45 feet diameter in the centre. These domes were to be supplied by Howard Grubb.

As early as 26 March 1873 H. Grubb told Stokes [Stokes, G486] that enquiries had been made about a new large instrument:

> "...the Vienna Observatory have written me about a 30 inch Achromatic. The question is how we are to get the glass. What a pity to have those fine 29 inch discs lying idle in Paris but I suppose the French would not sell them to the Germans for fear of being beaten in optical matters as well as Political ..."

In 1873 Grubb found a supplier of optical glass who promised well, as he related to Stokes [5 August, Stokes G489]:

> "I had a long interview in Paris with a Grandson[1] of Guinands (I forget whether I spell his name correctly) the original glass man. He (the grand-son) is a most interesting man & thoroughly up to his business. I have brought away specimens of all his optical glass & I consider what he showed me very superior to Chance. One

---

[1]Charles Feil; see 6.4

disc he showed me was 28″ dia × 24 thick (flint) & seemed perfect.
He said he could have a crown ready for this in 3 months."

Grubb went on to say that Merz[2], Steinheil[3] and all the other great continental makers also used this glass.

In 1874 Littrow sent Ed. Weiss, then First Assistant, on a tour of European and American observatories and workshops. Weiss recommended that a telescope of at least 26 inches diameter should be ordered from Grubb's. In June 1875 a contract was signed between Grubb and the Austro-Hungarian Government for the supply of a 27-inch telescope. A Local Committee was set up to report on the telescope, consisting of Prof. R.S. Ball[4], Astronomer Royal for Ireland, The Earl of Crawford[5], Mr. Huggins, Prof. J.E. Reynolds[6], the Earl of Rosse, Prof. Stokes, Dr G.J. Stoney[7] and Mr. Richard Walsh, the Austrian Consul in Dublin (Anon 1881). The telescope was to cost £8000 and delivery was to be made within three years after delivery of the lens blanks, failing which penalties were to be paid. Progress payments were to be made and the telescope was to be erected first in Dublin.

4.2   The 'Optical and Mechanical Works'

To have the contract for the largest refracting telescope in the world was to have arrived at the top of the telescope-making league. The future was obviously going to be rosy if the product turned out well. Grubb immediately began work on a new building at his plant in Rathmines which was to serve him until the firm moved from Dublin in 1918. The edifice was described by Robinson (1878):

> "The basis is a regular dodecagon (12-sided figure), 42 feet
> least diameter, and 42 feet from its floor to the summit of the
> dome. Round it, at 10 feet from the ground, runs a gallery 2 feet
> wide, with a light iron railing, from which several doors give access
> to workshops in which polishing and other light work is executed.
> On the ground, open arches communicate with shops, in which
> large lathes and other heavy tools are established."

The roof of the dodecagon was designed to allow the large dome for the Vienna Observatory to be erected over it. This factory became known as 'The Optical and Mechanical Works, Rathmines'. It was connected, apparently by blocking off the intervening laneway, to the back garden of 51, Rathmines Road, where the offices of the company were located.

---

[2] George Merz (1793–1867), the successor to Fraunhofer.
[3] Karl August von Steilheil (1804–1870), noted German telescope maker.
[4] Sir Robert Stawell Ball (1840–1913) noted Irish-born astronomer and popular writer.
[5] Formerly Lord Lindsay.
[6] James Emerson Reynolds FRS 1843-?, Professor of Chemistry, Trinity College, Dublin.
[7] George Johnstone Stoney (1826–1911), Irish physicist and inventor of the word *electron* for the natural unit of electricity.

Figure 4.1: Roof-wetting ceremony of the 'Optical and Mechanical Works' at the time of its completion, Nov 8, 1875. The view is from the northeast (Astronomical Institute of the University of Vienna).

Figure 4.2: Domes under construction in Grubb's yard. The new works are seen to the left in this picture (Astronomical Institute of the University of Vienna).

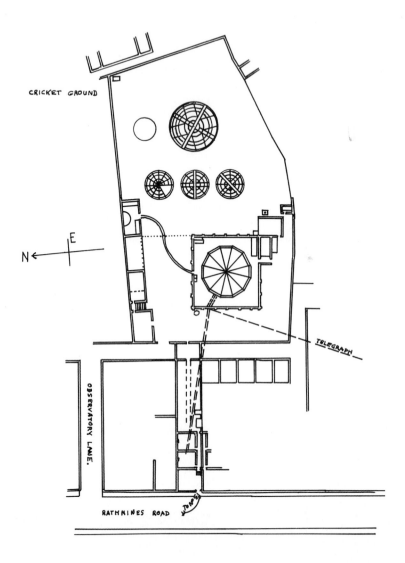

CRICKET GROUND

N ← ⊢E

OBSERVATORY LANE.

TELEGRAPH

RATHMINES ROAD

Figure 4.3: Layout of Grubb's works, re-drawn from his Catalogue of 1877. The position of the neighbouring cricket ground is also shown.

In a progress report published in *Nature* (Anon 1876) in September, 1876,[8] we learn

[8]*Nature* had been founded in 1869 by the astronomer Joseph Norman Lockyer (1836–1920)

"The work is going on smoothly and successfully ... Mr Grubb had contracted with Feil of Paris for the supply of discs of glass for the great objective, and the flint disc is already in Dublin, where it is now undergoing a rigid examination. The crown disc M. Feil expects to have ready in a few weeks; meanwhile active preparations are going on for the grinding and polishing of the objective. Parts of the general framing have been cast; the polar pillar is completely finished, and the declination circle and adapter nearly so. The clockwork and many of the other parts of the elaborate apparatus necessary for the working of the telescope are also complete, and Mr. Grubb is preparing a travelling gantry across the observatory, and proposes commencing shortly to put together the general framework and erect the larger portions of the mounting ... The telescope is expected to be ready by the autumn of 1878."

The frames of the domes were constructed in Dublin and were installed in Vienna under the superintendance of Mr W.K. Davis, 'Mr. Grubb's Engineer'.

"The great central dome is 45 feet in diameter, and its dome and the revolving machinery to work it have been supplied by Mr. Howard Grubb, who has put up all the domes of the smaller towers. The great dome is of a very peculiar construction. It is formed of two thin shells of steel plate varying in thickness; these are riveted on the inside and outside of a very light set of steel plate girders 18 inches deep at base and 9 inches at crown, the whole forming a cellular construction like the top and bottom of the Britannia Tubular Bridge[9]. This form gives enormous stiffness for the amount of material used, besides possessing several points of peculiar usefulness for astronomical work, such, the more specially, as keeping the temperature of the dome wonderfully constant, even under most trying circumstances. The total weight of this steel dome, with its ribs and girders, the cast-iron sole plate, and fitting, is about 15 tons, and as the result of a series of very ingenious mechanical contrivances thought out by Mr. Grubb, the tractive force necessary to pull round this huge drum, even when resting, as at Dublin, on a temporary support and insufficiently levelled, was only 70 lbs."

Unfortunately, the work on the objective did not, in the event, go well because Feil did not manage to supply sufficiently good blanks until the end of 1879. On 22 December 1875 Grubb wrote to Stokes [Stokes, G505]:

---

[9] A famous railway bridge over the Menai straights in North Wales, designed by Sir I.K. Brunel

"I have got no glass as yet nor do I expect to get any for at least 3 months ... At present I am pushing forward the Mechanical part very actively so as to leave me more leisure to work at the glass when I do get it but I shall take no steps without availing myself of your great kindness in offering me your assistance in determining form &c. I have not even got the sample discs yet."

[A small notebook containing measurements of the optical constants of the glasses for the Vienna telescope was found at Grubb Parsons' works in Newcastle and is preserved at the Tyne and Wear Archives.]

A report to the Committee in August 1876 mentions [Stokes, G508a] that a flint disc had arrived in March and was being tried. By November [Stokes, G510], a crown disc 'quite perfect as to homogeneity and the best annealed piece of glass I ever met with of a large size' had come and had had sample pieces cut from it for testing. Tables of indicies were sent to Stokes for his calculations. The crown disc was very thin and Grubb stated to Stokes that he preferred it should be worked into an equi-convex form, like other lenses he had made from Feil's glasses and which had given no difficulties in regard to spherical aberration [Stokes, G531, 24 April 1877]. However, this disc was rejected by Weiss during a visit in July 1877 on account of a 'feather-like' defect.

4.3   Visit from the Emperor of Brazil

Grubb was subjected to frequent interruptions in the shape of visitors. One of these was Dom Pedro, Emperor of Brazil, who turned up in 1876. Ball (1915) relates the story, perhaps with a little embroidery:

"It was known in a general way that the Emperor was about to visit Dublin. One fine morning he landed in the North of Ireland. By dint of a tremendous effort he visited the Giant's Causeway and a number of places in Belfast during the early part of the day. He then took a special train to Dublin, where he arrived late in the evening. He at once proceeded to Guinness' Brewery; after which he inspected another large factory in another part of the town. Finally, he attended a performance at the Gaiety Theatre. On returning late at night to the Shelbourne Hotel he sent for the Lord Mayor.

When that dignitary arrived, ready to place the whole of the city at His Majesty's disposal, the Emperor at once cut conversation short by saying that his particular object in coming to Dublin, was to see the great telescope which was being constructed by an instrument-maker in Dublin of worldwide celebrity. 'I cannot,' said His Majesty, 'remember exactly the name of this great man of science, but, of course, you know whom I mean'. The Lord

Mayor looked at his secretary and the secretary looked at him!
They were both at a loss. The Chief Citizen of Dublin then haz-
arded the name of a worthy spectacle-maker who lived nearby,
but the Emperor at once pooh-poohed that notion, saying that
the name of the man he was looking for was something like 'mub'
or 'tub'. This hint failed to produce any effect, and the Emperor
expressed his surprise that a man who called himself Lord Mayor
of the city should be so ignorant of so elementary a matter. 'At all
events', he went on, 'you must find out for me in the course of the
night where the famous optician is, and take me to him tomorrow
morning'. By this time it was twelve o'clock on a Saturday night.
The Lord Mayor and his secretary retired to the Mansion House,
where I have no doubt they spent an anxious hour in considering
how they could extricate the reputation of the city from the oblo-
quy which Dom Pedro was inclined to cast upon it. Suddenly it
was remembered that there was a person in the vicinity of Dublin
known as the Astronomer Royal. Although I don't suppose they
imagined that that humble individual was the person whom the
Emperor wanted to see, yet it occurred to them that it was within
the bounds of possibility that the Astronomer Royal might know
whether in fact there was an eminent optician in Dublin. To con-
sult him might be to find a way out of the difficulty. I was at
that time Astronomer Royal of Ireland. Once or twice I had said,
half in jest, to my wife that when the Emperor of Brazil came to
Dublin he would probably pay us a visit at Dunsink. So we had
the Emperor somewhat on our minds. At about eight o'clock on
the morning of Sunday I heard the sound of wheels on the avenue.
For any wheeled vehicle to arrive there at that hour of the morning
was rather unusual, but when I looked out of the window I was
truly astonished at the apparition. There was the Lord Mayor's
coach and pair driving up the avenue! I came down at once. The
Lord Mayor's secretary rushed in to tell me of the terrible anxiety
under which his chief was labouring. He asked me whether there
was any truth in the suggestion that some very big and famous
telescope was being made in Dublin for Vienna. I replied that I
did happen to know something about the matter; that indeed, I
was one of the committee to whom the general supervision of the
work had been entrusted. He then begged me to come to Dublin at
once, and forthwith to take the Emperor off to see Grubb and the
telescope. I said 'Grubb's place will be shut up as it is Sunday'.
The agonised secretary replied, 'Oh the Emperor cares nothing
about that, and we must do what we can'. So there was nothing
for it, but for me to go to Dublin and breakfast with the Lord
Mayor, while we sent off messengers to Mr Grubb at Rathmines,
telling him of the visitation with which he was threatened, and

imploring him to collect a few of his hands so as to open up his works as far as possible.

When we arrived at Grubb's we found the famous telescope-maker waiting for us. He had succeeded in getting together a few of his exceptionally skilled workmen. At once the Emperor showed himself thoroughly informed on all matters relating to the great object-glass. He was also well-acquainted with the particular requirements of the Vienna telescope. In accordance with his usual custom, he declined to look at anything which he had not decided would be worth his time. When he bade Grubb good-bye an amusing incident took place. His Majesty, though well-furnished intellectually, was, to put it mildly, by no means conspicuous for the regal splendour of his attire. As he was leaving he took up what he no doubt supposed to be his hat. In reality it was a beautiful new 'Lincoln and Bennett' belonging to Grubb. The Emperor had left behind what we call in Ireland an old 'cawbeen'. He was on the point of stepping into his carriage when the secretary, who was evidently accustomed to these little lapses, effected the necessary change of head-dress! ... '

4.4   Honorary Master of Engineering

In 1876 Howard Grubb's contribution to engineering in Ireland was recognized by his being granted the honorary degree of Master in Engineering by Trinity College, where he had been a student some twelve years before.

The Crown Prince of Austria visited Grubb in February 1878, just as the replacement crown disc arrived. Unfortunately it had too many veins and had also to be rejected. Yet another crown disc was procured and the flint was subjected to deeper scrutiny which ultimately led to its rejection for want of homogeneity. By this time Grubb's correspondence with Feil amounted to 350 letters and he had paid 5 or 6 visits to his workshop in Paris!

A year later the strain was beginning to tell. Grubb wrote to Stokes on 3 August 1878 [Stokes, G535]:

> "I wished to explain that for the last few weeks I have done very little to objective & do not intend starting again at it till I get rid of the British Association [for Advancement of Science, which met in Dublin that year, partly at Grubb's suggestion (see also Stokes, G502)].
>
> Several matters combined to force me to relinquish the work for a few weeks. The Vienna people desire now to have their great dome erected in Vienna before winter instead of leaving it here with me till after telescope is tried so we have to work at it night & day. We are working a large staff of hands up tp 9 p.m. in the evenings at it. Also I am anxious (as I cannot have objective

Figure 4.4: The Vienna 27-inch refractor when completed, shown in the do-decagonal room of Grubb's works, *ca* 1878 (Astronomical Institute of the University of Vienna).

ready) at least to have the stand in partial working order & we are now putting it together. This interferes with any arrangements for the first rough trial of objective but the principal reason of all is that in the present fuss and worry I have daily to go through I cannot find that indispensable quietude & leisure that is absolutely necessary when working at a large lens & it would be positively dangerous for me to go on just at present."

On 11 November Grubb remarked to Stokes (Stokes, G536) that 'The failure of the crown disc is very sad.' What this failure was due to is not stated. However, it is clear that it resulted in neither the flint or crown being ready—presumably the disc for the first had never been acceptable.

By 10 March 1879 [Shane] the mounting was finished and Grubb could boast to Floyd of Lick Observatory 'It is finished and is universally admired. The facility with which the huge mass is managed & the convenience of the arrangements for reading [and] setting excite the astonishment of all that have visited it.' However, by this time Grubb reckoned he had suffered £1000 loss in wasted work on the defective discs. He went on 'We had an enormous number of visitors to the Vienna Telescope last year & all were much pleased even those who came determined not to be pleased.'

Grubb's letters to Gill around this time are full of anxiety about the outcome of the project and the financial problems he was experiencing: 'Could you like a good fellow oblige me with some cash payment on account before you go [to the Cape] this failure of the Vienna glass has knocked all my arrangements about sadly' [SAAO, 26 April 1879].

... "I am busy just at present measuring and examining the new discs that have come—we got an awful fright about the crown. I took a set of measures & had only just time to dispatch them to Stokes (having only reduced a few) before I left Dublin in going to erect some instruments at Cork. On my return I found a few 'reams' of paper from Stokes in a dreadful fright for it appeared Feil must have altered the materials of his glass and the dispersion came out so high that the crown would come to a thin edge before it would be the right curve. I also got a fright but I sat down, worked away & before I went to bed convinced myself. Something was wrong in Stokes calculation and the next day I found out he had transposed some figures. I should think it cost him about 20/- worth of paper!!!' [SAAO, 27 August 1879]

In the meantime Grubb's wife, May, had been so ill that her life was almost despaired of and 'of course in the middle of all one of the servants has to go off to get married and the other has to go off ill so affairs are here something like what Mark Taply [a character in *Martin Chuzzlewit* by Charles Dickens (pub. 1844)] would call "awfully jolly".' [17 Sept 1879, RGO 15/72]

4.5   'A Splendid Success'

By early 1880 things were looking up.'... the Vienna Objective on its first trial
gave promise of very good results—I think the glass is very good. Another 3
months may now see the completion of this weary job.' [SAAO, 25 Feb 1880].
'I am awfully close (?) at work now at the Gt. objective which promises well.
I am in hope the figuring will be finished before the summer. It is a tough
job but so far we have experienced no special difficulties. We are testing it 3
times a day now.' [21 Apr 1880, RGO 15/72] ... 'working hard at the final
figuring of the Gt Glass. I hope another month will see the end of it ...'
[27 July 1880] '... Great excitement now about Vienna Glass. It is now in
tube and our roof opened. I got a glimpse at a star thro' cloud & it looked
promising. Every night since was clouded but today it has cleared & we are
anxiously waiting' [3 Nov 1880].

On 2 March 1881, Grubb wrote to Gill [SAAO]:

> "You will be glad to hear that the big telescope has turned
> out as Stoney says 'a splendid success'. All the members of the
> Committee on this side of the channel Lord Rosse, Stoney, Ball,
> Reynolds have seen it & are all delighted. I was able to show Ld
> Rosse more stars in Orion Nebula in 1/4 hour than he saw all his
> life before with the 3 foot or 6 foot. Several others have seen it
> and all without exception find it faultless. Erck, Hunter, Dreyer,
> Lord Crawford & Huggins & Stokes have not as yet come over. I
> am just beginning to feel a great load lifted off my shoulders for
> indeed I have had an anxious time of it and a couple of years ago
> or even 18 months since everything looked hopeless."

Writing on 28 Mar 1882 [SAAO] to explain how one of Gill's orders was
being delayed 'by red tapeism', Grubb goes on—'like the Vienna Telescope,
the cases of which are still in my yard waiting till the Foreign Office in Vienna
and Embassy in London settle how it is to be sent which you may imagine is
a slow process as it takes 10 weeks for an official letter to find its way from
Vienna to Dublin if sent through the Government offices'

At last, on 17 May 1882 [SAAO], the instrument left for Vienna: '... today
& all this week we are very much pressed as the Austrian Embassy have
after seven months negociating concluded a contract with the carriers for
transmitting the Telescope to Vienna & they are at this moment being carted
out of the yard.' Several visits to Vienna were apparently necessary before the
project could be considered complete. We learn on 3 October 1883[10] [SAAO]
'My [recent] visit to Vienna was most satisfactory and I am glad to find the
Great Instrument has done good work already though only in the hands of
outsiders as the staff at the observatory is so small. It was very satisfactory to
me to hear such good accounts of its performance from all who have worked
with it.'

---

[10]This was the first Grubb letterhead mentioning a telephone number, Dublin 603!

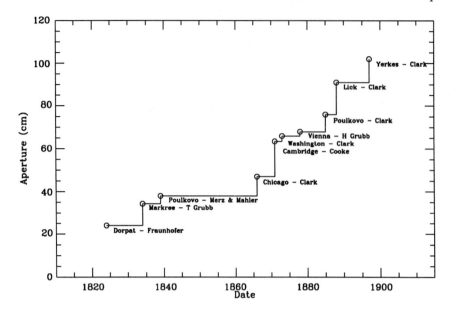

Figure 4.5: Growth in the size of refracting telescope objectives during the nineteenth century, taken from Danjon & Couder (1935), with amendments.

In the spring and summer of 1883, Simon Newcomb made an official factfinding trip to Europe and, during April, examined the Vienna telescope quite critically. Until its completion, the 26-inch at his own institution, the U.S. Naval Observatory in Washington, D.C., had been the largest refractor. Grubb had been fairly outspoken about the weaknesses of Clark's mounting such as the small diameters of its axes in relation to the size of the tube and the cumbersome method that had to be employed for setting it on a star (It was, in fact, re-mounted in 1893 by Warner and Swasey). Here are some of his (Newcomb's 1884) comparative comments:

> "The leading points of difference are, that the mounting of the Vienna telescope is much larger, stronger, and heavier in all its parts, that the appliances for using it are more elaborate and numerous, and that an elaborate system of friction rollers in declination is provided, while the Washington telescope has none. A more convenient system of illuminating the field and the divisions on the several circles has also been introduced. As a piece of mechanical engineering it reflects great credit upon its designer and constructor.
>
> Ease of Motion.- In moving the Vienna telescope one is at first struck with the fact that mere weight is a serious drawback in the management of such an instrument, but, when the motion is once commenced, the movement in right ascension is almost as easy as

in the Washington instrument. It is, however, very different in declination. For reasons which neither Dr. Weiss nor myself was able to perceive, the friction rollers seemed to be of little benefit in easing the motion in declination, which was much more difficult than in the Washington telescope, and, in fact, quite a tax upon the strength of the observer at the eye-piece."

He was also critical of the steering wheel-operated quick motion which he found dangerous to the knuckles. The stability against wind-pressure etc of the mounting was much better though still not perfect. The right ascension drive showed irregularity with an amplitude of two arcsec. Grubb's sector style of driving was not to be preferred over the continuous worm and wheel system on account of having to stop and rewind periodically. The slow motion in right ascension he approved of, however, since it was not screw-based and did not require re-winding. The fact that the setting circles could only be read from the eyepiece end of the tube he found very inconvenient for rough setting. The weather was not perfect enough that a definite opinion could be given as to the quality of the objective. Some of these objections seem to have a slight flavour of sour grapes about them but others were clearly valid.

Gill, always a staunch supporter of Grubb's, in spite of many temporary periods of mutual irritation, replied in kind in the article on *Telescope* which he wrote for the Encyclopaedia Britannica (1887). He mentions *inter alia* how awkward the Washington instrument was to set in declination, quoting from Washington Observations, 1874 (Anon 1877): 'The instrument is brought into the meridian and set by the observer within a degree by means of coarse divisions painted on the edge of the declination circle. These divisions are rendered visible by lighting one or two of the gas burners of the dome, and viewed by the astronomer with an opera-glass. Then an assistant mounts by a ladder to a high platform and holds a gas lamp near the vernier, and the fine setting is accomplished by the observer seated in the observing chair, the declination clamp and slow-motion screw being convenient to his hand.

He goes on 'In his official report on the instruments of European observatories Newcomb defends the want of solidity and convenience of this instrument as compared with the Vienna telescope, because its smaller axes (notwithstanding Grubb's anti-friction arrangements) permit it to turn more easily and the mounting to be of far simpler design. But at the time of Newcomb's visit the Vienna telescope had not been brought into work, and cannot have been in proper working order if the motion in declination was so stiff as he describes it, at least when the present writer tested the instrument in Dublin that motion was surprisingly easy.'

The Vienna telescope remained the largest refractor only until the completion of the Pulkovo 30-inch in 1885. This had an objective by Clark but the mounting was from the Repsolds of Hamburg.

4.6   Last Years of Thomas Grubb

Thomas Grubb's active participation in the firm seems have to have slowed
down in the early 1870s. We know that he suffered from rheumatism, as he
commenced a letter to C.P. Smyth on 27 December 1872 [ROE] 'I have now for
several weeks been much crippled by rheumatism, today, my right hand being
pretty well I wish to induce you to lose no time in making some experiments
on the pier [of the Edinburgh 24-inch reflector] ...

Again, in a letter on 16 May 1877 [Shane] to Captain Floyd, Secretary to
the Lick Trustees, Howard Grubb wrote:

> "I have to go to London for a few days this week to take my
> Father over on his way to Bournemouth for his health which is
> failing, he is most anxious to see you if possible."

Thomas Grubb died on the 19th September 1878 and was buried on the
23rd in Mount Jerome Cemetery, where the cause of his death is rather
quaintly listed in the register as 'decline of life'. His tombstone reads:

IN
REMEMBRANCE OF
THOMAS GRUBB
FELLOW OF
THE ROYAL SOCIETY OF LONDON
WHO DIED ON THE 19TH SEPTEMBER 1878
AGED 78 YEARS
ALSO OF
EMILY
DAUGHTER OF THE ABOVE
WHO DIED ON THE 8TH JUNE 1859
AGED 21 YEARS
ALSO OF
SARAH
WIFE OF THE ABOVE
THOMAS GRUBB
WHO DIED ON THE 10TH JANUARY 1883
AGED 84 YEARS

Although several obituaries of Thomas Grubb appeared soon afterwards
(see DNB 1890) for a list, they were almost all short and perfunctory. Only
that in *Nature* (Anon 1878) did justice to his memory. The more comprehensive entry in DNB was written by 'A.M.C.', presumably Agnes M. Clarke,
writer of *History of Astronomy in the Nineteenth Century* (1893).

Chapter 5

Grubb and the Lick telescope

5.1 Wooing the Lick Trustees

James Lick (1796–1876) was an energetic businessman who made a fortune out of land speculation in San Franscisco, benefiting greatly from the gold rush of 1848. In his old age, around 1874, he turned over many ideas as to how he should perpetuate his name, ranging from the erection of a huge pyramid in San Franscisco to giant statues of himself and family and finally to a telescope, larger than any yet built. Various eminent scientists, egged on by George Davidson, President of the California Academy of Sciences, persuaded Lick that the telescope was the project he should go for.

A board of trustees was appointed to carry out Lick's wishes and the secretary and prime mover of this was Captain Richard S. Floyd, a Georgia-born veteran of the Civil War (confederate side) and graduate of the US Naval Academy in Annapolis. The main scientific adviser to the board was Simon Newcomb, the leading astronomer of the United States, based at the US Naval Observatory in Washington DC. At that time, the Naval Observatory had just acquired a 26-inch telescope constructed by Alvan Clark[1] and Sons of Cambridge, Massachusetts, generally reckoned to have been the best maker of telescope lenses of the 19th century. This instrument was, for a time, the largest in the world.

Newcomb made a trip to Europe from December 1874 to March 1875 in order to visit European telescope manufacturers. Although he intended to visit Grubb on 2nd January, it appears that he only got to Dublin on 7th February. As already mentioned, Gill had given Newcomb his opinion of Grubb in a letter of 21st February, 1875. Newcomb later remarked in his

---

[1]Alvan Clark (1804–1887) was the founder of the company. His son was Alvan Graham Clark (1832–1897); see Warner 1968.

> "...Dec 1874, I was invited to visit the European workshops as
> an agent of the Lick trustees, with a view of determining whether
> there was any chance of getting the telescope made abroad ... The
> outcome of the matter was that Howard Grubb, of Dublin, was
> the only man abroad with whom negociations could be opened
> with any chance of success. He was evidently a genius who meant
> business. Yet he had not produced a work which would justify
> unlimited confidence in his ability to meet Mr. Lick's requirements.
> The great Vienna telescope which he afterwards constructed was
> then only projected."

In 1876, Floyd also made a trip to Europe. Grubb cultivated his acquaintance quite assiduously and gave him lists of suitable contacts such as Huggins, Stokes and Pritchard who might be expected to give a good opinion of his work. Grubb was very keen to promote the idea of using a reflector to get the best light-grasp, but orthodox opinion was then very much in favour of the refractor.

Floyd was bombarded with propaganda about the incompetence of other manufacturers, for example the letters already quoted about the 'Great Paris Reflector' in section 3.10.

Grubb encouraged Floyd to visit the British Association meeting in Edinburgh that year, as he intended to exhibit a 6.5 inch refractor 'of very perfect construction which I am particularly desirous for you to see as it contains many nice points never before applied' [described in Grubb 1876]. He suggested a complete itinerary of places worth seeing as a tourist. However 'The Caledonian canal is I think monotonous & tame'. He was advised to visit David Gill at Dun Echt and warned about the peculiarities of Piazzi Smyth.

> [4 Oct 1876][2] "Feil could I suppose procure you an invitation to
> the St Gobain Glass Works. These you would be much interested
> in seeing & at the same time might get some information as to
> what is the maximum size of glass disc they could make for a
> silvered glass mirror. They wrote me they could not undertake
> anything but something very small (about 2 feet I think) but they
> are I believe making 4 feet for Paris Observatory. It would be
> interesting to know what they say."

On 1 October 1876 Lick died, causing a series of disputes over his legacies; in particular his illegitimate son John Lick was claiming a large share of the estate. Still in Europe, Floyd received the news by telegram and passed on the information to Grubb, commenting on the problems which had arisen.

---

[2] References in this chapter are to the Grubb–Floyd correspondence in the Mary Lea Shane Archives of Lick Observatory, unless otherwise attributed.

Figure 5.1: Grubb's 'Portable Equatorial', of 1877. National Air and Space Museum, Washington D.C., courtesy of David DeVorkin. Ref SI neg. no.92-5806.

[Grubb to Floyd 6 Oct 1876] "Your letter of 5th reached me today. The news it contains is indeed bad, bad for all parties concerned & I fear in the end perhaps bad for the sake of science which would otherwise have been enriched by an unprecedented gift—curiously enough it was only last night I was sitting up late writing out my ideas for you. Curious also that the very event which naturally would have cleared up all difficulties should have been just that to create new ones ... As to the contesting of the Deed on the ground of insanity I of course know nothing except that it is generally considered a very nice question to draw the line between eccentricity & insanity ...If the new Trustees are appointed I suppose everything will go on smoothly but if the validity of the Deed be questioned I suppose the Lawyers & not science will ultimately be enriched.

However even should this affair now come to nothing I shall not regret at least the pleasure of making your acquaintance & the pleasant little chats we have had which I suppose would never have taken place but for the Lick trust. ...I had been planning out some nice ideas for working the telescope & dome, chair etc by hydraulic machinery.

[Grubb to Floyd 23 Jan 1877] ...I have arranged with the Royal Dublin Society here to have my paper on the comparison of Reflectors & Refractors published immediately on being completed without waiting for it to be read so I hope about middle of next month to send you copies.

I have now had the Vienna Dome Committee meeting here & astonished them by pulling round one of the Domes 4 tons weight with a piece of common thread, the power on the wheel & pinion being only 5 to 1. We are hard at work on the Gt. Objective now. I hope in another week to have quite decided on the curves ...

Could you give me a few rough sketches, from memory, of Mount Hamilton that would enable me to make a model in plaster and amuse myself planning out the underground observatory.

[Grubb to Floyd, 23 Feb 1877] Your kind letter from Rome to hand for which with its enclosures (3 tracings survey, 2 photos & newspaper cutting). I am much obliged. I gather from the newspaper cutting that the dispute between the Trustees & Mr John Lick has now ended and cannot well be revived so it is to be hoped now that matters will go on smoothly. I am sure this news must have been pleasant to you for I feared you would have been much troubled with the matter when you got back to America. I read my paper on 'Great Telescopes of the Future' at the Royal Dublin Society [Grubb 1877] last Monday evening & it will be in print in a month or so when I will send you 20 copies (or more if you wish) or if you desire me will send any directly to any address you give me. As regards the glass for mirrors I did write St Gobain Cy & Chance & they both refused to make a 7 foot mirror & one at least refused to make more than 4 feet—but if you desire it I shall write again.

I do not believe however that this would be of much consequence for I have been making some very important experiments & I believe I will be able to produce mirrors of large size (up to say 8 feet) embracing all the advantages of both metallic & silver-on-glass mirrors. I have been debating with myself what to do with this invention if it turns out a success. Patents are almost useless in this country so my present idea is to 'keep it quiet'—at same time I have no objection to show you the experiments & results when you call on me here. I believe I will be able to produce 8 feet mirrors with a greater Reflective power even than the silver on glass & almost imperishable. Dr Robinson of Armagh who is the only one who knows about it is quite sanguine of success. A 5 foot Reflector of this kind would be more powerful than Ld Rosse's 6 foot.

From the tracings you have sent me I have had sketches made & I am making a plastic model of the mountain top on which I will lay out ideal plans for the Observatory. I have already roughed out what appears promising. It embraces room for

Small Equatorial say 8 in for ordinary work

Meridian Room with Transit & Transit circle

Great Refractor Room 70 feet diameter with Dome (40″ Refractor)

Great Reflector Room capable of holding a 7 foot Reflector

Computing Room

Chronograph & Electric Room

& a set of apartments for use of observers.

It requires no small amount of economising to make all these fit but I think you will be pleased when you see it. When finished I could photograph it & send you a copy. I do hope you will be able to call here on your way back I have so much to show you now ...

[13 July 1877] I now send the model & hope it will arrive safe ... I see by 'Nature' the New York Tribune states you have definitely decided against the Reflector. I should hope that this is not yet decided for if it is from what I lately hear there will very likely be a telescope made (which could be finished long before a large Refractor) & which will exceed in power anything likely to be produced in Refractors for many years to come. However I take the matter only as a newspaper report.

The report also said you had great difficulty in keeping down the estimates of the European Opticians to anything like reasonable limits—this is surely not mine for I have been told by some of the first English Astronomers that my estimate was absurdly low & that I will surely lose by it—but I am quite willing to do it for the glory of it, for if this instrument is put in my hands I intend that it shall be the great work of my life & on it my reputation will stand or fall. Excuse this gossipy rambling letter & pray convey my kind regards to Mrs Floyd."

Figure 5.2: Grubb's plaster model of how he envisaged the new Lick Observatory should appear, from a damaged photograph in the Mary Lea Shane Archives of Lick Observatory. The large dome, of 70 feet diamater, was intended to contain a 40-inch refractor. A 72-inch reflector with a special sliding and rotating roof is seen to the right. A meridian circle and a transit instrument were also to be incorporated.

With the model was sent a formal letter 'Allow me to beg that the Trustees of the Lick Estate may accept this model from me if they are of opinion that it may be of any use to them in their deliberations'.

The newspaper report was evidently not correct:

> [4 Sept 1877] "...I am ...glad to see you have not changed your ideas quite so quickly as the New York Tribune would have us to suppose. I began to fear that a bad passage [back to America] had had some dreadful effect on your Scientific Notions.
>
> I do wish those academicians would give over fighting & let us have a chance. Everything is most promising for a commencement & it is even quite possible that in a few months I may have a second establishment on my hands with larger & more powerful machines than at present.
>
> There are one or two matters I have to mention. One is this. I would ask you not to be in a hurry in deciding about the Transit Circle for I believe there will soon be a revolution in that way & you would not like to be 'behind the times'. So if you are deciding

about this let me have 'my say' at all events[3].

Another matter. I know there is a strong feeling in America against giving the Gt Objective to be done out of the Country when you have so good a man as Clarke in it.

Now I have a great Respect for Clark & I would be very sorry if he thought I was trying in any way to take his work away & I say honestly that while I believe I could make you quite as good an Objective as Clark I do not guarantee that I would make you better for I believe his work to be first class in the optical way but I do think & know & indeed it is everywhere acknowledged that my mountings are very superior to his & therefore I would say that if the Trustees had any decided feeling against giving the Objective to be made out of the Country & that still they desired to have the best of Mountings I will not stand in their way by refusing to make the mounting only tho' I need hardly say I would rather have all. I mention this matter because I had a visit from Mr Waldo[4] of Cambridge Obsy a friend of Clark's & he seemed to say that Clark had set his heart on making the big object glass & I do not want to create any bad feeling in your country against myself.

There are many matters of course to be decided in this case & a divided responsibility is in no case desirable but I mention this to you thus privately so that you may be fully aware of my own personal feelings in the matter & can shape your course as you think best for the interests of the Trust.

Have you been able as yet to think about your own little telescope & decide on the kind of mounting? Remember we opticians are dreadfully slow (so we are told) so don't wait till you want it ..."

5.2   Grubb Pushes for a Reflector

[10 March 1879 Grubb to Floyd] "... In consequence of the failure of the [Vienna] glass my ideas with respect to the extension of size of great telescopes has undergone considerable modification since I wrote my paper on 'Great Telescopes of the Future'.

I do not want to lay any blame on Mr Feil who I am sure has done his best, but the fact remains that he has been unable as yet to produce a perfect pair of 27 inch discs tho' he contracted to have them finished in 12 months and has now had about 3 years work on them. I consider therefore (and it is but a matter of

---

[3] Grubb's new ideas on Transit Circles were described with his article on the Cork Observatory (Grubb 1880).

[4] Leonard Waldo, later of Yale Observatory.

common sense) that under these circumstances it would be absurd to expect there would be any chance of getting discs many inches larger in the present state of the art of glassmaking. Feil I believe offered to make discs of 40 inches diameter. Now if we estimate the difficulty as the cube of the diameter (I believe it to be much more) there would be about $3\frac{1}{2}$ times the difficulty in making a 40 inch than a 27 inch. Even if it could be made at all it would appear to take over 11 years at all events to perfect it.

Now the practical lesson we learn from this is that if we want great extension of power we must look to Reflectors rather than Refractors unless someone invents some new process of glassmaking. I am therefore more than ever inclined to press the adoption of an 8 foot Reflector.

On this matter permit me to say one word more. No doubt I shall be alone and single (among instrument makers) in recommending this but I would ask the Trustees to enquire the reason & I think they will find it is for this reason viz: That I am the only instrument maker who is at present in a position to make such an instrument and also the only Instrument maker in the world who has turned out successful mirrors over 3 feet in diameter (You are aware I suppose that the Paris Reflector is a failure).

The Great Melbourne Mirrors are therefore the only large mirrors ever perfected by an instrument maker (Lord Rosse & Mr Lassel being of course Amateurs).

Should the Trustees be inclined to ask me to contract for a large Reflector or Refractor I will be able I think to offer them such terms as will practically guarantee success (provided in the case of the Refractor the discs are procurable).

[30 May 1879 Grubb to Floyd] ... There is quite a stir about large Reflectors in England just now. Bessemer the great steel man is working hard at [?] enormous mirror but from what I hear of his method of working I venture (as I did in the case of the French 4 foot) to predict his total failure. There is also a Mr Common[5] working at this & his ideas seem to me more practical. When men like Bessemer[6] go to work at optical instruments they all split on one rock viz They look to attaining mechanical perfection in the figuring of the mirror not appreciating that optical perfection and mechanical perfection are 2 quite different things ...

---

[5]Andrew Ainslee Common (1841–1903). Born in Newcastle upon Tyne, he was a plumbing and heating engineer as well as an amateur telescope builder on a heroic scale. He constructed several large reflecting telescopes such as the 36-inch mentioned here, which eventually ended up at Lick Observatory, and a 60-inch whose mirrors were used later at Boyden Observatory near Bloemfontein, South Africa.

[6]Sir Henry Bessemer [1813–1898] was the millionaire inventor of the Bessemer converter for making steel. He was knighted and made an FRS in 1879.

I do not know if you are acquainted with Mr Clark but I hear the old man is now getting beyond his work & the sons will not be likely to carry it on in the same spirit at least so I am told by Americans coming over here but I only give it for what it is worth ...

[11 Jul 1879, Grubb to Floyd] ... One matter connected with my own work I wish to mention. A year or so ago I sent an 8 inch Telescope to Berlin to the New Government Observatory at Potsdam. I was very much annoyed however to hear that although they accepted the instrument they were not satisfied with the performance of the objective so tho' they said it was sufficiently good for their purpose I begged them to let me try again. On questioning them as to their objections I found the Germans as a rule prefer a slightly lower correction for colour than the English astronomers ie they like less blue & a little red round the star. Bearing this in mind I made another glass keeping the correction a little lower & I now have the satisfaction to hear from Dr Vogel[7] as follows 'I am very happy to make the communication to you that the new objective is not only good but is <u>very</u> good' (the underlining is Vogel's).

This is very satisfactory to me as this was the only single instance in which my work was ever objected to & I dare say you know the Germans are so jealous of me they don't like to acknowledge my work to be good.

[12 July 1879] ... Reflectors are looking up in England [!]. Several people have them in hands & Dr Huggins is negociating with me for a 3 foot to replace his Refractor. When such men as Dr Huggins who have used both prefer the Reflector it is a strong argument ...

[1 Oct 1879 private] ... Mrs Grubb has been very ill & is not yet out of danger but we hope a few days may make an improvement. She caught cold after a confinement & caught an inflammation ...

[1 Oct 1879 Grubb to Floyd] Agreeable to my promise to let you know everything that goes on here which would be likely to help the Lick Trustees to a settlement of the question of the Great Telescope I beg to send you a few notes:

1. Sir Henry Bessemer's Telescope

Since writing to you I have had a talk with Lord Rosse about this Instrument & I hope soon to see it myself. It would appear however from what Lord Rosse says

'To all an example but to no-one a pattern'

The mirror is not larger if as large as the Melbourne & the mounting is to be of an Altitude & Azimuth construction & there-

---

[7] Herman Charles Vogel (1841–1892).

fore there can be no clockwork & the observer must keep turning away continually at 2 handles to keep the star in view. This is going back to the 'real old times' of telescopes[8]. I don't suppose the California Trustees would commit themselves to such a retrograde step.

In his hydraulic machinery however for turning the dome &c there will probably be found some usefull lessons so I intend as soon as possible to visit it ...

2. Paris 4 foot Reflector

I see that the mirror for this has been delivered at the Paris Observatory and that 'nearly one metre' is good the rest is unusable. This can therefore be hardly called more than a 3 foot Telescope on a 4 foot mounting & from sundry private accounts I have heard of the difficulty of any outsiders seeing it I suspect that even the 3 foot is not perfect. Prof Newcomb will remember that before this mirror was half finished I predicted that it could not be a success.

3. Mr A A Common's new 3 foot Reflector

This instrument appears to be a decided success. I hope to see it soon & report upon it to you also I expect to hear more about its performance in a few days but I see Mr Common was able to pick up 'Deimos' the outer satellite of Mars with it on the 21st Ult°, that is, about 3 weeks before the Washington Astronomers hoped to see it with their 26 in Washington Refractor. If this be so it is a remarkable performance & it goes far to answer the question of what a Reflector will do in comparison with a Refractor. Mr Common has also been able to improve the silvering process so much that he can now deposit the silver without turning the mirror upside down which will be a considerable saving of trouble & risk when we come to deal with very large Reflectors.

4. The Great Refractor for Pulkowa

Prof Struve called on me a few days since. He has, as you are no doubt aware, ordered a refractor (objective only) from Alvan Clark— Alvan Clark having completed 2 objectives & I being only at my first of this very large size it was natural that Struve should order from him & I do not grumble at all at his doing so. Another reason he seems to have had is that 'time' appears to be of considerable moment to him & as I had the Vienna in hands he thought my hands were full enough. He was however much pleased with the mounting which he saw here & our Domes which he saw in Vienna and he has asked me to send in estimates to him for both Equatorial & Domes. Alvan Clark is to call to see me next week.

---

[8]This remark is ironic, in that all really large modern telescopes have alt-azimuth mounts, thanks to computer-controlled driving.

5. Great Vienna Refractor

We are at last I hope getting out of the troubles we have had in procuring the discs. Those last received from Feil appear much better. The last flint was only received last month but we hope to have the objective ready in the spring. If however Feil takes 4 years to produce 2 - 28 inch discs how long will he be in producing the 3[?] inch if he gets the order?

6. Proposed Lick Telescope

... So convinced am I that a large Reflector will be the right form of instrument I am giving some attention to the planning out of a suitable mounting for the monster. It appears to me that it will be necessary to effect all the motions by hydraulic power. The weight of an 8 foot would be about 8 times that of the Melbourne & as this last was just comfortable for one person to work of course the 8 foot would require something like 8 men to work it. This is undesirable for I consider every movement should be completely under control of the observer. I think you told me that an abundant supply of water is obtainable somewhere on the summit of Mt Hamilton. I would be much obliged if you could give me an idea how far (perpendicularly) from the top the water is obtainable & about in what quantity ... "

5.3 Meeting with Alvan Graham Clark

[18 Oct 1879 Grubb to Floyd, marked Private] "... I had a visit a week ago from Mr Alvan Clark[9] & of course among other things we talked of the Lick Telescope. Following out the practice I have invariably adhered to in all our correspondence of letting you know everything that bears on the question without reference to whether it may support or contradict my own ideas I think it well to let you know exactly what passed as nearly as I can recollect. You will however of course consider this as private information.

I found Mr Clark a most uncompromising opponent of Reflectors (as might be expected).

He told me he had offered the Lick Trustees that if they got the most powerful Reflector I could undertake for them he would make a Refractor of 15 inches only which would beat it. He modified that a little however afterwards & said he did not say now that he would do that but he had made the offer. He did not say what had caused him to modify his ideas. He said it was impossible to make a Reflector perfect. Why he said have the satellites of Mars never been seen with a Reflector—But they have said I.

---

[9]This must have been Alvan Graham Clark, since Alvan Clark visited Europe only once, in 1859, according to Warner (1968).

M^r C - Where

G - In England

C - When

G - Tell me first have they been seen this year yet in Washington & when do they expect to see them

Mr C - Oh not yet they hardly expect to see them yet but just about this time or very soon.

Mr G - Well then is it not curious that they have been seen in England in a much worse situation of altitude no less than 4 weeks since in a Reflector?

Some doubts were expressed by Mr Clarke of the authenticity of my story but I soon relieved his mind of that then he asked me the size of the Reflector & I told him 18 inches (This was a mistake see further on).

Oh then he said I see how it is. It is I believe possible to make Reflectors perfect up to 18 ins—but not beyond. I venture to say that they would not have seen it if the mirror had been much larger. As this was a mere matter of opinion I had nothing to say but after he left on looking over the account of the matter I saw that the mirror was one of 36 inch aperture so I went down to see Mr Clark at the hotel but he was out so I left a card for him & wrote on the back that I had made a mistake that the mirror was 36 not 18 dia & therefore his theory about the impossibility of making large mirrors perfect fell to the ground.

He seemed to be annoyed that the Lick Trustees ever went beyond his own recommendation. I gave them he said my best advice & as they don't choose to do with it why they may come to ask me to make a telescope for them but I can't trouble myself about them. He also appeared to be under the impression that the Lick Trustees would not do anything definite for the next 20 years or so but would be fiddling about & not be able to make up their minds. He also seemed to be annoyed with Prof Newcomb who he said was always his friend and backed him up until this Lick affair. I suppose he thinks Prof Newcomb is bound to support him against his own convictions.

As all this occurred at a private interview of course I must ask you to consider this communication strictly private tho' he spoke quite openly & did not ask me to consider it private therefore I do not consider I am doing anything but what is right in telling you of it as a friend particularly as I would be much pleased & not annoyed if he reported all I said to you also.

When I spoke of you above as a friend I was emboldened to do so by the great kindness with which you treated me in our several personal interviews while you were in Europe quite apart from any business transactions. And now as the time is I suppose coming round in which you will be called upon to make some decisions (notwithstanding Mr Clarks gloomy forebodings) I would repeat what I think I once said before. Whether it be a Refractor or a Reflector you decide upon I believe I can satisfy you as well as any other optical firm in the world. If it be a Reflector I can honestly & conscientiously say that I believe I can do better in both mirror & stand than you can get elsewhere. If it be a Refractor I can say the same of the mounting but I will not promise to make you a better objective than Mr Clark. I can promise to make you as good but from what I hear of their work I believe it to be as good as you will get anywhere. Although they are my Rivals I would be sorry to be thought to depreciate their work. I can admire good work even if it comes from the workshops of a Rival House.

In a few days I hope to go to London and will then write you again my impressions about the Bessemer Telescope & Mr Commons 3 foot Telescope.

Prof Struve did not at all admire the mounting of the Washington Telescope. He has asked me to send him an estimate for mounting his new 30 inch. Curiously enough Prof Struve told me the Lick Trustees had quite made up their mind to have a Reflector[;] a week afterwards Mr Clark tells me the Lick Trustees are at last convinced that they must have a Refractor. Say which is nearest the truth? Mr Clark tells me he does not care for the mountings he only wants to make the glass.

All this is gossip but no doubt interesting to you & I am watching anxiously the results of your deliberations for if I am to have anything to do with it I will devote the next few years of my life to it & it will be a success if it be in my power to make it so.

I forgot to mention that when I combatted some of Mr Clarks arguments about Reflectors & Refractors he said that at least in California a Reflector must be a failure for a Reflector always requires someone who understood them & there was no one there of any mechanical ability to undertake such a post. As to this objection you ought to know better how far it is valid than I can but I think this will not be the most difficult problem to solve.'

[5 Nov 1879] 'I have just returned form London & according to my promise I send you a few notes of my experiences.
Bessemer's Telescope

I had an introduction to Sir H. Bessemer from a nephew-in-law of his but I got him to write to Sir Henry first & he wrote back that he was 'not yet ready but the next time I go to London he will be happy to show me all'. I am not however much disappointed at this for hear from all sides that his work will be nothing but a costly experiment. Even at best his telescope is only the size of the Melbourne. Alt-azimuth mounting estimated to cost £40,000!!!

Mr Common's Telescope (3 foot Reflector)

This Instrument I have seen and am much pleased with. I am indebted to Mr Common (who is almost a stranger to me) for allowing me to inspect his telescope closely & for the readiness with which he gave me every information I asked for. I consider that Mr Common's Telescope is decidedly the best attempt to mount a large Newtonian Reflector conveniently & although it would not fulfill all the conditions I think essential in a large Reflector I think it is well worth carefull consideration & that many valuable hints may be obtained from it. Mr Common also showed me his observation book; & his observations I am convinced bear favourable comparison with those of the largest Refractors in existence. He can certainly see with his instrument anything that has been seen with the very largest Refractors & considering he has only had it for about 3 months this is saying a great deal. If then Mr Common can see with his 3 foot mirror even as much as can be seen with a 26 in Refractor in a much better situation what an incomparably more powerful instrument an 8 foot Reflector would be than any Refractor in existence or likely to be in existence for many years to come. Mr Common has courteously intimated that if the Lick Trustees desire to communicate with him he will be most happy to give them all the information in his power.

Dr Huggins has been as you are aware working his 18 inch Reflector for the last 2 years or so although we supplied him with a 15 inch Refractor to fit on same mount & now he has got on so well with the Reflector that he has given me orders to design a 3-foot Reflector[10] for his Observatory so everything at present tells in favour of large Reflectors ...

[4 Sept 1880] ...We are at work now on a 2 foot mirror for a private gentleman & I would certainly like some of you American Astronomers to see this when finished ..." [11]

5.4   First Disappointment

In December 1880, the Lick Trustees gave the contract for the supply of the lens to Alvan Clark. The cost was $50,000. Grubb was duly informed and asked to submit a detailed proposal for the construction of the equatorial mounting.

[12 Feb 1881] "...I do not at present see any necessity for entering into any discussion regarding the details & design for [mount] for several reasons

---

[10]Never constructed

[11]This was W.E. Wilson's 24-inch reflector.

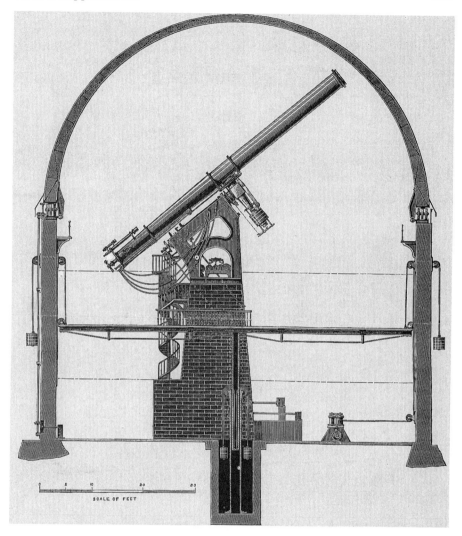

Figure 5.3: Grubb's design for the mounting of the 36-inch refractor at Lick (Grubb 1886c).

1° - Because it does not appear from your letter whether the Trustees intend entering into any contract for the equatorial till the discs of glass for the 36 in objective are obtained & the date of this is, to say the least, 'problematical'.

2° - Because after my experience in constructing what is now acknowledged to be the finest equatorial in the world I can forsee the conditions necessary to fulfil, & the difficulties to be encountered, in the construction of a still larger instrument; & I have already devised special appliances to meet these difficulties, but it would clearly be against my own interests to divulge these matters at present. I therefore though willing to submit estimates & specifications of what the instrument will be guaranteed to do I will not be prepared to submit plans of details until I obtain the contract.

3rd - Because it will be within your recollection that I took a large amount of trouble & interest in the plans & arrangements for the Lick Observatory the only outcome of which was that the Trustees proceeded to order an objective from the Messrs Clark without even asking tenders from my house & I must frankly confess that I consider the Trustees did not act towards me with that courtesy which I think I had a right to expect at their hands & therefore while quite willing to undertake the construction of the Lick Equatorial I would, before entering a tender, desire to see the conditions under which I enter my estimates & that I am placed at least on equal terms with other houses ..."

These reasons were repeated in a letter to Simon Newcomb *ca* 10 May 1881.

"...I do not like the idea of actually entering into competition in such matters with other makers, which seems to me too much treating them [telescopes] like Agricultural Implements or Steam Engines ..."

5.5 Quotes for Dome and Equatorial Mounting

Very little happened for the next few years, largely due to the disintegration of the Feil company. It was only in November 1885 that the company, resurrected by Feil senior, was able to complete the contract for the lens blanks. The crown glass was successful at the 19th attempt. Grubb was asked in November 1885 whether he was still interested in bidding for the equatorial and dome. He replied on 8 December 1885, asking for details of the specifications:

"...I do not anticipate that the extra cost of carriage [from Ireland to the USA] would form any serious addition to the expense of the work while the special machinery which I have & which is suitable for this particular work would more than balance any disadvantage I may be under due to such causes. Perhaps it might be well if I were to add that I am about to patent some new inventions for labour saving apparatus connected with Equatorial Telescopes & specially usefull in the case of very large sized instruments ..."

On 30 January 1886 Grubb sent in rough estimates and a description of his plans for the equatorial and dome. The dome by itself would cost £6500 in Dublin, or £7,000 if the shutters were to open beyond the centre. The equatorial would be £8,000. The whole installation with electrical control and a rising floor would be £18,000. The formal quotation was sent on 13 March.

Grubb was very proud of his design for the new Lick Observatory and it formed quite an important part of his public lecture to the Royal Institution, delivered on 2 April 1886, entitled *Telescope Objectives and Mirrors, their Preparation and Testing* [Grubb 1886a, 1887a]. William Huggins was in the chair. The model he had made according to his design was shown for the first time.

"Whether this design will ever be carried out or not I cannot tell, but even as a proposal I trust it may be interesting enough to excuse my introducing it (somewhat irrelevantly perhaps) to your notice to-night ...

The conditions I laid down for myself in designing this observatory were that it would be possible for the observer single-handed to enter the equatorial room at any time, and that, without using more physical exertion than is necessary for working the smallest-sized telescope, or even a table microscope, he should be able to open the 70-foot dome, turn it round backwards and forwards, point the equatorial to any point of the heavens, revolving it in right ascension and declination to any extent, and finally (the most difficult of all) to bring his own person into a convenient position for observing. I say this last is the most difficult of all, for I think any who have worked with larger instruments will allow that there is generally far more trouble in moving the observatory chair (so called) and placing it in proper position than in pointing the instrument itself. In this instrument the 'chair' would require to be 25 feet high, and with its movable platform, ladder, balance weight, &c. would weigh probably some tons. Even if very perfect arrangements were made for the working of this chair, the mere fact that the observer while attempting to make the most delicate observations is perched upon a small and very unprotected platform 25 feet above the floor and in perfect darkness, tends to reduce his value as an observer to an extent only to be appreciated by those who have tried it.

No matter how enthusiastic a man may be at his work, I would not put a high value on his determinations if made while in a position which calls for constant anxiety for his own personal safety. I would go even further still, and say that even personal comforts or discomforts have much to do with the value of observations.

I propose, therefore, that all the various motions should be effected by water power. There are water engines of various forms now made, some of which have no dead point, and having little *vis inertia*, are easily stopped and started, and are consequently well adapted for this work.

I propose to use four of them: one for the right ascension motion of the instrument, and one for the declination; one for revolving the dome, and one for raising and lowering the observer himself; but instead of having anything of the nature of a 26-foot chair or scaffold, I propose to make the 70-foot floor of the observatory movable. It is balanced by counterpoise weights, and raised and lowered at will by the observer. Then the observer can without any effort raise and lower the whole floor, carrying himself and twenty people if desired, to whatever height is most convenient for observation; and wherever he is observing, he is conscious that he has a 70-foot floor to walk about on, which even in perfect darkness he can do in safety.

The valves and reversing gear of the water engines are actuated by a piece of mechanism, the motive power of which may be a heavy weight raised into position sometime during the previous day by man or water power. By means of a simple electrical contrivance, this piece of machinery is itself under the complete control of the observer, in whatever part of the room he may be, and he carries with him a commutator of a compact and convenient form, with eight keys in four pairs, each giving forward and backward movements respectively to

A. Telescope movement in right ascension;

B. Telescope movement in declination;

C. Revolution of dome;

D. Raising of floor.

The remaining operation, opening of shutter, is easily effected without any additional complications.

It is only necessary to anchor the shutter (which moves back horizontally) to a hook in the wall and move the dome in the opposite direction ... the shutter must of course be opened by this motion."

5.6   The Contract Lost

The Lick Trustees in the end decided to favour the American firm of Warner and Swasey, in spite of the fact that their quotation had initially been higher than Grubb's. This partnership was a relatively young concern, having been started only in 1880, and had hitherto constructed only quite small instruments (Pershey 1984). Worcester Warner[12] and Ambrose Swasey[13] had met as apprentices in the Pratt and Whitney machine tool company in 1866. The Lick contract did for them what the Vienna had done for Grubb. Most of the succeeding generation of American telescopes were mounted by Warner and Swasey.

On being told that the contracts had been awarded elsewhere, Grubb sent the following letter to the Secretary of the Trustees, H.E. Matthews, on 31 July 1886:

> "I have the pleasure to acknowledge receipt of your favor of 10 inst, informing me the contracts for supply of Equatorial & Dome to the Lick Observatory have been entrusted to other firms & containing bank order for $600, stamped receipt for which is enclosed herewith.
>
> I beg to thank you for your courteous letters & will ask you to convey my thanks to Captain Floyd for his kind acknowledgement of the merits of my design for the moveable floor &c, which I hope the Trustees will see their way to adopting, as I am convinced that it is the best solution of the difficulty.
>
> I shall always feel a great interest in the Lick observatory & (if not asking too much) would be obliged if you would kindly let me have from time to time such information respecting the progress of the work as may be available to the general public.
>
> I desire to express my sincere wishes that for the sake of Astronomical Science generally this great undertaking of the Lick Trustees may be brought to a perfectly successful issue."

On 7 October, in a letter thanking Matthews for a positive reply to the above, Grubb ended up '...& you can tell Captain Floyd that if at any time he thinks that my experience might be of any use I shall be most happy to give my advice or opinion upon any doubtful points.'

That Grubb was very upset by the Trustees' decision is understandable, given all the work and enthusiasm that he had put into it. There was an interesting come-back in *Observatory* for August 1890 [Dated 19 June 1890]:

> "GENTLEMEN, -
>
> In the 'Observatory' for April 1890, p.158, a reviewer (who does not sign his name) speaks of the lifting-floor of the Gesellschaft Urania in Berlin, and says that it is 'on the plan devised by Sir Howard Grubb, and so coolly appropriated by the Lick Observatory.' The right to use the ingenious idea of Sir Howard Grubb was purchased by a money-payment, and a receipt for the money in question was signed by Sir Howard Grubb on July 31st, 1886.

---

[12] Worcester Reed Warner, 1846–1929.
[13] 1846–1937.

The original papers, together with letters from Sir Howard Grubb, signifying his entire satisfaction with the whole arrangement, are on file in this office, and copies of them will be furnished, should you so desire. Under these circumstances it is no more than right that you should insert the present note in the 'Observatory' in order that the correction of an unjust criticism may have equal prominence with the criticism itself.

I am, Gentlemen, respectfully,
H.E. Mathews
Secretary of the Lick Trustees"

Chapter 6

Never so Busy—the 1880s

6.1   The Transit of Venus Telescopes

The 1880s saw Grubb at the peak of his career. They started out with the successful completion by him of the largest refractor then built, The Great Vienna Telescope, and finished with the construction of the 'Astrographic' telescopes for the *Carte du Ciel* project. It was also a decade of frequent interaction with David Gill who by then was well ensconced at the Royal Observatory, Cape of Good Hope. Amongst the major items that Grubb made for Gill during this period were a mounting for the Dun Echt heliometer (which Gill had purchased from Lord Crawford), a 6-inch telescope for transit of Venus observations, an 8-inch telescope and dome to be used at the Durban Observatory, an observatory structure to house a larger heliometer made by Repsold, a photographic lens paid for by Nasmyth and, of course, a 13-inch astrographic camera for the *Carte du Ciel* project. Gill and Grubb frequently exchanged ideas concerning the design of these and other instruments.

Fortunately for us Grubb had a habit of tucking private notes in with his official correspondence. These were in his own handwriting which certainly obeyed the 19th century maxim that a gentleman's letters should not be unduly legible—legibility was the mark of the humble clerk! They provide an insight into many of his private thoughts and tell something of his family life. Every few years the succession of letters was interrupted by Gill's home visits to the British Isles, during which he invariably took the opportunity to stay with his friend and catch up on the latest family news.

The transit of Venus of 1882 (i.e. an occasion when Venus crossed the face of the Sun) was considered an event of major astronomical significance, offering an opportunity to determine solar system distances more accurately. Astronomers of several nations, in particular those forming the British Transit of Venus Committee, organized a number of observing stations. Several new 6-inch instruments had to be built, including one for Gill. Grubb got the order and their construction made life very full indeed for him. In November

1881 he wrote to Gill:

> "I never was so busy. We are taking in every hand we can get
> & getting new lathes &c. We have 14 telescopes from 6 in up in
> hand, all in a desperate hurry! also 5 domes from 15 to 24 feet.
>   The largest we have is for the Mexican Government 15in Equa-
> torial 24 feet Dome & we have 2 Equatorials for Spain & the whole
> of Houzeau's new Heliometers & mountings for Belgian Govern-
> ment. No grass growing under our feet I assure you."

On 2nd December 1881 he gave some further details of work in hand:

> "I do wish that the transit committee had made up their minds
> a few months earlier; matters have been left altogether too long
> and it will be very hard for us to get all done in time. We have
> six of these 6 inch telescopes. We have also your 8-inch for Dur-
> ban and two ... for Brussells, also one 5 inch telescope and one
> 6 inch Telescope, all to be finished in February. Besides which
> we are remodelling Dr Huggins Telescope mounting Reflector and
> Refractor at opposite ends of the Crosshead on two Declination
> axes independent of each other one inside the other ... all in a
> desperate hurry."

On 1st February 1882 he replied to pressure from Gill:

> "I am doing the best I can for you. I have ordered your work to
> be pressed forward in all departments in preference to any other
> & certainly you will have them all as soon as possible ... I enclose
> some bills which I ought indeed have sent long since—I need not
> tell you that with £60 a week going out in wages a remittance
> would be very acceptable ..."

By March Gill's demands had become too much for him:

> "Then I wish to say a few words about your late letters—
> When I got your letter in which you threatened me with the dire
> consequences of your wrath I treated it as a joke—Once before you
> said something like it & because I did not take it as a joke you made
> some satirical remarks about my not being able to appreciate one
> so I was determined to treat it this time as one. Your last letter
> however makes it plain that no joke was intended and this being
> so I must say I think you have not treated me well to write as you
> have done.
>   You know, as you ought to know, that for old friendship's sake
> if for nothing else I would be sorry to see you placed at any disad-
> vantage and I have told you that I am doing the very best I can

for you. Now you may take your choice of either of two positions.
Either you disbelieve what I say or, if you do believe me, you commit a very unjust act in threatening me with pains & penalties for
what I cannot help. A man can do no more than his best & when
he is doing that it is hard to be told that if he succeeds he gets
just what he is legally entitled to & if he fails he gets odium &
disgrace. I will go even further & say it was unwise to write so for
I may tell you I felt very much inclined on receipt of your letter
to write you to say I gave up the job. If it had been someone else
I certainly would have done so with no loss to myself for I have
7 other customers waiting for this size of telescope. In doing as I
am & pushing your work in preference to all others I am getting
into disgrace in other quarters & run the risk of serious pecuniary
loss ... Well may I say 'Save me from my friends'.

I really am at a loss to understand some of your letters. Is it
a case of 'Darwinism' and are you beginning to 'harmonize with
the surroundings' that you write in such an uncivilized style? ...

If I were in your position & wanted work done well I would pick
out that man whom I could best depend upon. I would put all in
his hands asking him simply to do the best he could to have all
by such a time & instead of writing him threatening letters which
would only irritate and distract him I would try to encourage him
in his work. If he failed through want of attention I would give
him no more work. If he failed thro' circumstances not under his
control I would try him again & if he succeeded I would give him
all the credit possible. If you just try that plan I think you will
find it better, at least in dealing with natives of this country. ... "

Gill did, in fact, receive his instrument in time. Several subsequent letters
tell of the trouble Grubb was having with other clients because of his solicitude
for Gill.

6.2   Fenian Troubles Amongst the Workmen

The troubled political scene in Dublin did not leave Grubb unscathed. On 3
May 1882 he reported to Gill that all but the micrometer for the 8-in Durban
telescope (ordered about the same time as the Royal Observatory transit of
Venus instrument) had been sent and added:

"You have no conception of the hard push we have had to
get through our work. As it is I fear I will lose 2 orders for 6″
Telescopes as I have had to neglect them & will probably also lose
£180 which I was to have got from Mexico to hasten their work. I
am paying £70 a week away in wages & yet I cannot get through

it. This is partly due to causes which I mention in enclosed private note."

The note referred to was probably the following (undated):

"The simple fact is (but one I did not like to have noted in our copying book[1]) this: the minds of all our men are completely upset with the political situation they can think of nothing else but holding their Fenian meetings & when they are at work here they leave their heads behind them & we have had, oh[?] such messes made of some of our work & such loss of time it is heartbreaking."

In Ireland, this was a period of intense agitation over the reform of land ownership, characterized by many acts of violence. Between mid-October 1881 and the end of April 1882, there were 14 murders and 61 shooting attacks, mostly the result of activities by secret societies. On 6 May 1882 occurred the most dramatic assassination of the period, the so-called Phoenix Park murders, when the Chief Secretary, Lord Frederick Cavendish, and his Under-secretary, T.H. Burke, were stabbed to death by members of the 'Invincibles' (Lyons 1971).

An interesting letter dated 2 August 1882 gives further details of the the tense atmosphere Grubb was living in:

"... You do not regret more than I do that everything is not as it might be but I am too ill and seedy to argue with you. Davis is away in Vienna & I am utterly done up. If you knew all & how I worked to get off what I did you would pity & not abuse me. I did not take more than I could do provided the men worked fair but as I gave you a hint before we have had bad work here & the men especially Lamberts are not working fair. I have had to take all Lambert's hands away from him & put him to work in a room for himself & you can imagine what a state we are in when I tell you I have had to have some of the hands under Police Surveillance & I myself now never come down here at night to try an object glass without a loaded revolver in my hand.

When these micrometers were made for you I gave Lamberts his own time in order not to give him an excuse after he said he would have them done in 3 days. I gave him 3 weeks & when I came to examine them I found them so bad I had to spend a week at them myself & for 4 days I worked myself at them till 3 AM every night. You cannot conceive the trouble I had ... "

---

[1] Before typewriting and carbon paper came into use, copies of outgoing commercial correspondence were made by slightly dampening the original and pressing it against tissue paper in a large book. Soluble ink was used, and a mirror image of the original was transferred to the tissue paper. The copy could be read from the reverse side.

Unfortunately, Gill was very dissatisfied with the telescope he had received. His main complaints were that it lacked rigidity and also that a number of minor modifications he had requested seemed to have been ignored.

One letter from Gill was so intemperate that Grubb had to complain [31 March 1883]:

> "...The rest of your letter is simply a set of Piazzi-Smythian adjectives strung together in a manner which I think it best not to comment on; except to say; that I do not object to any amount of fair criticism, provided it be done in such a manner that it is possible to discuss & answer; but I do object to stringing a lot of adjectives together; without giving any data whatsoever to discuss or answer. Your letter contains not one definite statement except about the lamps. Such a letter I never before received from any scientific man except from the above-named Prof. I had thought that his style was 'to all an exception, to no one a pattern'. I finished some 14 Equatorials last year. In not one other case have I had a complaint except as regards the method of dividing the Decln circle which I did according to your ideas & which was the only point I got into trouble about. In no case did I take so much trouble as in yours & and in no case have I had any complaints at all but yours & let me add also all orders except those coming through you have been duly paid for but I have never yet received any paymnent whatsoever for the Durban Observatory; though I have your distinct statement that the money would be sent on its receipt."

Grubb quite rightly objected to Gill's habit of placing an order and afterwards bombarding him with design changes. He offered to take back any unsatisfactory work provided:

> "1. That you formulate your demands precisely in one document & not spread over many months of corrrespondence.
> 2. That the demands do not exceed what you originally presented.
> 3. That either you yourself or some properly qualified representative of yours tests and approves of the Instrument before it leaves Dublin."

Nearly a year of bitter recriminations over this telescope followed until both parties agreed that a replacement mount, of the proportions Grubb usually considered correct for an 8-inch, should be sent out. In spite of the bitter language that was flowing, when Gill and Grubb were simultaneously made Fellows of the Royal Society, Gill was able to write [3 June 1883]:

> "I ask you to accept our sincere congratulations on your FRS election. I had written to several friends expressing my pleasure at

entering that honourable body in the company of an old friend—
yourself—and therefore, tho' obliged to criticize your work,

> I am now as ever
>> Your sincere friend
>> David Gill."

The final making-up seems to have occurred during Gill's visit 'home' in
early 1884.

6.3   The Cork (Crawford) Observatory

In 1879 Grubb completed a small but interesting observatory for Queen's
College, Cork, where he seems to have been given *carte blanche* to follow out
out some of his own most interesting ideas (Grubb 1880). The chief instrument
was an 8-inch refractor, and it incorporated on a smaller scale many of the
innovations which had gone into the Dun Echt and Vienna designs. It was
shown at the Paris Exhibition of 1878 and earned Grubb a gold medal, which
he portrayed on his company letterhead for several years afterwards. The
most impressive of the new features was a means for regulating the driving
clock from an electrically controlled pendulum slaved to the main observatory
clock. He did not here use an electrical 'detector' as Gill had done, but instead
used a differential gear between the telescope drive and a clock driven by the
slave pendulum to control the friction applied to the governor of the drive.
This was, in effect, a mechanical version of Gill's system, but a faster-acting
one. It suffered from the same disadvantage, i.e. that it acted as a speed
control rather than as a position control. The dome of 15 feet diameter was
also of a new design. It opened in segmental fashion and ran on a 'live ring'
set of rollers.

A 4-inch telescope of this observatory was constructed as a siderostat. The
instrument could be rolled out from its housing and lowered to make firm
contact with its mounting pads on the ground. The position of the observer
did not change as the field of view moved around the sky.

There was to be a 5-inch transit instrument furnished with glass position
circles and a unique form of lifting and laterally moving roof on counter-
weights.

The observatory had a central time installation and several accessories
were also supplied by Grubb. These included two forms of micrometer and a
spectroscope.

The whole installation was housed in a small Victorian gothic building of
Cork limestone and has apparently survived much as Grubb left it up to the
present day.

Figure 6.1: The Cork 8-inch refractor at the Paris exhibition of 1878. This print, though reversed, was signed by Grubb. This telescope is a typical specimen of a 'Standard Equatorial' (Astronomical Institute of the University of Vienna).

6.4   Proposal to Buy Out Feil

Optical glass of good quality, especially large discs for telescope objectives, was then manufactured by only two concerns: Chance brothers of Birmingham and Charles Feil in Paris. The processes involved were trade secrets and had been developed by Pierre-Louis Guinand (1745–1823), a clockmaker of Les Brenets, Switzerland. Later, a Munich businessman, Geheimratsreferendar Joseph Utzschneider, financed experiments at Benediktbeuern in collaboration with Fraunhofer, which improved the process still further. Guinand parted ways with Utzschneider, and his son, Henri Guinand, founded a new glassworks at Choisy-le-Roi which was eventually inherited by Charles Feil, a grandson. However, Henri had sold the information to George Bontemps who moved to England during the 1848 revolution and joined the Chance Brothers' firm, bringing the technological secrets with him (Chance 1937).

About 1880, after the successful production of the Vienna discs, Charles Feil retired and handed over the firm to his son Edmond. However, the business soon started to go badly. In particular, Edmond was unable after almost twenty attempts to supply the 36-inch crown blank which formed part of the order placed by the Clarks for the Lick telescope. The business was about to fail and Charles sought to regain control. He informed Captain Floyd, chief trustee of the Lick project, that if he could regain possession of the business, the order could be completed very quickly. Evidently he did not have the money to bail out his son alone, for on 17 June 1884 Grubb wrote to Gill, then still in Britain, as follows:

> "There is a matter I would like to consult you about but I must ask you not to mention the matter elsewhere for the present except it be to Dr Huggins who is the only one at your side of the water I have as yet spoken to about it. You are aware I suppose that Feil the younger has come to grief. I never liked him. He was very different to the father & I never cared to have dealings with him. He has now gambled away everything & seems to owe about £3000 but it is possible that the assets if properly realized will nearly balance this. I have been often urged to take up the matter of optical glass but never saw my way, knowing there are trade secrets connected with it which it might take a large portion of a man's lifetime & capital to find out but it has occurred to me lately that in the present condition of Feil's some combination might be made between his house & mine. I have been thinking it would be possible to form a company over here which might be or might not be connected directly with my own Establishment & get old Feil here as manager. I had some preliminary correspondence with the old man about this, he seems inclined to take the idea but would rather form the company over there & also put his son into it; neither of these conditions would at all suit my views. I am sure there would be no difficulty in getting Capital. If I understand him he estimates the value of his stock, goodwill &c at £2000. He proposes to raise £2000 cash & that the capital of the Company should be £4000, made up of the £2000 cash & the £2000 of his stock in trade &c; in which case he would hold half the shares of the company. He says he has an offer something of this sort in Paris but still he seems very anxious that I should join him. I am writing to him now to say that under no circumstances would I care to put any money into or take any interest in the company

if formed in France but will try to get out of him what terms he would require to come over here & I certainly do not like the idea of his son having anything to do with it but I fear that will be a great difficulty as he evidently wants to provide for the son.

I am letting you know about this in case anything might occur to you as I know you would be glad to give me any advice which you think would be useful. The reason I ask you to keep it quiet for the present is that I hear Ross of London is building a great factory in Clapham Common which it will take the optical trade almost of the whole world to support & if they hear of this matter they might try to pick up Feil."

In the end, Grubb's scheme came to nothing for, in fact, Mantois gained control in February, 1885. After this the firm became Charles Feil, Mantois and Parra. Although the Lick blank was soon completed, production problems remained. In Grubb's interview of 1896 (FitzGerald 1896) he remarked 'I may get a 20in. disc in six months (phenomenal this), or—as is the case of the 28in. object-glass for the Greenwich telescope—I may have to wait three years for it. No fewer than sixteen failures were encountered during the making of this latter disc, owing merely to the presence of air bubbles and such-like faults'[2].

6.5   Reflectors of the 1880s

Why did reflectors have to wait until the 20th century to become the dominant type of telescope? Reflectors possess the great advantage that all rays are brought to the same focus, unlike refractors which even at best do not give equally sharp images at all wavelengths. It was also possible to make reflectors which were fairly 'fast' for photography, i.e., having a small ratio of focal length to size of main mirror. This could not be done with lenses. In addition, reflectors can be used with ultraviolet and infrared light whilst refractors cannot as these rays do not pass through glass. Furthermore, at first, it was easier to get a larger 'field', or area of sky with sharp images, with reflectors than with refractors. Although, later in the decade, developments by the Henry brothers of the Paris Observatory and by Grubb showed that refractor design could be modified fairly satisfactorily to overcome this disadvantage, it was still a real problem in the early 1880s. Before photography, this consideration had not been very important.

Nevertheless, reflectors remained relatively unpopular, especially with the professionals. This was partly due to the fact that they were usually poorly mounted on insecure stands, partly that they were felt to need adjustment too often, and partly to conservatism. It is noteworthy that the lead in using them was taken by amateur astronomers, particularly those who were developing the new field of astrophysics.

---

[2]Mantois (1894) gives an account of the processes involved in forming large optical blanks.

In spite of their relative unpopularity, Grubb constructed several note-worthy reflecting telescopes during the 1880s. The Huggins telescope of *ca.* 1870 with its interchangeable refractor and reflector was re-mounted in 1882, following a suggestion of Huggins himself, so as to make the changeover more convenient. The two tubes were placed on opposite sides of the mounting on separate axes one of which turned inside the other so that they could be moved independently in declination.

In 1881, W.E. Wilson (1851–1908), a landowner of Daramona, Co West-meath in Ireland, ordered a 24-inch reflector which, however, he placed on a mount for a 12-inch reflector that he had bought from Grubb in 1871. The best work with this instrument seems to have been done after 1890 when he had it 're-mounted by Sir Howard Grubb, and provided with his best form of driving clock and electrical control. The new mounting has given the greatest satisfaction' (Wilson 1900). It was used for pioneering work on photoelectric photometry (see Butler and Elliott 1992) in collaboration with several other Irish scientists—Minchin, Monck and Fitzgerald (the last-named, a profes-sor at Trinity College, Dublin, was a theorist in the field of electro-magnetic radiation and is remembered today by relativists for his suggestion of the 'Fitzgerald contraction' undergone by rapidly moving bodies). Wilson took a series of very fine photographs (Wilson 1900) with the telescope. After his death, the instrument was presented to University College, London, and re-erected at Mill Hill Observatory.

Another dual reflector was supplied to Isaac Roberts (1829–1904), a self-made building contractor who turned to astronomy at about the age of 50. His first telescope was a Cooke refractor of 7 inches aperture, but he soon decided to order a larger instrument from Grubb. His 20-inch reflector was mounted together with the Cooke on one of Grubb's 'twin' equatorials. Desiring as he did to take long photographic exposures, he soon found the the standard telescope driving clocks of the period were quite inadequate. Roberts felt that the clock drive of a telescope should be good enough to leave the telescope running without adjustment for long periods, and laid down the conditions which should be met by a satisfactory photographic instrument. Grubb made a major effort to meet his requirements (see next section).

In July 1884 Grubb was visited by 'a Parsee Professor of Physics', Mr K.D. Naegamvala[3] of the College of Science, Poona. This visit must have been in connection with the placing of an order, for in July 1885 Grubb mentioned to Gill that he was building a $16\frac{1}{2}$-in reflector for Bombay. A letter from Naegamvala (1888) in *The Observatory* mentions a Grubb spectrograph as being one of the accessories of this telescope, which appears to have been finished about then. The instrument was at first described as a Newtonian (see Kochhar 1988), but later it seems to have become a Cassegrain and, later still, a 20-inch Cassegrain! It would not have been difficult to convert from Newtonian to Cassegrain as the primary mirrors of Grubb's photographic

---

[3]Kavasji Dadabhai Naegamvala, 1857–1912.

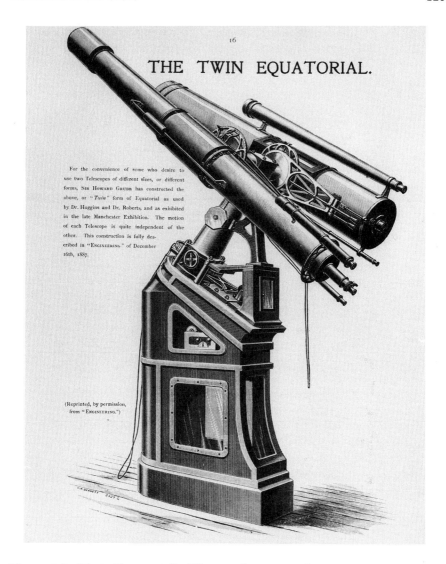

Figure 6.2: 'Twin Equatorial'. This combination reflector and refractor was described in *Engineering* **44** 667 (Grubb Catalogue 1903).

reflectors of the period had central holes for focussing. It was possible by means of a telescopic eyepiece at the mirror end to view the image on a screen put into the plateholder at the upper end. The tube of this telescope may have been one of those which formed part of a 'Twin Equatorial Telescope' exhibited by Grubb at the Manchester Exhibition in 1887 (Anon 1887). It was then described as a 17-inch reflector, and since there is no record of such a telescope anywhere else, it can probably be identified with the Poona instrument. The upgrading to a 20-inch may have been the reason for another visit which Naegamvala paid to Grubb in September, 1896, but we have no record of what transpired on that occasion. Naegamvala was a fairly active observer and published several papers on his results.

6.6   Improvements to Driving-Clock Design

In April, 1887, Grubb spoke at the meeting of the Royal Astronomical Society 'On the Choice of Instruments for Stellar Photography' (Grubb 1887b). He discussed whether refractors or reflectors were the more suitable, but the most interesting part is a description of an improved method for regulating driving clocks which he had applied to both Roberts' reflector and Pritchard's equatorial at Oxford.

This method incorporated a major advance over all previous schemes in that the correction was now applied to the position of the telescope and not as previously to the rate of movement. The means used to introduce an advance or a retard was a pair of planetary gear systems which could be engaged by means of electromagnets. The action was sufficiently gentle that a change of speed did not induce oscillation of the telescope, something that is very undesirable in photography as tending to blur the images. This part of the scheme was so successful that it was used in every large Grubb and Grubb Parsons telescope until after World War II.

The detector was an electrified version of Grubb's previous scheme as applied to the Cork observatory. A wheel turned by a pendulum slaved to the observatory clock was compared to the motion of a shaft geared to the final worm drive of the telescope. Any differential motion was detected by electrical contacts and current was applied to turn on one of the correctors—advancing or retarding as necessary. As the detector was mounted on a wheel turning at one revolution per minute, very fine tolerances had to be maintained if an accuracy approaching 1/20 of a second was to be achieved. This was the main weakness of the detector which led to its abandonment in favour of a better system.

6.7   First Photographic Refractor

As is well known, Gill was a pioneer of photographic sky surveys. In 1882 he had photographed a bright comet by means of a Ross camera lens of $2\frac{1}{2}$ inches aperture and 11 inches focal length attached to the mounting of his 6-inch telescope. He had been surprised by the number of background stars that appeared on the newly available 'dry' plates that he used. Deciding to experiment further, he obtained in 1883 a 'Rapid Rectilinear' lens of 4 inches aperture from the Dallmeyer photographic concern. In 1884 he borrowed from them a similar one of 6 inches aperture and 54 inches focal length. With this particular lens he was ultimately to make the sky survey known as the

Cape Photographic Durchmusterung (Gill 1896). The 'Rapid Rectilinear' lens was of symmetrical form and consisted of two well-separated 'old achromats' (so-called, i.e. cemented doublets rather like those of the old Thomas Grubb patent, made of pre-Jena glass) with a stop between them. The images it gave, for that time at least, were relatively sharp and free of distortion. It was, in addition, reasonably fast, an essential attribute in those days of insensitive plates. This lens was mounted by Gill at the end of a square wooden tube which slid for focussing purposes within a larger similar one forming the main body of a telescope. A simple plateholder was fixed to the other end and the whole 'instrument' was carried by the solid mounting which he had purchased with his own money in 1879 as a mount for the Dun Echt heliometer.

Early in 1885 Gill conceived the idea of constructing a special photographic instrument with three telescopes mounted together to do the definitive Durchmusterung. One was to be a 5-inch guide telescope, constructed from an old Dollond transit instrument. The next was to be fitted with an improved Rapid Rectilinear lens from Dallmeyer and the third was to have a specially made large objective, intended for photographing the centre of each Durchmusterung field to greater depth, the idea being to study the law of stellar distribution with magnitude.

6.8   Correspondence between Gill and Grubb

In February 1885 Gill wrote to Grubb:

> "Have you any ideas about a perfect photographic telescope to cover a field of at least $2\frac{1}{2}^{\circ}$ radius ... Dallmeyer has lent me a 6″ Rapid Rectilinear Lens which we shall try but I am doubtful about it. The brothers Henri [sic] of Paris have produced what appears to be a highly satisfactory lens. I write to know if you have considered the matter and to ask particulars & prices for such a lens of 6″, 7″ & 8″ aperture & whether you wd go in for a double combination."

Further negotiations were conducted partly through Huggins, who was perhaps Gill's most intimate friend in England and whom he often asked to undertake delicate tasks. Gill wrote to Grubb on 13 May, rather too optimistically as it later turned out:

> "... Dr Huggins writes to me that you that you will undertake to make a Photographic objective of 9 inches aperture and 9 feet focal length for £150 as good as Henrys of Paris— that is to say of the highest perfection in definition and to cover perfectly a field of $4\frac{1}{2}^{\circ}$ in diameter, and that you will complete such a lens within 5 months from date of order. I have wired to Dr Huggins to accept your offer, but I understand of course that you will guarantee the performance of the lens."

The new lens was to be a simple doublet, corrected for chromatic and spherical aberration, but without any particular specification as to size of field. However, it represented quite a challenge to Grubb as he had not before constructed an achromatic lens corrected for 'chemical rays', i.e. light from the blue end of the spectrum to which alone early photographic plates were sensitive. It was to be known as the Nasmyth lens because James Nasmyth had made a grant of £200 towards it.

Dallmeyer was to take care of the tube and photographic arrangements for the new 6-inch lens that he was to supply while Grubb was to provide the rest of the instrument.

In the middle of the negotiations there suddenly appears a letter of sympathy on the Grubbs' loss of their youngest boy (Herman, born 1882). Deaths of close relations and friends were often mentioned in the correspondence and they remind one forcefully how short the expectation of life was in the days before modern surgery and medicines.

In July 1885, the blanks for the lens were ordered from Chance. Business was good:

> "I have the new Robinson Memorial Observatory at Armagh just complete & will be sending off Dr Terby's 8 inch to Louvain in a few weeks. Just got off another 6″ to New Zealand, another to follow, and getting another in hands, also some Domes for Russia & United States & Observatory & $16\frac{1}{2}$ inch reflector for Bombay. These with some 5″ & 4″ keeps me pretty busy besides small matters.
>
> Gill (date missing): About the Photo lens I suppose you have duly got my letters. I have just received from Paris a photo of a part of the Milky Way with the new Henry lens. It is simply magnificent [right to the] edge and each star absolutely and perfectly round—for my sake, and if you love me—don't let the Frenchman beat you.
>
> Grubb [16 September 1885]: I have just received a pair of discs from Chance & am having a rough polish put on them in order to test them. One I have good hopes of but some fears that I will have to return the other. I have a 4″ trial lens in hands.
>
> Grubb [30 September]: I have been rather unfortunate about the discs. There are slight faults in both discs I have got from Chance. I have been polishing windows on various places on the edges to try and localize these faults & as far as I can see I think they will work out in the grinding but it will be 3 or 4 days more before I can quite determine this ... you speak of using a field of 8 inches which would be something like 4°; now I am very doubtfull if such an enormous field will be usefull or possible to get with good definition. The photographs I saw by the brothers Henry & which were probably the same as what you saw were only about

$1\frac{1}{2}^{\circ}$ in length by 1° in breadth ...

Grubb [14 October]: I am very glad to be able to tell you that by a little 'dodging' I have managed to escape any faults of both flint & crown for your objective and we are now free to go ahead, which we will do at once."

On 7 October Gill sent Grubb a set of detailed plans. Those for the photographic breechpiece were to become the standard for the later astrographic telescopes and are illustrated in Gill (1892) and Ambronn (1899). Provision was made for focussing by moving the end of the telescope barrel in or out instead of adjusting the lens itself. A scale enabled the focal position to be read. The location of the plate within the plateholder, and the mounting of the holder itself, utilized proper 'kinematic supports', as they would now be called. Grubb was at first a little shocked at the elaborateness of this design and feared that the construction would prove very costly. Later (see Gill's letter of 4 June, 1888), during the design phase of the *Carte du Ciel* telescopes, he almost came to believe the ideas had been his own and had to be reminded that they were due to Gill.

Grubb [20 January 1886]: "It is of course very hard for a draughtsman who is not acquainted with the available tools of the workshop or what they can do to work out details of such a job as this in economical manner; however I am sticking as near as possible to your drawings and will do the best I can. Re 9 inch Photographic Objective. Before next mail I hope to have had my first trials. I note you want a spring in cell to keep glass up against one side as in transit circle mounting ... There is a great cry here just at present for perfect clock movement for use in celestial photography. I am making what I believe will be the most [perfect] equatorial form in this respect for Mr Roberts (President Liverpool Astronomical Society). I have all the clock arrangements of the Moscow Equatorial on my hands; also Oxford (De La Rue reflector) I will have to re-model & another in Scotland for Lord McLaren.

Grubb [2 June 1886]: I am glad to be able to give you a favourable report. In making the calculation I ran it a little too fine & I found that the correction for photo rays was almost perfect when the lenses were absolutely in contact & that this would be undesirable as it would leave no room for final correction, so I re-worked the fourth surface & now I think I have the correction fully under control. The last trials I had today are very promising & I expect soon to be able to report its completion.

Gill [21 June]: It really is too bad of you to neglect me thus. Yr contract time for delivery of the photographic telescope is long long past—and there seems no sign yet of your finishing it. I must

insist on an immediate reply and yr sending it at once or not at
all ... If you want me to write you in a better humour you must
show that you deserve it.

Gill [28 June]: The [replacement for the 6-inch 'Transit of
Venus Telescope'] Equatorial I have erected hastily in a spare
room, till we get time to mount it in its own observatory ... As a
whole I am quite charmed with this new instrument. What wd I
not have given for it in 1882! If the final object glass is up to the
mark I have no hesitation in saying that it is the best equatorial
of its size in the world and the only equatorial I have ever seen
that realizes my ideas of stability ... I am quite delighted with
[the] slow motion, it is by far and away the best I know, and the
arrangements of the clamp in Decln are also most satisfactory. I
am thoroughly content.

Meanwhile I hope not an hour is being lost about the photographic telescope and I trust it has left before this reaches you.

Gill [7 September]: Just a line to say I shall lose all patience if
the Photo. Telescope does not arrive by mail [steamer] expected
tomorrow ... The new 6″ gets a high place of mention in the
E[ncyclopaedia] B[ritannica] Art. Telescope and I have come down
very hard on the Washington mounting ... "

(It should be mentioned that Gill wrote the articles on 'Telescope' and
'Micrometer' for the 9th edition of the *Encyclopaedia Britannica*, published
in 1887.)

6.9   The Instrument in Cape Town

The telescope finally was sent to Cape Town, but its shipping documents were
delayed—Gill had to have the custom house searched to find it.

Gill [6 October 1886]: "I had to make a few alterations to get
the thing together ... and put stronger spiral springs so that the
focussing arrangement would work when the Inst is directed to
the zenith. Now all is in perfect order—and so far as I can see the
whole thing will be a great success. So far as I can judge by one
night of bad definition the object glass is exceedingly good, the
chromatic correction just what it ought to be and the centering of
the lens very satisfactory."

The completion of this telescope occurred just before Gill left for the Paris
Astrographic Congress of 1887. Unfortunately, the Royal Society, which had
hitherto been financing the CPD (Cape Photographic Durchmusterung), was
negatively influenced by the Astronomer Royal, Christie, who was apparently
jealous of Gill (Warner 1979). They decided to withdraw their support on

the grounds that the CPD would be superseded by the *Carte du Ciel* project. Gill did not share this view and chose, after discussing the matter with his wife, to fund the survey out of his own pocket, devoting half his salary to it. His experimental work had, as a consequence, to be cut short.

The newer Dallmeyer lens turned out in any case to be inferior to the first one and the field of good definition of the Nasmyth lens was disappointingly small at only about 2° across. For these reasons, and the expectation that the soon to be furnished astrographic telescope would give superior results, this telescope was rather quickly abandoned. The Nasmyth lens was afterwards used as a collimator in connection with imposing 'réseaux' on Astrographic plates prior to their exposure in the telescope. The focussing system and plate-holding mechanism were attached to the original wooden Durchmusterung telescope and used for that survey. The eyepiece of the guide telescope, which was made movable in $r - \theta$ fashion, turned out to be inconvenient and was replaced in the astrographics by normal x–y slides. Also, instead of using a small circular hole in a piece of watch-spring as a reticle, normal cross-wires were employed.

The importance of this instrument lay not in any results it ever produced but rather in the fact that it provided a test-bed for many of the ideas which were later incorporated in the design of the Grubb *Carte du Ciel* and other photographic telescopes. The problem of designing and constructing a lens which was achromatic for 'photographic rays' and which at the same time gave satisfactory images over a large field was still to occupy several years of hard work.

Today, little of this telescope survives. The Nasmyth and 5-inch guider lenses remain at SAAO, though unused. The mounting was given by Gill to the newly-created Transvaal Observatory in 1906 (Hers 1987) where it now carries a 9-inch objective and tube completed by Grubb in 1907.

Chapter 7

Gill and the Astrographic Project

7.1 The Astrographic Telescopes

In 1886 the Henry brothers, opticians at the Paris Observatory, sent Gill some photographs taken with a photographic lens of their own design. This led him to propose an international congress to coordinate sky mapping by photography. At the meeting, which took place in 1887 under the leadership of Admiral Mouchez[1] and Gill, it was resolved that a *Carte du Ciel* [Map of the Sky] would be constructed, each participating observatory to map a particular zone of declination using instruments of a standard pattern. Their aperture was to be 33 cm and their focal length 3.43 m, with aplanatism and achromatism defined at 430.8 nm.

After the Congress Gill spent several months in Britain. Grubb was keen to get to work on a design and wrote [14 May 1887]:

> "I shall be glad to hear from you as soon as possible about the details of the photographic telescopes. Are there not one or two of them to be made for Australia as well as for Greenwich and the Cape? Of course, the greater number I have to make, the less price I can make them for.
>
> [1 June] I think it would be just as well if I attended at the next meeting of the Royal Astronomical Society on Friday week so I shall in all probability see you there .... I believe I can count on all the members of the Royal Society & Royal Astronomical Society Committees, except two, as acting friendly to me or at least as doing what is right and fair but I have reason to know that there is one at least who is working heaven & earth to give

---

[1] Ernest Amédée Barthélemy Mouchez (1821–1892), director of the Paris Observatory.

the order for all the telescopes to France, probably you know who I mean without my mentioning names.

Now I dont think there can be any reasonable doubt that these instruments can be made in our own Country at least as well, probably decidedly better, than in France & my estimate is lower than that of the Frenchman. If therefore the Government send their orders to France they will have to be prepared with a good reason for doing so as I shall certainly take steps to have the question raised in the House. I cannot however think it likely that the Government would go off hand & order instruments as this bombastic individual is telling everyone, without waiting for the advice of the two societies most interested; however this matter has put me upon my guard & I think I had better be on the spot whenever any discussion comes on.

This matter of course you will keep private just for the present. I count on your advice and assistance in the matter.

I have just completed experiments on a new form of objective suggested by Professor Stokes which forms the very best telescope for visual work as well as photographic by an alteration both in distance and position of a crown lens which has unequal curves. I thought of giving a short paper on this at next meeting of Royal Astronomical Society."

It is not now clear who 'this bombastic individual' might have been. Strong factions were a feature of British astronomy at this period. It is evident from contemporary issues of *The Observatory* that the Astronomer Royal, W.H.M. Christie[2], and his Chief Assistant H.H. Turner[3] tended to oppose anything suggested by Gill. They were often supported by A.A. Common and I. Roberts.

Grubb's domestic arrangements were upset in June as he mentioned in a letter to Christie [18 June 1887, RGO 7/43]:

"I write a line to ask you to pardon my not having answered your letter in ue course. The fact is that our eldest boy [Howard Jr] has taken scarlatina. I have had to remove all the other three boys out of the house. I am now stopping with them at my sister's house and all communication is cut off between this & my own home."

During the same month, Grubb roughed out his ideas for the 'Standard Photographic Telescope', or Astrographic as it is now usually called, and he wrote to Gill on the 24th for his comments. One point concerned the extra accuracy required in the final worm drive which came after his correcting mechanism and thus had to be essentially perfect.

---

[2] 1845–1922, Astronomer Royal 1881–1910.
[3] 1861–1930, later Professor at Oxford.

"I am about to construct a special tool for cutting the screws [worms]. Our micrometer screws are cut on a special machine & I have never known any case in which they did not compare favourably with those by other makers. Some of the results of examinations of my micrometer screws have been sent me by different observers & they were highly satisfactory; but the machine is not suitable for cutting screws as coarse as the clock screws of large Equatorials. Up to the present it has sufficed to cut these in a good screw cutting lathe. As I mentioned above however it is now my intention to make a new machine specially suitable for cutting these screws the master screw of which I will cut in my micrometer screw cutting engine. So far as the cutting of teeth in the sector is concerned I cannot see my way to any better system than what I use at present. The sector is first placed in the dividing engine & a set of divisions is cut corresponding to the number of teeth required; it is then placed in the cutting engine & each division is watched under a microscope while the corresponding tooth is cut."

The above letter also contained an estimate that the price would be about £1500. Gill's reply [25 June] contains several interesting points.

"There is much need for you taking extra precautions in screw cutting and wheel cutting. Roberts has had infinite trouble & Huggins finds a periodic error of over 20″ of arc!! recurring every 80 sec^{ds} of time so far as I remember.

No screw direct from the machine is of the slightest value— you must cut a tolerably long screw, make a long female screw & grind the two together till you get absolute freedom when the female screw fits as tight (by a split screw) as possible & equally tight at all places .... As to your plan of sector-cutting I prefer Gautier's[4] which I explained to you but every man must work in his own way, it is the <u>result</u> we want. You should be bound to some specific accuracy as to the result—e.g. there should be no periodic error amounting to +0″.2. Errors of long period are of less consequence as they can be corrected by the watch [guide] telescope but errors recurring in short periods like 60^{sec} or 80^{sec} are an intolerable nuisance."

The range of movement in hour angle without reversing the telescope was to be increased by $\frac{1}{2}$ hour to $1\frac{1}{2}$ hours on the opposite side from that which the tube was on. The sector itself was to be made longer by allowing it to protrude from the stand and protecting it by thin sheet metal covers. The

[4]P. Gautier designed the mountings of several French telescopes, including the astrographic instruments whose lenses were made by the Henry brothers.

Figure 7.1: Cutting a drive sector in Grubb's works. The tracking of the telescope depended on the accuracy of this part. The machines were driven by belts from shafts turned by a central steam engine. A drill press is seen to the right (SAAO collection).

friction relief roller of the right ascension axis was not of the correct cross section as Gill saw it. The guider telescope should be at least **of** 9 inches diameter. He went on:

> "I have today received a letter from Bamberg[5] of Berlin offering to make object glasses up to 20 inches aperture of the new Jena glass. If he can get such discs there is no reason why you should not do so also. There would be no difficulty then about difference of object glass for chemical & visual rays & you would be able to unite all the rays much more perfectly. I would strongly advise you to make immediate enquiry on the subject."

7.2   Knighthood

Grubb was knighted on August 22 1887 (Knight Bachelor) by the Lord Lieutenant of Ireland. Christie offered his congratulations [26 August, RGO 7/43] and Gill wrote [21 September] as follows:

---

[5]Carl Bamberg, German telescope maker.

"Accept my hearty congratulations, my dear old man, on the well deserved honours that have been conferred upon you. God grant you a long and happy life for you and her Ladyship to enjoy them. Yes, our wives enjoy these things most of all—probably the only others who approach the same enjoyment in such things are our mothers—and for you and me that is gone. But this I know that about the present moment the proudest and happiest little woman in Dublin is your little wife."

On 28 Sept Grubb wrote, crossing Gill's letter (mail to the Cape took two to three weeks):

"You heard I suppose of my having been knighted. Very unexpected, but I value it for the grounds on which it was given. I was very carefull to ascertain this before I accepted it. Don't think I have not been working—I have gone through an exhaustive series of experiments & I have got I think a photo objective which will give certainly 50% & probably 100% greater field than the Henrys i.e. 16 square degrees. Even if I got only the 9 it would be worth having."

At this point Grubb could not have realized the difficulties he was going to face in designing the astrographic lenses. He seem to have felt that he was ahead of his continental rivals, as the following letter to Christie shows [27 August, RGO 7/43]:

"May I ask if you will be in Manchester [for the meeting of the British Association]. I think it will be necessary that I should say a few words about my experiments & designs for these photo telescopes but I wish to say as little as possible about the experiments.

You will easily understand that while I am not only willing but anxious to communicate the result of all my experiments to you, Dr Huggins & Professor Stokes, &c & very thankful for your suggestions & help I am by no means as equally anxious that the French Opticians should get a hold of the results of my experiments & use them for their own advantages ... "

7.3 Technical Improvements

Grubb did not care for the 25 June letter [18 Oct]:

"While I fully recognise that the new conditions required for stellar photography necessitate extra precautions I can by no means allow your remarks .... to pass without correction. You say

Roberts has had infinite trouble. The fact being that Roberts set to work to do what no one ever yet succeeded in ie, to trust altogether to the rate of his clock. For 2 months he was fighting with an error of 0.2 seconds due to an eccentricity of one of the wheels of 1/600 of an inch. I mounted one of his wheels on an adjustable base & the error has since disappeared .... Today I have a letter from Pritchard in which he says that Roberts can now leave his clock for $\frac{1}{4}$ of an hour without any attention & gets quite perfectly round[?] stars. You then say that Huggins finds an error of 20″ of arc recurring every 80 sec of time. This is quite right but when I got back Huggins' screw to examine I found it in a sad state & on re-cutting it & sending it back the error has been reduced to 3″ of arc. I hardly expect to get this less in an old instrument .... Further on you say 'No screw direct from the machine is of the slightest value'. Now how can you reconcile this with your own statement to me that in the Dun Echt telescope which is worked by your own clock the motion is absolutely perfect & a star is kept perfectly bisected on spider's lines for a long time. The screw of that telescope was cut for you in the same manner & with the same lathe as Huggins' & in the manner you describe as not of the slightest value ... . I can show you letters from German Astronomers who have taken the errors of my screws and compared them with those of Repsold & others & they give the preference to mine.

You say I should be bound down to an accuracy of 0.2 of a second .... if of arc your limit is altogether too fine & no honest English mechanic would undertake a contract with such a clause. I say English for my experience of the French is that they will undertake anything provided you pay a deposit.

I see no use in employing a glass which is dissoluble in vinegar nor do I think it likely that in the short interval which has elapsed since your visit to Germany the makers have so far improved the glass as to be able to make good discs of 20″ diameter while they could only show a ruined disc of 5″ when you were there. I have been informed by experts in glass manufacture that any glass of the composition used for the Jena glass is liable to tarnish on surface & to get strongly tinged with colours in from 18 months to 3 years according to the amount of exposure to daylight. In view of the state of infancy of this new material & the uncertainty which rests as to its stability, an uncertainty which cannot be cleared up until some years have elapsed, I cannot recommend its adoption in the present case. I have within the last few months had opportunities of consulting Dr Huggins, Professor Stokes, Mr Christie[6] & many others & all agree with me as to the undesirability of adopting

---

[6]Sir William Henry Mahoney Christie, 1845–1922, Astronomer Royal 1881–1910.

this glass for the standard instruments. I am however about to procure some to experiment upon . . . .

I have been making a long & exhaustive series of experiments on the best form of objective & have I think arrived at a form which is quite certainly 50% & probably 80% greater field than the ordinary with the same perfection. The experiments were quite troublesome, costly & tedious for although theory guided me to some extent nothing but actual trial could satisfy one & I have made 10 or 12 objectives of 5″ aperture. Some worked several times over . . . . I have tried almost all possible or at least all promising forms; tried the effect of separating, modification of thickness & of triple combinations. The general form of the resulting lens is something like my Father's aplanatic photo lens reversed & this is something like what Dallmeyer used for the photo-heliograph.

I have also been working away at the clock-work & by a combination of your Dun Echt detector & my corrector I believe I will be able to produce something altogether beyond what has ever been done before.

I have now in hands standard objectives for Oxford, Cork, Sydney & Mexico & expect orders for the Melbourne in a few days . . . . Yours & Greenwich will probably be the last.

[19 October 1887] . . . . £1435 is the amount of the tender (accepted this very day) for Mexico & I don't believe I will make anything off this first one.

This instrument must be perfect in every respect to be of any use so please don't stint me in the estimates. One must live somehow."

Gill still wanted a hard specification for the accuracy of the drive [26 November 1887]:

"But if you are not prepared to guarantee freedom from periodic error amounting to 0″.2 (and I only say e.g. 0″.2) I ask <u>what</u> freedom from periodic error you are prepared to guarantee? The higher price of the telescope depends a good deal on the accuracy demanded in the driving gear—therefore it is necessary to define the accuracy that you contract to give. <u>This is an essential point.</u>"

Again [13 December], he comments on the Jena glass:

"It will be a very great pity if we make the blunder of employing the wrong glass from want of proper enquiry—that is to say if we adopt the ordinary glass when the other is really the glass of the future, or if we adopt the Jena glass and find that it does not last. I do not think the German Gov^t is likely, under the advice they have, to make such a blunder. Remember it is no private firm, but that Gov^t is aiding, and that the honour of German Science is involved.

[Grubb to Gill, 22 February 1888] We are well on now with the Mexican Telescope & I hope to have all the clock work with the control &c at the Astronomical Society on the 13th April next. I propose to mount it with a chronograph arrangement of sufficient scale to show errors of 1/20 of a second. I have promised to give a lecture at the Society of Arts on these photo telescopes on the 18th April.

[25 April] I am just back from London. I had the new clock working. A full description will be published in this week's 'Engineering'[7] & I will send them by next mail .... The performance of the clock has considerably exceeded my expectations. Even in the very rough way I had it mounted on a wooden box it detects and corrects errors not exceeding 1/40 of a second. I have therefore no longer any difficulty in my mind as to the question of clockwork. I attended a meeting at the Committee at the R.A.S. but at hat time there was no news from Government about either your or Christie's telescopes .... I would be glad to hear from you whether you would suggest any alterations in the frame for the photographic plate or any of the eye end arrangements as I am about to put that part of the Mexico telescope in hands & I may as well make yours & Greenwich at the same time .... I hope soon now to have both Greenwich & your instruments well in hands. In anticipation of receiving the orders I have got a large amount of the work done. In the wheel cutting for instance while cutting the Mexican wheels I cut three sets altogether & many other parts in same way I done [sic] in triplicate so I hope to get through the work very rapidly when I do get at it."

Gill replied cholerically as follows [20 May]:

".... I have no fears about the clock work and never had. The point about which most of my correspondence has been about, and about which you are still silent, is the accuracy of the driving arc and the driving gear. Well about that, I believe you will do your very best, and you can't do more even if you try—is that Irish? .... I am really at a loss to understand what all this delay about ordering the photographic telescopes means. It is a disgrace to England to be so behind hand. I wish I was at home to stir them up with a long pole .... Do not make the micrometer of the guiding telescope or any part of it till I send you a sketch —and

---

[7] *Engineering*, **45**, 402, 1888.

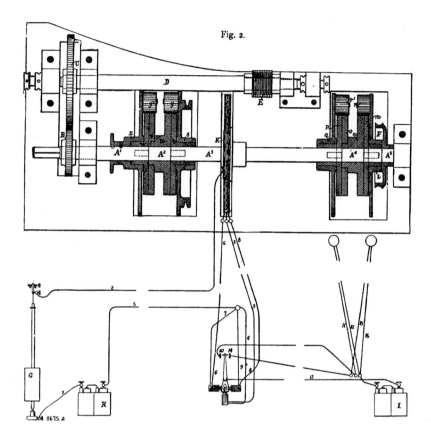

Figure 7.2: Grubb's phase-locked clock drive. The aim was to generate a precise sidereal drive speed from a powerful but free-running clockwork motor. It worked as follows: E is the final worm drive. It is driven from the lower shaft (consisting of several sections), which has on it two sets of differential gears A′ and a detector wheel K. The governor of the motor (not shown) is geared to the lower shaft at F. Seconds pulses are generated by the pendulum G, whose tip passes through a blob of mercury. They are fed to the detector wheel, which rotates once per 20 seconds. There are three sets of contacts on the detector. The left contact passes the pulses if the wheel is running ahead, the centre if it is on time and the right if it is running slow. The pulses then pull the relay (at centre bottom) arm in the appropriate direction and it, in turn, operates the electromagnets controlling the differential gears, so producing a correction. The left differential gears are used to make guiding and setting adjustments. This drive system was provided for all Grubb's photographic telescopes after 1888 (Grubb 1888).

do not forget that it must command a field of at least 1° in radius, to permit the selection of a suitable guiding star ...."

Again on 4 June Gill wrote:

"I have read your most interesting and clear article in Engineering .... The plan of relief friction of the polar axis is close to Repsold's as you will see in my article in the E[ncyclopaedia] B[ritannica] 'Telescope' (By the way I have not yet got separate copies else I wd have sent you one) therefore the credit is wrongly given to me .... It is not clear in the article that I designed the eye-end and plate mounting—only that you made it and I depicted it. These are trifles, but I think they should be mentioned."

7.4 Political Pressure Applied

A good part of the delays being experienced were due to minor quibbling about the specifications of the telescopes being put forward by Christie. On 3 July Gill was jubilant: 'I have just received a good bit of news—which though not all I could wish is still another step in advance.' Hydrographer, Gill's immediate superior at the Admiralty, had written to say that essentially all of Gill's requests had been forwarded officially to the treasury. Gill went on 'I am thankful to see that the Admiralty now at last, after reproving me for proposing a too extravagant scheme, have seen the truth of what I said.'

On 15 August Grubb had further good tidings:

"I am glad to be able to tell you good news at last. I went to London from Colwyn Bay[8] where my family were about a fortnight ago to a dinner at the Mansion House in connection with the Paris Exhibition. I was anxious to see Christie about the contracts for Photo Telescopes but did not like to call on him officially. However I was fortunate enough to find myself sitting by him at dinner: we had a long talk & I asked him why he did not get a question asked in the house about the contracts. After a long talk he expressed himself willing that a question should be asked at my instigation (not his). Well to make a long story short, before I left the room I had it partly arranged with Sir H. Roscoe & when I got home I wrote out a long statement & formulated a question but before I had it put I got advice from a friend (an old government official well up to Parliamentary work) & I followed his advice strictly. Sir H. Roscoe[9] (as an opponent of the government) asked the question

---

[8]In North Wales, where Grubb had a summer house.

[9]Sir Henry Enfield Roscoe FRS, 1833–1915, a chemist and spectral analyst who had taken a close interest in the early astrophysical work of Bunsen and Kirchoff. He was MP for Manchester 1885-95.

while I set Stokes[10] as a supporter of the government) on Smith[11] & Goschen[12] privately. This if necessary was to be followed by a question from Crossley (Liberal) & Sir J Lubbock & if necessary an Irish grievance was to be made of it by Russell[13] & Saunderson[14]. The result was a favourable answer from government but I gave up all hopes of hearing anything more of it till the Autumn session; however yesterday I heard from Stokes that while he was at the Admiralty a letter arrived from the Treasury authorizing the ordering of the Greenwich & Cape Instruments so now I hope all is well. The Melbourne Instrument was ordered last week."

Gill replied on 6th September:

"What a poor spirited creature Christie is not to have accepted responsibility [for having the question asked in parliament] himself. He is the real cause of all the delay we have had. He told the Admiralty that my plans for the observatory and for making the telescope were extravagant and got me an official censure for the 'costly character of all proposals coming from the Cape ...'.

Grubb [22 August]: Stokes is over here at present & we are working away to get the very best possible form for the objective. I am working out a number of trial forms to corroborate the result of his calculations. In this way it will be curious if we do not get at the best possible result ... p.s. I will write you as soon as our experiments come to a definite issue. So far Stokes' calculations go to show that the form I am making must be very near that of the very best possible."

In the summer of 1888 the works were visited by the Institution of Mechanical Engineers. The factory was described in detail in *Engineering* (Anon 1888). From 35 to 40 men were working there at the time.

A letter to Christie [7 February 1880, RGO 7/41] shows that the working day was then normally 9 hours. Clients were charged 12/6 per diem for each employee in the field, occupied either in working or travelling to and from Dublin.

In October, Grubb moved from his father's house, 141 Leinster Road, Rathmines, to 51 Kenilworth Square, Rathgar, presumably as a result of increasing prosperity. On 31 October he wrote to Gill:

---

[10]From 1887 to 1891 Stokes was member of Parliament for Cambridge University in addition to his other offices.

[11]William Henry Smith (Jr), 1825-91, First Lord of the Treasury and leader of the House of Commons

[12]George Joachim Goschen, 1831–1907, Chancellor of the Exchequer 1887-92.

[13]Probably Charles Russell, 1832–1900, a prominent supporter of home rule for Ireland.

[14]Col. E.J. Saunderson, d. 1906, leading Unionist M.P.

"I am getting up some more plant & increasing my staff for I will have an enormous quantity of work to get through in the next 12 months. The new screw cutting machine is ready for work & we are to have a new large lathe erected next week .... p.s. I am getting into our new house. It is an awful job but I think we will be very comfortable when we do get settled. I have at last a study for myself where I can shut myself up to work."

Gill requested many changes from Grubb's standard design, some of which the latter felt were not necessary, but he consented to go along with them. For example, the lower bearing of the polar axis was changed from a gentle taper to a much steeper one. The arrangement for aligning the direction of the axis was also altered to Gill's specification. Because of the long exposures of the photographic plates, this alignment had now to be much more precise than with visual instruments. Even the shape of the declination slow motion handle did not escape his attention. However, he had to give up on the idea of enclosing both photographic and guider tubes in one oval outer tube as Grubb could not do this within the agreed price. Quite a few lengthy letters, full of sketches, flowed between them until the final details were agreed.

The Mexican astrographic was finished first and photographs and a drawing were sent to Gill for examination. On 21 March 1889 Gill wrote:

"The feature of the Mexican telescope which strikes me as most ugly and unmechanical is the very clumsy attachment of the tubes to the declination axis. Even if you go in for the two tubes, which I only consent to under compulsion, and because you say that you cannot make the oval tube for the money, you certainly must flange both tubes upon a central iron piece, designed so as to give the smallest possible overhang from the shoulder of the decl^n axis. The huge unsightly block to which apparently only one of the tubes of the Brazilian [sic] Telescope is attached appears to me a mechanical barbarity, contrasting most unfavourably with Repsold's elegant arrangement in the Potsdam photo telescope, a photo of which (unfortunately torn & a part lost) I send you. I think Repsold's driving and slow motion in RA arrangements very inferior to yours—but I think there is an advantage in a complete driving circle, which is never unclamped from the screw, because it wears absolutely uniformly ....

Grubb [28 Mar]: .... The experiments on the best form of object glass have been prolonged far beyond what I expected. I have got two forms now either of which are better than anything I had before. I have had an opportunity lately of comparing with one of the French negatives under the microscope, at the Oxford Observatory with the most satisfactory results. In a few days I hope to have made up my mind as to which of these two forms is

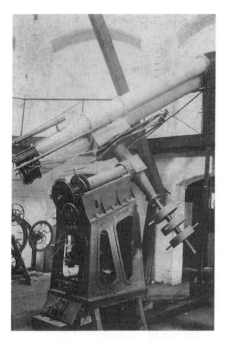

Figure 7.3: Astrographic telescopes in Grubb's works. The instrument on the left was the first to be constructed, destined for Mexico. That on the right may be the one made for Cape Town. A belt-driven band saw can be seen in the background (SAAO collection).

the better and then I can go straight ahead on the big glasses." Going on to Repsold's Astrographic for Berlin, a picture of which Repsold himself had just sent him, he says 'No doubt it is a beautiful instrument as all Repsold's are, but as a piece of engineering I would say it was 'To all an example, to no one a pattern'."

In June, Grubb had to take a holiday [10 July 1889]:

"Just returned from Switzerland a very different man to what I was when I left. I had been working very hard for some months & got into a very bad state. Everything seemed to go wrong with me & I got into such a nervous irritable state that tho' I seemed to be working very hard I could get thro' no work at all. So at last I had to give up & for the first time since I was married I went off for 3 weeks complete holiday not even leaving my address behind except with my wife & have come back an entirely new man. I could not have believed that a few weeks could have made such a change. I believe I have been saved from a bad illness & I am thankful to say I am now in grand health & everything is going on splendidly ...."

7.5   Difficulties with the Lenses

The design for the astrographic objectives was still not satisfactory. Pritchard
at Oxford had been spending much of his time on the testing of the experimental lenses. Gill wrote [14 August]:

> "I am convinced that you have been getting into trouble in an
> attempt to do the impossible viz: to get a sharp square field greater
> than 2 × 2°. Pritchard seems to be greatly discouraged by your
> non success & fears that he is not going to get a satisfactory O.G.
> for Oxford. I hope you are now satisfied that it is impossible to
> get fields of 3° radius, & that you will devote yourself to doing the
> possible, viz: producing an object glass which shall give a sharp
> definition over as large a field as the Henrys'. I shall be satisfied
> when this is done but with nothing less .... About the Mexican
> telescope .... I now see that the tubes are flanged but the point
> which raises my ire still is the huge unnecessary projection beyond
> the end of the $Decl^n$ axis. It looks as if the cross-head had been
> originally made too short, and this had been stuck on to give more
> range of hour angle without reversal. Hence my adjectives, and I
> rejoice to find that no such useless overhang of the tube will occur
> in the Cape telescope."

Things were still not going well for Grubb in his private life or indeed at
work [25 Sept 1889]:

> "I have been greatly knocked about & had an anxious time
> about my wife who you will have seen by the papers I sent you
> had a daughter [Mary, 1889–1969] 3 weeks ago but has been very
> weakly & ill. I think however we are over the worst now & in a
> few days I expect & trust all anxiety will cease. [9 October]: 'I
> would have sent you some drawings by this mail but that is just
> one of the departments in which I have been upset in consequence
> of the sudden death of my draughts-man, and I am at present
> looking out for another which is by no means an easy post for one
> to fill .... You are quite right about the Mexican telescope; that
> objectionable part will not appear in any others.
> Respecting the object glasses. I have had great trouble cer-
> tainly with respect to these, but I think I am approaching a
> satisfactory conclusion. I have been working under a very great
> difficulty, not having any Equatorial here that I can use for pho-
> tographing celestial objects. I will however be out of this difficulty
> in a few days, as I am now erecting the Greenwich instrument (the
> only one whose latitude is near that of Dublin) in my tower, so I
> will then be in a position to take photographs myself. Up to the
> present time every object glass I have had ready for trial, I had

to send to Oxford, and consequently Professor Pritchard has got discouraged. I am now working for two square degrees [sic] only as this is the size which has become determined by the Congress, and with the very high quality of definition required it will probably be not possible to get any more. What form the Henry object glass is I do not know, but as I have tried a great variety of forms, and I find very little to choose from between one and another, but there are some points which are absolutely essential to be attended to. The object glass form which you speak of would not answer at all, as it gives strong coma in the lateral pencils pointing towards the centre. The form however which appears to be about the simplest and best is very like that of any ordinary object glass, that is to say a nearly equi-convex crown, and plano-concave flint, but it is necessary in order to correct the coma of the lateral pencils to bend the crown forward, that is, making it deeper on the 2nd surface than the 1st, or bending the flint backwards, making the lenses touch in the centre, or rather, more nearly touch in centre than on edge. This it is necessary to do, and with very great precision, for if over-done it will throw the coma out from centre and in either case you get an image in which the greatest condensation of light is not in the centre of the disc.

Alteration of distance between the lenses also makes a considerable difference in the coma and this is also very determinate. But the unfortunate part of it is that in whatever way we attempt to correct the coma the conditions involve curves which give a very much lower correction for spherical aberration than the ordinary form, consequently the curves require to be forced very much out of the spherical in order to correct that. You will see that the introduction of these 3 conditions that is of field, in addition to the 2 which we have to combat in an ordinary object glass, i.e. spherical & chromatic aberration, increase the difficulties enormously. In the ordinary object glass we have the facility of slightly altering the distance between the lenses to give a final correction for achromatism, here we have no possibility of doing this, as the field would be instantly destroyed. Again in our ordinary form of object glass we have the facility of ascertaining in what surface an error in figure exists by cementing one side or other of the crown, which we have no chance whatever of doing in this case.

I have just got some photographs from Oxford done with the last glass, along with the photograph taken by the brothers Henry. I can see that I have not yet hit off exactly the right chromatic correction, but when that is done, I think I will have quite as good an object glass as they have. You must remember they have had great advantages over me; they had 2 years start to work quietly at the object glasses and they had the opportunity of trying them whenever they like at the Paris Observatory. Up to the present time I have been obliged to work on artificial stars, or on the Pole star, on which I can only give an exposure of 8″ [sic] without showing elongation. I expect however that this next month will see me quite square, and when I get the first quite satisfactory I will have no trouble in duplicating them."

The letter quoted above seems to indicate that Grubb was not up-to-date on the theory of optical aberrations. As early as 1856, Seidel[15] had shown that the conditions of achromatism, flatness of field and freedom from spherical aberration could not be satisfied simultaneously in the way he was attempting. The solution that he pointed out was to use a glass of high refractive index and lower dispersion paired off with another of lower refractive index and higher dispersion. Before the new 'Jena', or anomalous, glasses produced by Schott and Co., dispersion and refractive index increased together (Lummer 1900). The new glasses, about which Grubb was so dubious, initiated a revolution in lens design.

Gill [1 November 1889]: ".... I know you have suffered in this way, [in being expected to produce an impossibly large field] but it has not been in my power to help you. I have protested as far as my official position would allow, I could not do more. The Henrys have had another great pull which you also ought to have, viz, a large perfect plane. Of course the ultimate appeal is to the sky, but you can test the object glass with such a plane with artificial stars in the focus for parallel rays, & this you cannot conveniently do in any other way."

The Astronomer Royal, Christie, visited Grubb's works during December and commented favourably:

"With regard to the object glasses, it must be remembered that they require the study of quite a new branch of optics, because it is quite a different matter to get a good definite centre of field and to deal with a field extending over a degree from the centre. On a photograph taken with the Mexican object-glass very fair results were obtained at 80′ or 90′ from the centre." (Christie 1890)

By January Gill was getting very impatient at the delay in the delivery of his telescope.

Grubb [5 February 1890]:

".... I plead guilty to all your accusations but under very extenuating circumstances. If you only knew how I have been pressed

---

[15]Philipp Ludwig Seidel (1821–1896), Professor of Mathematics at the University of Munich.

on all sides during the last 12 months you would not wonder at my letters being unsatisfactory. It is all very well working at high pressure for a month or so but when it comes to 12 months it is very hard to keep up the steam. Two or three times I thought I would collapse altogether but I managed to stick together still .... I have had a sharp attack of the wretched epidemic [influenza] which left me rather weak but am getting right. I can say however that if you were to lay £1000 on my table as a bribe for putting on more steam I could not do so. I am working every hour I am not sleeping. I have given up all social invitations & never lose a single opportunity for observation—more I cannot do. I am working just as closely as my health will permit and if I go one step further I will break down & all will be delayed instead of forwarded ....

[6 February 1890]: .... Object glass: Mr Christie has passed his and yours I am now engaged on literally night & day. I was very much pleased to see at Greenwich some plates taken at Paris of 20 minutes exposure placed beside mine. They were both of the Pleiades. In mine of 20^{min} there are two doubles distinctly shown while I got another very small with a shorter exposure. In the Paris 20 min there is not one. Even the larger widely separated one which in my 20 min have almost clear glass between their discs, is absolutely covered over in the Paris one by the large size of the disc of the big star. There is not even a pimple shown on side of disc. I believe I have got a decidedly better result."

7.6   Finished at Last

By 26 February 1890 Grubb believed that the Cape objective was finished. The mechanical parts were received in Cape Town on 11 June. Gill was basically pleased with the new instrument, though, as usual, he had many minor complaints. The objectives for the main and guide telescopes were sent out somewhat later after approval and acceptance by Christie. On 19 July Gill sent the following:

"I do think you are the most careless and happy go lucky chap that ever took to building instruments astronomical. The O.G. of guiding telescope came safely to hand six days ago. The obj. seems to be a very good one indeed. I am not quite certain about its centering, because I could not be quite certain of the centering of my eyepiece—for I had to shorten the tube by $1\frac{1}{4}$ inches before it was possible to focus!! How on earth did this happen—was the telescope inspected?"

By August 12 the photographic objective had arrived and had been mounted

Figure 7.4: Typical Grubb 13-inch astrographic telescope. This illustration first appeared in *Engineering* **50** 720, 1890. Later, it was reproduced in Grubb's catalogues.

"The images are good as far as 40′ from the centre of the plate and perhaps they are sufficiently good to 62′ but I cannot say until I have made some more experiments and until I have got further trial pictures .... The guiding telescope O.G. bothered me a little .... Now I find that there is a very small error of centering of the two lenses and a considerable error in the spherical aberration correction. I have never seen anything finer than the central part of the lens, but to make a good telescope some further figuring must be done."

7.7   Excuses, Excuses

Grubb admitted responsibility for the faults mentioned in the 19 July 1890 letter (18 August), excusing himself on the grounds of overwork and months of strain. He had again gone to the Continent on holiday but 'I am sorry to say my trip was a 'fiasco' this time as both my travelling companions were prevented from coming at the last moment & I only got 8 days instead of 3 weeks & never got to Switzerland at all. However I am now much better.' When Gill's August 12 letter, complaining about the photographic objective, arrived, he must have felt very taken aback as the following reply shows:

"Respecting the Photo O.G.: There is something very extraordinary about this. I looked at the plates taken with it and certainly never saw with any O.G. better definition in field; but I remember distinctly that after the O.G. was finished it was, as you are aware, laid aside awaiting Mr. Christies' to have it sent to Greenwich for trial. Before sending it away it was put in the tube again for some purpose, I forget what, and rough photos taken with it. I think it was to obtain the length of the tube; and there was something about the images on that photo which seemed to me as you describe. Knowing that such an appearance could not proceed from want of adjustment, and that it had given perfect photographs before, I attributed this to some outside cause, and did not hesitate to send it forward; but I have since then been thinking that there may be another cause for it. I do not know whether I told of all the trouble I went through with the glass-grinder I had in my employment and the strong suspicion, almost certainty I had that in some cases he actually did acts which tended to delay the progress of these glasses.

On several occasions, just as an O.G. was ready to be dispatched after months of work, I found several deep scratches which were not to be accounted for, and which necessitated re-working the glass. Such accidents do occasionally happen, but they happened so strangely and persistently with this man that my suspicions were aroused, and I fear there was little doubt that this was done on many occasions maliciously. Now it has occurred to me as the only possible solution of your O.G not being right, that it had been tampered with during the time it was laid aside awaiting trial at Greenwich ....

Respecting 10″ [guider]: This I had great hopes from what you told me in a former letter would be a very perfect O.G. It is possible however a little want of centering which you have detected may account for the whole fault; however what-ever is to be done of course I shall do cheerfully for you if you bring the O.G. over with you in November."

The work to be done on the telescope to make it satisfactory, besides the refiguring of the object glass, was summarized by Gill on September 12:

> "1. To partly reconstruct the breech end in the way I proposed for adjusting orientation etc.
> 2. To refigure the object glass of the guiding telescope.
> 3. To provide springs to keep the object glasses rigourously in place in their cells.
> 4. To provide a dew cap to finding telescope.
> 5. To alter the scales and eyepiece of the micrometer of guiding telescope. No one can work with such an eyepiece in the zenith during long exposures. The scale readings are much to coarse . . . ."

On December 16 Gill announced that he would leave Cape Town for 'home' on 21 January, 1890, bringing with him the two objectives and the breech ends. He added:

> "Pritchard sent me a Henry picture, an Oxford picture and a Greenwich one. I found the Henry best, then the Greenwich and last the Cape, in fact the Cape obj cannot make such images as Henrys—and it must & I know you will make all right as you have promised to do."

The defective parts were sent straight to Grubb's so that he could get to work immediately. The outer surface of the crown component of the objective was found to have a serious error which Grubb was certain did not exist when he had done his final tests on the lens. In March Gill proposed to bring Elkin[16] of Yale with him on a visit to Dublin. Grubb did not appear too happy about this [14 March 1891]:

> "I would be pleased to see Dr. Elkin, though I fear just at present we wont have very much to show him, and unfortunately our accomodation is so limited, that I could only be able to offer a bed to one. If he does come therefore I suppose I must let you do just as you like in the way of going to an hotel. There is only one decent hotel here & that is the 'Shelbourne".

On 12 May, Grubb sent Gill copies of photographs to show the extent of progress with the refiguring of the photographic objective which he had tried out temporarily mounted on a telescope destined for Cork. Gill was not, however, satisfied. Grubb felt that the problem lay with the testing rather than the objective itself, and sent it to Oxford where it could be mounted properly. Tests were done by Plummer[17] under the supervision of Prof Pritchard (Gill 1913). In a private letter Grubb talked of his holiday plans:

---

[16]Elkin, W.L., 1854–1933, Yale University. Later director of Yale Observatory.
[17]William Edward Plummer, 1849–1928.

"..... I think of getting away for a few weeks. I have not been feeling up to the mark at all lately & I have a chance of joining some friends in Switzerland which will probably not occur again this year. They are leaving on Tuesday & I thought of following a few days after, dropping in to see Ethel on the Rhine & then joining my friends for 10 days in Switzerland .... I really feel that I want this just now & I only wish I could take my wife with me but she hates travelling .... Ethel tells us in her letters that it is lovely warm weather on the Rhine. I was in Cork 3 days & it never stopped night & day pouring rain and blowing a hurricane.

(24 July 1891)· [My wife] and the boys are at the seaside in the North & my daughter is coming home 'for good' from Germany on Monday."

Gill sailed again for Cape Town in July. As on several occasions before, he did not send explicit instructions to Grubb as to what should be done next. Grubb knew very well by now that Gill would never pay for anything he had not properly ordered, and was appropriately cautious.

(19 August): "The letter which you wrote me immediately before leaving was evidently sent off in great haste and was not very definite as regards forwarding the breech-pieces. You appeared to want them in a hurry, and yet as I had definite instructions to send all through the Admiralty, I did not like without some authority to deviate from this. I thought the best plan therefore was to write to Mr Wharton (Hydrographer) which I did, and after some delays and correspondence, I determined to send you the articles by mail steamer instead of through the Admiralty. They did not actually take the responsibility of ordering me to do so, but they gave me to understand from their letters, that they had no means of getting the things out rapidly so I thought it best to send by the mail steamer, and I hope I have done right .... I enclose account for additional work done to the breech pieces &c."

Only on 26 July 1892 did regular work on the survey finally begin.

7.8 Other Grubb Astrographic Telescopes

Grubb supplied Astrographic telescopes to seven observatories for the Carte du Ciel. Oxford, Sydney (lens only), Melbourne and probably Tacubaya (Mexico) received objectives with the flint component in front while the Greenwich and Cape Observatories had lenses with crown in front (O'Hora 1988). He discussed the problems he had had to face with these lenses in a very bland manner at a meeting of the Royal Dublin Society in 1890 (Grubb 1890a), but did not mention the fact that he had actually delivered lenses of two different designs.

The Greenwich and Cape telescope have curved focal planes to this day (Jones 1988; the late J. Churms, private communication), and are usually focussed for stars at 40 to 50 mm distance from the plate centre in order to get the best overall images. The former was removed to Herstmonceux in 1957 and placed on a new mount in 1969. Examination of the plates produced by the Cape astrographic shows slight elongation of the images situated towards the corners.

The Mexican instrument was inspected before leaving Dublin but, after installation in Tacubaya, the images did not appear to be equal to those obtained in Dublin. Although adjustment of the lenses was tried, faults still remained and the lens was sent to the Clark optical company in Cambridge, Massachusetts, for comment. They found a) that the lenses were incorrectly centred, b) spherical aberration manifested by the fact that the central and outer zones had longer focal length than the intermediate ones and c) that there were striae in the glass, shown up by polarized light. The Clarks did some work on the lenses, but comparison of plates taken before and after this showed that 'radial distortion' persisted, although the images after re-working were more evenly illuminated (Anon 1913).

In spite of the troubles experienced in the construction of these instruments they served their purpose adequately and made made lasting contributions to astronomy as general-purpose wide-field photographic telescopes. Whether the *Carte du Ciel* project was, as a whole, a 'good thing' is another question, absorbing as it did a large fraction of the available astronomical effort for many years.

Chapter 8

The McClean Telescope

8.1 Introduction

The main telescopes manufactured by Grubb during the 1890s were the 26-inch Thompson refractor of the Royal Greenwich Observatory and the Mc-Clean 24-inch refractor of the Royal Observatory, Cape. Both of these instruments were gifts from private individuals.

Frank McClean, FRS, LLD, (1837–1905) was a wealthy engineer who retired in 1870 to devote his life to scientific and artistic interests. He built an observatory at his house and became quite well known as a spectroscopist. He discovered the presence of oxygen in β Crucis. The foundation of the Isaac Newton Studentships at Cambridge was due to a gift from him of £12,500 and he was also a major benefactor of the Fitzwilliam Museum in Cambridge. At his private observatory he installed around 1894 a Grubb 12-inch photographic refractor with 10.5-inch guider and objective prism.

Sir Henry Thompson (1820–1905) was a successful surgeon and something of a dillettante. He studied painting under Alma-Tadema[1], exhibited at the Royal Academy and wrote several novels including *Charley Kingston's Aunt*, which ran into 15 editions! He had strong views on dietary matters, on which he wrote two books, and was largely responsible for the adoption of cremation in England. 'At the age of eighty he became an enthusiastic automobilist, and in 1902 wrote a small book on the motor car' (Anon 1905). His astronomical enthusiasm seems to have existed for several years from about 1888.

8.2 Offer of the McClean Telescope

In September 1894 Gill received the following letter, which was not entirely unexpected:

---

[1]Sir Lawrence Alma-Taddema 1836–1912.

Rusthall House - Tunbridge Wells
10th August 1894

Dear Dr Gill

It has been my wish for some time past to offer a large Telescope, equipped for Photographic and Spectroscopic work, to one of the Public Observatories in the Southern Hemisphere—and by preference to the Royal Observatory at the Cape of Good Hope.

With this object I have now arranged with Sir Howard Grubb for the construction of a Photographic Refracting Telescope of 24 inches aperture and 22 ft 6 in focal length—also for an Object Glass Prism to work with it, having a refracting angle of $7\frac{1}{2}$ degrees, and the same aperture. Coupled with the Photographic Telescope there is to be a Visual Refracting Telescope of 18 inches aperture ...

May I ask if you, as Astronomer Royal at the Cape, would be willing to accept such an Instrument, and in that case if the Official Trustees of the Observatory would be prepared to provide any assistance necessary for its efficient use?

I remain, dear Dr Gill
Yours faithfully
Frank McClean

Copies of the three-sided correspondence concerning this telescope exist at the SAAO, and occupy six thick volumes.

8.3   Negotiations over Design

Gill seems to have learned on a visit to Grubb in about April 1893 that something was in the offing, although there are indications that correspondence between McClean and Grubb started as early as October 1892 (see Gill to Grubb, 13 June 1896). A letter of 18th May 1893 from Grubb coyly states: 'The consultation with my correspondent was satisfactory in some respects, and not in others. He is not at all altered in his views by the arguments that you have used in your letter, or those which you armed me with before seeing him.' From his reply, it appears that Gill disagreed with the idea of having an objective as fast as f/10, rather than the more tractable f/15, and also about the range of wavelength for which achromatism was desired. However, in spite of these difficulties, an objective prism had already been ordered. Gill (to Grubb, November 3) emphasized his desire for a mounting that would allow proper circumpolar movement of the telescope: he had found the astrographic too limited. He preferred an 'English' or yoke mounting.

"You once denounced rather strongly the Potsdam photo telescope mounting and I think if the details of its engineering could be improved that it secures a minimum of weight in the moving

Figure 8.1: Frank McClean FRS of Rusthall, Kent, a retired sanitary engineer who had his own observatory and presented a large telescope to the Royal Observatory, Cape of Good Hope (SAAO collection).

parts with very great convenience of working. In its existing form the driving circle is rather small, but this could be easily remedied. I will gladly write again when I know in what direction yr client's views point ..."

Meanwhile, Grubb was making experimental lenses: (13 December, to Gill)

"In a few days I hope to have photos taken with different kinds of objectives, all of about 4″ aperture and 44″ focus. Firstly, a two lens combination like the ordinary stellar photo O.Gs. Secondly, a 3-lens combination of peculiar construction, probably the best we can make, and Thirdly, a 4 lens combination something like the original Petzval[2] portrait lens. I think when all these are laid before my correspondent he ought to be able to come to a decision."

---

[2] Joseph Petzval (1807–1891), Professor of Higher Mathematics at the University of Vienna.

In a letter of 19 January 1894 to McClean Grubb mentions a preliminary model of the instrument, which was then to consist of the 24-inch O.G. and prism, with a 12-inch guider. A lifting floor was suggested, similar to one which Grubb was then building for Mr Dunn's Observatory at Maidenhead. An important point was the form of the stand, to allow the maximum of circumpolar motion. The focal length was to be 24 feet and the quoted cost £2150-0-0. By the end of January, the prism had been ordered as well as the blanks for the 24-inch lens.

An interesting letter from Grubb to McClean written on 5 February, shortly after they had met face-to-face, mentions the possiblity of a 34-foot focal length instrument at a cost of £3000.

"I further explained to you that in consequence of the present position of work at my establishment which necessitated an un-usually large and efficient staff, it would be a considerable saving to me if this work could be put in hands without further delay, for otherwise I would probably be obliged to discharge a number of useful hands which could not be obtained again, and whose places would have to be filled with men who for a time at least would not be equally efficient; in consequence of this, and as an inducement to come to terms in the matter, I offered to take 10% off the price of either of these instruments . . .

I am exceedingly sorry that you appear to think still that the prices I mention for these instruments are high; I think if you will enquire from anyone who has got estimates for similar size instruments that exactly the reverse is the case, and the sums I mention are extremely low.

As regards the prices of other makers about which you asked me. You may perhaps think it curious that I have not studied their prices in making up my own price lists. The fact is that it is im-possible in the case of these telescopes as in many other instances of mechanical work to compare the prices of one maker's instru-ments with another, unless one has a very intimate knowledge of the construction and design of each instrument.

I work altogether to my own designs, believing them, (rightly or wrongly) to be the best, and I am content to make these with a small profit, and it is no concern of mine whether the prices of other makers are higher or lower than mine . . . I could not make my instruments at a lower price without losing money over them . . .

I have now been for about 15 months working at a consider-able number of experiments at your request. I looked upon these experiments as pilot work for the large instrument, and in fact as the commencement of work on this instrument; and these exper-iments have cost me no little time, trouble and expense. I have had to devote a considerable portion of my time to them besides the time occupied more especially in my glass department and I specially engaged Mr Taylor[3] to help me to carry out the experiments and hasten the work on the various trials, etc. However I looked on this work as directly connected with the work on the large instrument and in case of receiving the order from you for the instrument, have not any intention of making any charge to you for this work ... "

Grubb to Gill (7 February 1894) "His latest idea, which he was very hot on while I was in London, was to make the instrument very long, 34 feet focus ... The worst of the long focus is that the stand would become such a prodigious affair, and naturally the cost is running up, and he does not like this."

Perhaps to persuade McClean to make up his mind, Grubb told him on 27th February that after lecturing at the Birmingham and Midland Institute he would be in London:

"One business I have in London this time is to talk over the details of a new photo telescope which some person unknown has offered to present to the Greenwich Observatory. The proportions are to be exactly double that of the Survey telescopes, ie:—26 inches aperture and 22 feet 6 inches focus. I am proposing a mounting for this on the plan of the last I showed you, that is, with a considerable amount of circumpolar motion."

The telescope mentioned was to be the Thompson refractor. Nevertheless, McClean refused to be hurried.

Grubb to Gill (21 Mar): "We are now at work on the big prism of 25 inches aperture, $4\frac{1}{4}''$ thick on one side and $1\frac{1}{2}''$ on the other: it is a magnificent piece of glass, the finest I ever saw, and 214 lbs weight.

I suppose you have heard of Sir Henry Thompson's gift to Greenwich. This I am working away at, that is to say the design.

I have designed an Equatorial for it which will have all the good points of the stellar photographic telescopes combined with circumpolar motion; it will approach in appearance something of

---

[3]H.D. Taylor (1862–1943) worked for Cooke of York, a rival telescope manufacturer, and invented his famous 'Cooke Triplet', a wide-angle lens, about this time, perhaps as a result of his consulting work for Grubb. He reported on his new 'perfectly achromatic' object-glass at a meeting of the Royal Astronomical Society in April, 1894, which was, in fact, attended by Grubb (see section 9.4). On this occasion, Grubb repeated his remarks on the impermanence of the new Schott glasses (see sect. 7.3) and was quite sharply corrected by Taylor.

that of the Potsdam instrument but you will find that I have arranged it so that there will be no overhanging strain on the polar
pillar.

By the way, I was looking at the instrument at Glasgow which
my father made so many years ago and it is almost identical with
the Potsdam instrument, or rather the Potsdam is identical with
it."

The decision to have the visual refractor of 18 inches diameter was reached
only at the beginning of August.

Writing to Grubb on 11 September, just after receiving the official offer
from McClean quoted above, Gill says:

"There is only one point in which I have a little difficulty. I
know that Mr McClean has devoted a great deal of thought and
consideration to the question, and therefore it is the more difficult
for me to offer an opinion apart entirely from the old saying that
one should not look a gift horse in the mouth. Still I cannot help
telling you privately that I should feel much happier about the
success of the instrument if the focus were 30 to 36 feet instead of
$22\frac{1}{2}$ ft ... "

On 2nd October Grubb wrote to Gill

"I need hardly tell you that I am delighted to hear that this
telescope is to fall into the hands of an old friend, & I suppose
there is no harm in telling you now that anything I could do with
Mr McClean I did to induce him to offer the instrument to you
...I am doing this instrument at a very low price for Mr Mc-
Clean, partly in consequence of his having given me very large
orders [Maclean had a Grubb-equipped observatory at his home,
Rusthall, Kent], something like £2000 of orders besides what he is
doing for you, and partly because at one time during the negocia-
tions things appeared to be in a very critical way and in fact I had
almost given up hope of carrying them through, and it was only by
putting matters in the most favourable possible light before him
that we got round what might be called a very 'close corner' ...I
am making him a 24″ obj-glass for £1,600, an 18″ for £800, and
the mounting for £2,250, and the large prism with its attachments
for £1,300, Total £5,950, say £6,000."

Gill made a strong representation to McClean in favour of a higher f-ratio
during October, but he was answered by a telegram on December 6 'Wish
accepted length maintained' and this put an end to the matter. The result
of McClean's hard bargaining was to delay the signing of the contract until
after that of the Thompson telescope for Greenwich, and to generate bad

feeling between Grubb and him. Unusually, the contract for the instrument was spelt out in minute detail, and all detailed drawings had to be submitted for McClean's approval before the commencement of construction.

8.4 Trouble with McClean

On 22 August 1895 Grubb wrote a confidential letter to Gill complaining about McClean's attitude:

> "Since I last wrote to you Mr McClean has taken action about the dome and observatory, but I am afraid very injudiciously.
>
> While I was at his place he spoke to me about this portion of the work, & seeing that he was of the opinion that it could be done off in a few months, I told him it would take about 12 months to make a Dome, Lifting Floor and Observatory. I heard nothing more until I got a letter from him to say that he had ordered a dome from Cooke, who offered to finish the dome in half the time I mentioned for all; and in a very peremptory manner he told me to have everything ready for shipment by the 1st May next.
>
> I was extremely disappointed at getting this letter from him. I don't know whether you are aware that I took this contract from him at an extremely low figure, but knowing that there would be other work to be done, and being under the impression from his attitude all along that I would have that work (He consulted with me about every single point in the whole installation and got my ideas on all), I accepted his terms as to price which he laid down himself hoping that even if I made nothing on the telescope, I might have some little profit on the rest of the work. Now however by his late action he has completely cut me off from that, and considering he has lately expressed himself highly satisfied with the work I have already done for him to his own telescope, and with which he has already done most excellent work himself, I do think he has treated me with very little consideration. I was obliged to write to him to tell him so. As to the matter of time [to complete the telescope], it was understood I was to get a clear 18 months for the mechanical part of the telescope, and it is absurd to think that a great instrument like this could possibly be completed by the 1st May next, when he has only just now put me in a position to make the final designs for the major portion of the work.
>
> I have worked hard and well at this work for Mr McClean thinking the installation would be all mine, and wished to make it one that I would be proud of but Mr McClean has spoiled all this, and were it not that I am anxious that you should have your largest instrument made by myself, knowing what a good use you

will make of it, I would be very much inclined to carry out what was my first impulse on receiving his note, and that is, to write him to say that I would be glad to throw the whole thing up and let him get anyone else to make it he likes.

You have no idea how worrying and annoying it is to have to deal with people who make perfectly unreasonable demands; a man can do no more than his best; I have been doing that up to the present but I cannot be expected to have the same interest in the work in the future ...

[25 September] I hope that he will leave with you the arrangement of these breech pieces &c because it is almost impossible and terribly delaying to have to correspond in this triple fashion, and try to please two people as well as satisfy myself as to the conditions of various parts."

Gill 's reply, also on 25th September, to the August letter, was marked 'Strictly Confidential'

"I am very sorry indeed to hear from Mr McClean as well as yourself of the sudden change of front[?] and the ordering of the Dome from Cookes. I am very much afraid that I shall get a Dome by no means as convenient to work as one of yrs would have been— nor a design so well considered from point of view of convenience of adaptation to the instrument.

I observe however that whenever there are notes from an Oxford note book in 'the Observatory' shewing that Turner[4] has been on a visit to Mr McClean there always comes some letter from McClean showing a sudden (and generally unwise) resolution to make the Cape Telescope and Observatory a mere copy of what they have at Greenwich ..."

8.5 Troubles at Home

Grubb's troubles with McClean were bad enough, but he was also experiencing various domestic crises which depressed him still further. This handwritten note of 5th December shows some of his preoccupations:

"I would have had the general drawing of the inst ready before this but for home troubles. I have had my wife very ill—her old trouble the throat but one of the worst attacks she ever had.

Probably her recovery is retarded by other trials. Our eldest (Ethel) who has always been a very headstrong wilfull girl tho very clever has left us I fear for good. The monotony of home life was

---

[4]H.H. Turner, professor at Oxford and writer of an idiosyncratic column 'From an Oxford Notebook' in the *Observatory* magazine. See also section 7.1.

irksome to her & nothing would do her but the one thing repugnant to us viz to go on the stage. We have at present consented to her having 6 months training only, but eventually I fear it will end by her going on the stage altogether.

Our youngest living boy Romney, a dear fine fellow, caught cold in school, got a rheumatic attack & now the doctors tell us his heart is at fault & as yet give us no hope of his final recovery. So you see we all have our troubles & sometimes they crowd together in a way hard to bear ... One bright little spot is that my second boy [George Rudolph] is getting on grandly at Trinity [College Dublin] & got first place in his entrance to Engineering Schools.

[Grubb to Gill, 27 February 1896]: 'Every single suggestion that comes from you, on being sent to him [McClean], is met with some counter suggestion, which if it does not negative it altogether, at least renders it impossible to carry out, and my brain is getting perfectly distracted with the whole thing. If only I knew what to do, and what would please each to do, I would do it, and get rid of the job, and sing, Oh be joyful!! but whatever I do, even if it be more than the contract requires, is, as you see, met by a letter full of 'musts' and 'insists' all scratched under. I look forward with great hope to your coming over here as being the means of putting an end to this chaotic state of affairs ...

I may tell you however, for your own private satisfaction that altho' I have told him that the work must be arrested, I have given orders, and I am going on with, all the lower portion of the frame, and all the pillar & stay, arresting only the work on the intermediate piece ... doing this is a considerable risk in dealing with one like Mr McClean who seems to shift his opinion every other day.

I cannot understand Mr McClean's attitude at present. He was extremely nice in the beginning of this business, & altho' he drove a very hard bargain and insisted in getting a great deal more than he was entitled to, still I found him fairly reasonable, and always pleasant, but from a certain time, about 12 months ago, he completely changed, and I hate the sight of his letters, for there is always something disagreeable in them.

I am certain that some one is putting him against me in some way or other. I think it very likely I know who this is, but I reserve this for your private ear ... "

8.6   Death of Howard Grubb Junior

To add to these troubles, Grubb was about to suffer a really heavy blow: [Grubb to Gill, then on leave in England, 15 April 1896]

"How I wish you had come [to England] at a happier time. We are in terrible trouble. Our eldest boy Howard is dying. I forget whether I told you the long story about his illness & the operations he had to go thru' but I will not trouble you now. For 15 weeks he has been very ill & for the last 7 weeks he has been lying on a water bed & for the last 3 weeks all the doctors have given him up. The doctors call it lung disease but I believe it to be blood poisoning from the after effects of the operation. Some nights last week we hesitated to take off our clothes & we had no hope on Sunday night that he would live till the morning. His temperature went down so low that no clinical thermometer would register it. This morning again the temperature went down & it is quite possible that before this reaches you our dear boy will be taken from us.

It has come to that point that we hardly know whether to pray for his recovery or his release. Thank God however he suffers little or no pain & he is quite happy in his mind."

Howard Grubb Junior evidently died the following day. Following Victorian custom, Grubb's letters carried black rims until September of that year.

8.7   Strange Behaviour of Roberts

The person Grubb felt was poisoning his relationship with McClean was apparently Roberts, as the following letter reveals: [Grubb to Gill, 25 April]

"There is one matter which I had it on my mind to write you about on arrival in England, but which recent events rather knocked out of my head, but I think it is just as well you should know about it because it is quite possible it may contain an explanation of the sudden change that appears to me to have occurred in Mr McClean's relations to me. It is a matter quite unconnected with Mr McClean himself, but it is very possible that if he heard a garbled account of it, it might render him suspicious and cautious in his dealings with me.

You are aware that in the early part of his work, Dr Roberts came to me and got me to, first of all, make an instrument for him, and gradually improved it until he got it to a pitch of perfection enabling him to do the work for which he got so much credit. Some time afterwards he came to me and told me that he had a 15 inch reflector of With's, which was a very good mirror, and that he proposed to mount this on his old equatorial [someone has written in the margin of the letter the words '6 in Cooke'] which he had discarded as useless for his photo work, and to make a presentation of all this to Trinity College, Dublin. I think, if I remember rightly, the instrument was actually in my works at the time. He told me he wanted it put into thorough working order; by that, I understood that he meant in as good order as it ever was before when a new instrument, but of course I never thought that he would expect me to make the instrument as perfect as our modern telescopes which are constructed from the very beginning for photographic work.

I put the instrument into order and made some great improvements in it, and erected it at Dunsink. Dr Roberts got great credit for this, and an Honorary degree from Trinity College on the head of it.

As long as Sir Robert Ball was at the Observatory I got very good accounts of the working of this instrument, but when Dr Rambaut[5] got there, he wished to do with it work comparable with the work done by the regular standard photo telescopes, and of course it was found wanting; the old Cooke's clock was unable for the work, and the sector was so short that it was impossible to get really good driving.

I did various things to it, such as cutting a new screw in our screw cutting engine, and put on a new driving circle (it was not possible to put on a long arc) but I told them all through that the instrument without radical alteration from the beginning to the end could not be expected to do the finest class of work.

Rambaut was anxious to do the best work, and therefore applied to the Board to get the telescope either modified or replaced. The board of T.C.D. did not like to do this without consulting Dr Roberts, and when he was consulted, he, I believe got very angry and abused me up hill and down dale for doing bad work. I have not seen the letters but I have been told that his letters were absolutely libellous. He then came over, unfortunately when I happened to be absent, and left word that certain things were to be done to the telescope. I reported that I would do these things under Dr Roberts' orders, but it was my belief they would not cure the faults, but still as I predicted the instrument was not up to the standard stellar photo telescopes. When the small account, (about £12) was sent in to Dr Roberts, he wrote a most abusive letter and has not, I understand ceased to villify me in every possible way he could to everyone he meets.

I have never spoken to Mr McClean or indeed to any but intimate friends about Dr Roberts' conduct, but I think it more than likely that this may be at the bottom of Mr McClean's suspicions
. . .

---

[5]Arthur Alcock Rambaut (1859–1923), successor to Ball as the Royal Astronomer of Ireland.

There is a general feeling, I know that Dr Roberts had no right to present an instrument to Dunsink Observatory for work which he found it was impossible for him to do with that instrument, no matter how modified, otherwise of course he would not have got a new instrument for himself. I do not think there is much chance of Dr Roberts ever getting himself another honorary degree in this City! ...

I was anxious that you yourself should know the facts of the matter so that you can correct any erroneous views if they happen ever to crop up in connection with those around you.

I was not the only one who came in for abuse, for Dr Rambaut, Sir R. Ball and the Board of Trinity College came in for a large share of vulgar innuendoes.

p.s. ... My dear wife is better but still very weary and tired. It will be some time before she is herself again ..."

8.8   More Problems

In May there arose a bitter dispute, which was to cause serious delays, about the casting to form the base part of the equatorial stand. Grubb wanted to cast it in several manageable pieces, whereas McClean alleged that the contract had stipulated that it be one very large casting. It was eventually, after much friction, agreed that a single casting should be used, and this had to be made in Great Britain at extra expense as the Dublin foundries could not cope with it. Even so, it was considered a difficult job.

[Grubb to Gill 26 May 1896] "... Show me any doccument signed with my name, in which I undertake to make that casting in one piece and I will acknowledge that I am wrong, but until this is done, Mr McClean's position repeating as he does in every letter, 'I insist, I insist' without bringing forward any evidence, is utterly illogical and unreasonable ... Mr McClean may insist as much as he likes, but he cannot insist on my doing anything that I have not covenanted to do, and you must now be perfectly aware that the only bit of evidence he has brought forward as to my intentions of how I was going to make that frame, was, a design drawing, which like every other design drawing, did not of course show the joints; this evidence as you must see is utterly useless ... your mention of Mr McClean's idea of claiming the design of the telescope, is of course, too absurd to give me a moment's thought, at the same time it shows me quite plainly the object that has been underlying all this weary and wretched correspondence since I undertook the work, & it certainly does not make me any more inclined to oblige Mr McClean by doing anything that I am not obligated to do ...

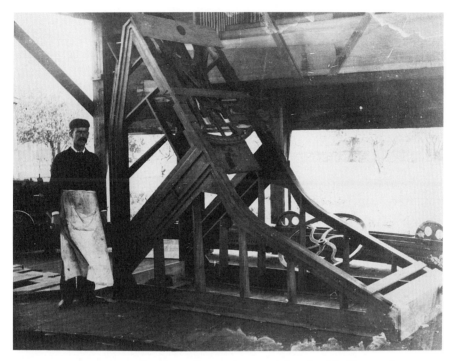

Figure 8.2: Pattern maker at work on the stand for the McClean telescope at Grubb's works in Dublin. Dated 1 May 1896. (SAAO collection).

[Grubb to Gill, 19 September 1896] ... I wish very much you had been with me at the Carron[6] foundry, and heard what Mr Bamforth the head of their heavy foundry had to say about this casting. He enquired from me most particularly why it was this was required in one piece, for he said 'It would be a very much better, firmer, and stronger job if you will allow me to cast it in pieces, plane the joints & bolt them together; any engineer who knows his business will tell you that!! ... "

8.9 Progress on the Thompson Telescope

While the McClean telescope was the subject of acrimonious disputes, work had been going ahead full steam on the Thompson 26-inch refractor. However, Grubb was feeling the strain, as he informed Christie, the Astronomer Royal [16 June 1896, RGO 7/39]:

---

[6]The Carron Foundry in Glasgow was founded in 1760 by Dr John Roebuck (1719–1794). It was used extensively by Boulton and Watt.

"I can assure you that I have been just as anxious as you or Sir H. Thompson to get the work done and for a long time past we have been working very long hours on it, from 6 in the morning till 9 at night, not even stopping for meals, and the men are pretty well done up by this time. I have also changed all my own arrangements, and put off my own holiday which was settled for the 12th of this month, until the 24th ..."

To a letter from Grubb stating that the objective was finished, the following postscript was attached [17 June 1896, RGO 7/39]:

"Since Sir Howard dictated the above he has been feeling very unwell and was obliged to go home and see his medical man, who says that it is incumbent on him to get away from work at once as the strain caused by the night & day exertions to get the 26" OG finished has been a great deal too much for him.

F.E. Ladd, Secretary"

8.10   Grubb Explains Delay of McClean Telescope

The evident progress on the Thompson telescope while the McClean telescope was proceeding rather slowly was a source of irritation to Gill and McClean, who felt that Grubb was favouring their rivals. Grubb's letter of 19 September 1895 continued:

"While we were talking in Aberdeen, you told me that according to your information, Mr McClean's telescope was ordered before the Greenwich one, whereas my recollection was the reverse. I have looked into this matter and the fact is the Greenwich contract was signed on the 6th April 1894, and Mr McClean did not finally accept and obligate himself in the matter of the telescope until he paid the first installment and that was on the 30th May, nearly two months afterwards; besides which it ought to be remembered that in the case of the Greenwich contract, there was, for a considerable time before a moral certitude that the order would come, whereas in Mr McClean's case he had been so many times on and off the job, and had changed his mind so often as to whether he would or would not have it, there was no certitude whatever until that date viz:-30th May. Practically the Greenwich telescope was 3 months ahead of his: also, it should be remembered that from the time the Greenwich contract was signed I have had no trouble whatever in arranging any details with Mr Christie, and nothing has led to delay. Little matters that did crop in such as pitch of screw for the Decln movement were merely trivial matters and no alteration whatever was made or suggested in my design, whereas in Mr McClean's it was one continual series of objections to everything I proposed, and to undertake an instrument under such conditions would really require double the time. On this matter of the frame fully 4 months have been lost."

By March 1897 the castings for all the major parts had at last arrived. Grubb claimed that, because of their size, the telescope would have to be assembled outdoors. The lenses were also nearing completion. Testing was done in a 'polar tube' when, as in this case, no suitable equatorial stand was available in the works, and short exposures could be made without trailing due to the effect of the earth's rotation. Grubb mentioned in a note to Gill in April that they had had trouble with the 24-inch objective, but that he was 'devoting myself to it personally' and had got it nearly right.

8.11   Illness of Rudolph Grubb

In April, 1897, tragedy almost struck the family for a second time: [Grubb to Gill, 29 April]:

> "I have had a fearful week of worry. My eldest [surviving] boy [George Rudolph] is very ill in Typhoid fever which as you can imagine after last years sad experience makes us very anxious and Mr McClean in the middle of all this has been worrying me with letters and telegrams so that I am nearly off my head.
>
> He refused to pay an installment due in the mechanical part because the base casting was not ready which he said was part and parcel of the original design ... I had to tell him at last that I would not go on with the work unless he paid it, and he has at last done so ..."

After nine weeks the boy recovered and was pronounced out of danger.

8.12   Grubb on Holiday in Switzerland

In June, it was possible to send some trial photos taken with the 24-inch lens on the polar stand. Grubb then took a much-needed holiday in Switzerland and Germany, leaving his younger son, Romney, in Wiesbaden to learn German for a year. Grubb's Swiss holidays appear to have been walking tours. In a letter to Max Wolf of Heidelberg (see section 9.5) he gives us a brief glance at his holiday style [Heidelberg 28 July 1897]:

> "... in anticipation of your coming visit to Switzerland. I would like to suggest to you to spend a day, or a few days in the Maderaner Hotel. We enjoyed it very much and you will find comfortable accommodation there. The proprietor of the Hotel (Le Croix

Figure 8.3: Grubb with the McClean Telescope. He claimed that the castings were too large to get inside the building (SAAO collection).

Blanche) at Amsteg is also proprietor of the hotel at the head of the pass and you will be very comfortable at both places.

It is a walk of about 8 miles with an ascent of about 3,000 ft going up the thal, and if you want to take luggage it can go up on a mule. The valley is well worth a visit, and if you are in the St Gothard valley you should not miss it."

Gill, on seeing the first plate, felt that 'the images are nice and round but very fluffy at the margin—probably on account of the atmospheric definition—as you describe no-one could from the plate alone form a judgment as to the quality of the object glass—but I am sure you will see that it is perfect before it is sent out.' In July the mechanical parts were being erected in Grubb's yard.

> [Grubb to Gill, 29 July]: I write a line specially to thank you for your kind and friendly note and enquiries about my poor boy. We had indeed a terrble time. I felt that if I lost him I had lost hope of what I live for & for many weeks the doctors would give no hope. I was not absent from my work for a single day but there were some days I hardly knew whether I was standing on my head or my heels and I fear I sometimes did more mischief than good at the works. We feel now as if we had a son that was lost & found again—was dead & is alive again. He is thank God getting on splendidly & is getting quite stout (comparatively).
>
> I thank you very sincerely for your letter. Such a letter I assure you is a greater incentive to pushing on work than pages of abuse for it gives me heart to tackle it. The amount of work on this instrument is enormous far more than on the Vienna Telescope for which I got double the money & between ourselves I will be a heavy loser by it ... "

8.13 Problems with the Thompson Telescope

The objective of the Thompson refractor, whose erection on site at Greenwich had been completed in May 1897, now turned out unfortunately to be unsatisfactory. In August Grubb was told by Christie that there was outstanding coma which could not be got rid of by adjustment of the lens. He visited the Royal Greenwich Observatory to see the problems for himself and offered [4 August 1897, RGO 7/39] to return the objective to Dublin and corrrect it as his own expense. Its final acceptance occurred in 1898 [5 October 1898, RGO 7/39].

Grubb informed Gill of the problems that he had been having:

> [Grubb to Gill , 12 August, 1897]: "...I fear I shall have to work two surfaces of the [Thompson telescope] O.G. over again. This unfortunate matter has shaken my faith very much in the efficacy of the tests that I employ, and I certainly do not feel justified in making preparations to send the [McClean] O.G. out to Cape Town until I satisfy myself, you or Mr McClean or whoever he may appoint that no error of this sort exists."

Figure 8.4: The Thompson Telescope for the Royal Greenwich Observatory being assembled inside the Optical and Mechanical Works (SAAO collection).

8.14   Gill's Lack of Sympathy

At the time Gill received this letter, McClean was visiting Cape Town and had already been there for two weeks. Gill was unfortunately beginning to agree with his view of Grubb, and was not inclined to be sympathetic:

> [Gill to Grubb, 8 September.]: "I am sorry to learn by your letter ... that the 26-in [Thompson] object glass has not turned out perfect. I gathered from reports made by Christie to the R.A.S. that it was quite perfect but this apparently referred only to trials on double stars, i.e. to central pencils.
>
> No one could form any definite judgement about the quality of an O.G. from such photos as you sent to me. I am ready to admit that a man with great experience in making an O.G. and from the trials of the same O.G. in successive stages of its figuring and testing must know much more about it than anyone else—and may be able to pronounce it perfect by means of trials which could not satisfy an astronomer ...
>
> If the telescope had been mounted upon a proper stand and properly adjusted in a proper observatory it might have possible to secure photographs in Dublin in the most perfect conditions and to decide about the quality of the O.G. there.
>
> But I do not understand that you now propose this ...
>
> But whatever you do we must fall back on the fact that you are responsible for the delivery of a perfect O.G. which is to be guaranteed 'from defects of construction and workmanship for 15 months after delivery.'
>
> There is no other way open which is fair to us and to you.
>
> I am to add that Mr McClean entirely concurs ... "

McClean had for some considerable time been making nasty remarks concerning Grubb in his letters to Gill : [7 February 1896] 'Grubb has skimped the stand'; [13 February 1896] 'I can make nothing of Grubb'; [30 May 1896] 'deliberate deception by Grubb'; [19 June 1896] 'Grubb adept at unscrupulous fencing'; and so on. Gill's letters for some years after this visit show his changed attitude with such remarks as: [21 December 1897] 'Grubb has not got a leg to stand on'; [29 December 1897] 'What a fellow Grubb is!'; [19 January 1898] 'don't know what to make of the man'; [5 Mar 1898] 'Don't give in to Grubb'.

McClean and Gill evidently got on very well together and probably shared the same political views, described at least in Gill's case as being of 'the old crusted Tory type' (Forbes 1916). Their later exchanges of letters on the conduct of the Boer War reinforce this impression.

Grubb, for his part, kept labouring certain points (such as the fact that he was losing money on the McClean contract) and he also made much of the fact that the large size of the base casting had forced erection of the telescope in the open air.

> [Grubb to Gill, 8 September 1897]: "... Only for having to erect in the open air we would have been ready before this but

you have no idea how much time and valuable labour is expended in consequence of the impossibility of getting it into our building and using the travelling gantry and arrangements we have specially for erecting instruments there and which we were able to use in the case of the Greenwich one and would have been able to use in this case but for the enormous casting.

I can of course understand your anxiety and Mr McClean's to get the instrument out, but you have no conception of the amount of trouble and labour involved in getting a large instrument like this into perfect order more particularly under the exceptionally disadvantageous conditions under which this telescope was constructed.

I can assure you I need no spur for pressing forward the work, and as hinted to you before the cost of the work on this telescope is altogether in excess of what I am getting for it; I am at least £1,000 out of pocket in cash at the present moment and I owe a lot besides, and I cannot get in money until the instrument is delivered. You may rest assured that not a moment will be lost that can be helped, at the same time I don't want to send the instrument out of the place in an imperfect or hastily finished state.

[Grubb to Gill 14 September:] I am very much pleased to be able to tell you that I have satisfied myself as to the excellence of the 24″ O.G., and I think when you see the photograph I am sending, you will also be satisfied ... I was, I confess, staggered by the results obtained at Greenwich, and I was afraid that something of a similar character might be wrong with your glass. I may mention that the curves are not quite the same in both cases because the quality of the glass was not identical."

On McClean's behalf, Dr Common inspected the completed telescope in Dublin in October and professed himself satisfied. Grubb put twelve men onto finishing off the details after dismantling the telescope. He expressed his displeasure to Gill at the tone of his recent letters, which had been supporting McClean's point of view:

"...I think you must have forgotten that you wrote me on the 24th May of this year saying that you desired to keep yourself aloof from any controversy between Mr McClean & myself. I think this would have been a wise course for you to adhere to, and with your permission I will act on the wish expressed in that letter of May 24 and will not, just now, enter into details on the points referred to by you. I must, however, in justice to myself simply say that a good many of your statements are evidently based on a total misconception as they are distinctly inaccurate, and I do not admit the correctness either of your facts or deductions.

I feel confident you would never have written this letter if you knew all the facts.

We have had 12 men on the instrument since it was taken down. The wedge casting, pillar & stay are ready to go, and a second consignment in a fortnight after."

8.15 The Instrument Shipped: Arbitration

The actual shipment of the instrument was delayed by the dispute between McClean and Grubb. The details of the arguments are tedious: suffice it to say that McClean was withholding the final progress payment (about one third of the total cost) until he had had word that the instrument was shipped. Grubb, for his part, refused to ship until he had received his money. Both men felt that any concessions would weaken their case during the expected arbitration proceedings, to be judged by A.A. Common. Only by the intervention of the arbitrator, and after a great many intemperate letters, did the impasse get resolved. In effect, McClean agreed to pay the third amount, together with the cost of packing, the Carron Company's bill for the large casting and an extra amount for 'anti-friction apparatus' as soon as he received the steamship company's receipts for the goods. The agreement to ship was reached on 24 February, 1898.

The telescope was shipped the following month from Liverpool, Grubb having gone there personally to supervise the transshipment from the Dublin boat and its stowage. It arrived in Cape Town early in April, together with three pages of typewritten instructions on how it should be assembled.

[Gill to Grubb, 27 April 1898] "The 50 packages containing the McClean Telescope reached Table Bay 18 days ago, but it was only last Monday week that the wedge casting (the last of the lot) reached the Observatory.

You seem to have inspired the Captain and Officers of the ship with a true notion of care required, and nothing was hoisted out of the ship except in presence of one of my assistants.

It took three days to mount the wedge-casting, as it is a foot higher than the entrance door and had to be brought in thus [sketch showing how casting was tilted] to clear the doorway, then slewed 90° on its corner inside the entrance hall (12 ft × 12 feet) and be dropped on its base ...I cannot understand how you did not get it into your workshops—our door is a bare 8 feet high— surely yours is as high as that, in any case it would not have been a very big matter to have knocked down a few square feet of wall if necessary—and the casting is perfectly easy to handle.

I don't forsee any difficulty in erecting the mounting—and if the object glasses are all right I shall be able to send you my blessing ... "

It was not long (23 June) before Gill sent the usual letter of complaint that followed the delivery of a new instrument. First of all there were two pages grumbling that Grubb had not made provision for automatically winding the driving clock by hydraulic means, as had been requested.

> "You leave me as I guarded you against doing—with a clock that could not be made to go. This is not the way to treat me ...[The next complaint was that the focussing did not occur within the range of the adjustments] ...I am happy to say that the 18 inch is a very good object glass, and I shall be most thankful if the 24″ is as good. I am sorry to say that the stand does not seem to be steady ...I think I shall manage to stiffen it by cross stays ...But it is most wearysome and annoying to find that instead of merely erecting a telescope one has an endless amount of work to do besides. [Then follow complaints about the wiring] ...I wrote you long ago about all three things and how they should be done but you paid no more attention than you did about the hydraulic winding."

Grubb's reply [28 July] diplomatically started by noting Gill 's satisfaction with the 18-inch objective. With regard to getting the large casting into his workshop he said:

> "It would serve no usefull purpose to argue this point on paper. I have already in a former letter pointed out that it is your want of knowledge of local circumstances here which probably led you into the error of thinking it was possible. All I can say is that the model of that casting is at my Works:- send over someone and let them get it in if they can without such alterations as would endanger the safety of the building. The only possible way as I said of doing it is the Irishman's way of raising the roof, in other words to rip up the floor and dig a trench in the ground, but I did not care to endanger the stability of my building by doing this."

He denied responsibility for providing the hydraulic ram for the winder:

> "You have based your deductions as to my want of attention to your directions &c on the supposition that some certain piece of apparatus was ordered. I cannot find this order. Unless you can show that I am wrong in this I expect you will retract what you have said about the matter. Respecting your remarks about the stand. I have to say nothing as it was made in this way directly contrary to my recommendations and advice. As regards the small matters you speak of such as switches &c, all I can say is they are the same as have been furnished elsewhere & about which I have had no complaints."

In spite of everything, the 24″ objective was not satisfactory. Tests showed [Gill to Grubb, 5 Oct] that there was strong inward coma for all stars near the plate edges. The discs of the faint stars were not as small as they should have been. Minimum focus, instead of being just short of Hβ, was found to be considerably to the red of it. 'If there is any further trial I can make I am willing to make it—but I think you will see for yourself that it is necessary to put the object glass right in Dublin, and to see that it is right before it is sent out again'.

8.16   Common's Judgment

Again, the dispute delayed matters for somewhat over a year. After numerous submissions from both parties, Common was able to make his judgment on 26 September 1899:

> "NOW KNOW YE AND THESE PRESENTS WITNESS that I the said Andrew Ainslie Common having taken upon myself the burthen of the said Reference and having fully considered the allegations and evidence submitted to me by the parties do make and publish this my Award in writing of and concerning the matters in dispute, that is to say I DO AWARD AND DETERMINE that on the claims and counterclaims the sum of Ninety three pounds six shillings is due from the said Sir Howard Grubb to the said Frank McClean F.R.S. ..."

The defective objective was to be returned at McClean's expense to Liverpool for perfection at Grubb's, Grubb to pay the passage to and from Liverpool and to do the work at his expense. The return trip outward was to be paid by McClean also. However, if there were further problems, their rectification was to be entirely at Grubb's expense. Each party was to bear his own expenses in the arbitration, and Common's were to be shared between them.

It appears from this judgment that Common did not regard either party as being clearly in the right.

8.17   Re-working of the Objective

Gill had avoided writing to Grubb for about a year while the arbitration was in progress and the correspondence did not re-start until 1 November 1899, when it concerned the shipment back to England of the objective. Although Grubb took his time over the work, at least he had installed some proper test apparatus. On 14 May 1900 he wrote to Gill :

> "... We are pushing on with the work on the O.G. but it is a great pity it was not sent at the time I suggested for I could in

all probability have turned off the work in 6 months; I was not consulted as to the convenience of the time in sending it and it arrived at the most inconvenient possible time, when we had taken down our optical house for re-erecting it anew with the mirror arrangement &c. I have got what I believe will be a very perfect arrangement for trial with a great sliding bench of over 20 feet long formed of turned steel bars 3 inches in diameter with different parts sliding upon these and supplied with all facilities for trial, but this of course all took time and then came too the press of all this eclipse work which is only now just over. Notwithstanding all this however I think it probable that I will have the O.G. ready in the time I named that is 8 months after its delivery to me, (that is Aug 1st). I write in haste as I am just starting for Madrid. (For the eclipse of 28 May 1900; see below, Chapter 9.)

[13 August]: ... The plane mirror has been very useful to me more especially in testing the correction for achromatism but I find there is a slight difference between the appearance of the section of the cone of rays inside and outside the focus when using the mirror and when looking directly at an artificial star, which leads me to suspect that the large plane is not quite perfect in figure towards the edge, therefore it is that I think it all the more necessary to get photos of the Pole star, consequently I am making preparations to do this and as I found I could get no good definition through the aperture in the roof, I am mounting it outside the building altogether, and as it is necessary in this case to provide proper protection for it will be some 10 days or a fortnight before I can expect to get a definite result.

[22 September]; I am back in town again and working away. While I was away there were a few good nights but not many as we have had a good many fogs here, but my son has got some very promising images with the glass ... The lateral images appear to be perfectly free from coma ... "

Other progress reports followed: that of 1 January 1901 explained the trouble Grubb was having in determining the wavelengh of shortest focus:

"Since you left [for S.Africa] I have been trying to get some satisfactory results with the 12 inch prism which Mr McClean was kind enough to lend, worked in combination with the 24 inch O.G.; I am sorry to say, however that I have not succeeded. [By taking photos of spectra at different focal settings it should have possible to determine the narrowest part of each and hence the wavelength of shortest focus.] I have taken scores of photos of spectra, and altho' they all show that the shortest focus as somewhere about the centre of the spectrum, it would be quite impossible to say from any of them where the minimum point is exactly. I attribute this to the fact that the pencil of light is of so slight a vergency that it is not possible to determine very accurately where the best focus is ... I then went to a great deal of trouble and rigged it up and took photos of the solar spectrum for which I had to wait a considerable time, and in these, tho' I got nice fine lines they were no better as to the determining of the precise position of the minimum focus.

I got nothing at all so satisfactory as with the former method I adopted, which is on very much the same principle as that which Vogel used for determining the different foci of the parts of the visual spectrum ... the minimum focus appeared to be as nearly as possible in the centre of the impressed spectrum, or if anything perhaps a shade towards the blue end.

Without having a prism of the full size of the O.G. I don't think we can get any more decisive result than this and I am quite satisfied that this O.G. is as near perfection as the 26 inch at Greenwich. I cannot see therefore, (unless some further experiments be suggested) that I can do any good by keeping it longer ... I have not seen anything to lead me to suppose it wants further correction in any way, but I have taken a very large amount of trouble to obtain photos that would give a more satisfactory result than what sent you, and without success.

I am quite satisfied to send the O.G. to you unless some further course can be suggested by which it is thought probable more decisive results can be obtained, and I am sending a duplicate of this letter to Mr. McClean, and if he cannot suggest any more likely method of crucially testing the glass I am willing to deliver it.

[In handwriting] My kindest regards & good wishes for the new century."

It was decided that the objective should be sent out for actual trial in the telescope. Grubb mentioned to Gill [7 February] that he had provided for some adjustment of the separation between components of the lens, which he thought would be within $\frac{1}{8}$ of an inch of 2.5 inches, so that experiments could be done to seek the best position. Unfortunately, this information arrived in Cape Town after the lens itself, and Gill grumbled at having to 'pull the whole thing to pieces again' to measure the distance.

8.18 Further Correspondence

Around 1904 there was further correspondence over the drive sector which had been damaged by carelessly rewinding while it was clamped to the telescope. Gill was just then preparing for a visit by the British Association for the

Figure 8.5: Sir David Gill near the end of his time at the Royal Observatory, Cape of Good Hope (SAAO collection).

Advancement of Science and asked Grubb (11 January 1905) 'Is there any chance of your coming out in August next? I think you could do the trip for nothing and it would be a grand holiday for you.' Grubb did not mention this in his reply, but says:

> "I suppose by the time this reaches you, you will be back at Cape Town from Johannesburgh [sic]. My younger son [Romney Robinson Grubb] is not far from that, at Germiston, working away there in the mines.

> I enclose account for work done and hope you will find it right. The re-cutting of the sector was a very ticklish job and had to be done with extraordinary care involving practically more work than making a new sector for an instrument in hands as I had to rig up a temporary polar axis and fit up its own gearing plate and everything in situ for doing the ratching under the same circumstances as when the sector was in its proper place."

The opportunity was also taken to install a 'quick slow motion' on the worm plate. This was found necessary to aid with setting the telescope accurately and worked in a similar way to the normal slow motion [guide speed] adjustment except that the planetary gear was driven by a small motor which could go in either direction. A similar arrangement had been installed on the Radcliffe 24-inch for Oxford. It is described in detail in a paper laid before the Royal Dublin Society (Grubb 1905).

Gill 's time at the Cape was drawing to a close, and in his last letter to him there [19 September, 1906] Grubb gave some family news:

> "We are all fairly well here, but the 'all' does not mean very much now, as one of my sons as you know is in India [George Rudolph] and the other in the Transvaal and we have no one at home now except our little girl [Mary, usually called May]."

Gill retired to England early in 1907.

Chapter 9

End of the 19th Century

9.1 The Public Man

Following his success with the Vienna telescope, Grubb began to be in demand for prestigious popular scientific lectures. The first of these, and perhaps the most interesting, was *Telescope Objectives and Mirrors, Their Preparation and Testing*, given at the Royal Institution (Grubb 1886a,b,c) and already referred to in chapter 5 in connection with the Lick telescope. On this occasion he appeared at his best: he gave a very frank and explicit account of his methods of working, no doubt feeling that he could only impress and lose nothing by being open.

He described the processes involved in lens making from the selection of the glass, through the grinding and polishing, to the final tests. He explained his use of stars, real and artificial, as well as the Foucault method in his tests. He gave, for example, one of his favourite demonstrations: a delicate spherometer which could detect the flexure of a typically thick flat glass mirror under its own weight.

The difficulty of polishing lenses he represented by the following:

"In order to convey some idea of the relative quantities of material removed by the various processes [of polishing and grinding], I have placed upon the walls [of the lecture theatre] a diagram which will illustrate this point in two distinct ways.

The diagram itself represents a section of a lens of about 8 inches aperture and 1 inch thick, magnified 100 times, and shows the relative thickness of material abraded by the four processes.

The quantity removed by the rough grinding process is represented on this diagram by a band 25 inches wide, the fine grinding by $1\frac{8}{10}$ inch wide, the polishing by a line $\frac{1}{50}$ inch wide, while the quantity removed by the figuring process cannot be shown even on this scale, as it would be represented by a line only $\frac{1}{10000}$ inch thick.

I have also marked on this diagram the approximate cost of abrasion of a gramme of material by each of the four processes, viz.:–

		£	s.	d.	
Rough Grinding,	about	0	0	1	per gramme
Fine Grinding,	”	0	0	$7\frac{1}{2}$	”
Polishing,	”	0	10	0	”
Figuring,	”	48	0	0	”

Although he firmly believed in the use of machinery for grinding and polishing, he was the first to admit that lens-making was an art and depended on intuition:

> "I may safely say that I have never finished an objective over 10 inches diameter, in the working of which I did not meet with some new experience, some new set of conditions which I had not met with before, and which had then to be met by special and newly devised arrangements.
>
> A well-known English astronomer once told me that he considered a large objective, when finished, as much a work of art as a fine painting.
>
> I have myself always looked upon it less as a mechanical operation than a work of art. It is, moreover, an art most difficult to communicate. It is only to be acquired by some persons, and that after years of toilsome effort, and even the most experienced find it impossible to reduce their method to any fixed rules or formulae."

Another lecture, *Telescopes for Stellar Photography*, was delivered at the Society of Arts in Grubb (1889). This was partly an historical account of the subject, but mainly a description of the various means that had been devised for the steady driving of telescopes during long exposures, with particular emphasis, of course, on his own contributions. One interesting piece of information is a description of how he could generate artificial stars in any chosen colour, to test the objectives he was constructing.

The Royal Institution lecture *The Development of the Astronomical Telescope* (Grubb 1894a), was concerned with the great advances being made in astronomy, both in Europe and the USA, through the use of photography, not neglecting the techniques Grubb himself had developed. He took the opportunity to mention his water-supported large telescope and his ideas, developed at the time of the Lick bid, for convenient operation of telescopes by electrical control.

A most interesting interview with Grubb was published in *Strand Magazine* (FitzGerald 1896). It shows Grubb the raconteur and contains several detailed stories, in particular the description of the pouring of the Melbourne Specula quoted from earlier. At the time of the interview, the Thompson refractor for Greenwich was under construction at the Optical and Mechanical Works, and photographs of it were included. He told the story of the South telescope (see section 1.14) and discussed the giant refractors recently built for the Lick and Yerkes Observatories in the USA. He pointed out that his giant floating reflector could be constructed for a mere £33,000, a trifling sum to any millionaire desirous of immortality!

9.2 Siderostatic Telescopes

For the Crawford Observatory, Cork, (Grubb 1880) a new form of telescope had been designed, incorporating a tube that formed the polar axis and was driven at the sidereal rate. The eyepiece was at the upper end of the tube and viewing from the zenith to the equator was obtained by means of a small flat mirror at the bottom of the instrument. This could be adjusted from the eye end to give different declinations. Thus, the observer hardly had to move. The 4-inch telescope for Cork was placed on rollers so that it could be wheeled into a housing when not in use.

A more appropriate name for these instruments than Grubb's 'siderostatic telescopes' is perhaps the 'polar refractor' (Dewhirst 1982).

In 1884 (Grubb 1884a) his attention turned to making siderostatic telescopes of larger aperture. To save on the size of the optics, particularly the flat mirror, which he claimed was almost impossible to make in large sizes, Grubb proposed reviving the 'dialyte' form of refractor, where a single large crown lens is used to collect the light but the chromatic correction is provided by a much smaller flint component in the converging beam. The flat mirror is also in the converging beam and much smaller than it would have to be if placed in front of the objective. In Grubb's illustration, the astronomer sits at the eyepiece in his study, beside the fire, controlling the telescope outside by means of wire ropes connected to handles and indicators.

Although a telescope of this pattern was proposed for the Robinson Memorial Telescope at Armagh and was approved by two of the trustees appointed for the purpose, R.S. Ball and G.J. Stoney (Stoney and Ball 1884), J.L.E. Dreyer as director was opposed to such a radical innovation even though it would have resulted in a much larger aperture for the same price. Mainly, he feared that the extra flat mirror would increase the amount of scatttered light in the field, making faint objects hard to see. The changing angle of the flat mirror would also change the transmission of the optics, making photometry difficult. He quoted Provost Lloyd[1] that 'no matter how large it would be-

---

[1]Humphrey Lloyd (1800–1881), Provost of of Trinity College Dublin from 1867 until his death.

Figure 9.1: Dialytic siderostatic telescope proposed by Grubb. The crown
lens is at the top of the tube and the flint just above the cube where the axes
cross. The observer sits in comfort within the building (Grubb 1884a).

come possible to make telescopes, still, the great mass of Observatory work
will be performed with moderate sized refractors of 10 or 12 inches aperture'
(Dreyer 1884).

Grubb's 1884 article contained some negative remarks about the Paris
coudé (elbow) telescope of Loewy[2], who rose to its defence in two letters to
Nature (Loéwy 1884). Mainly he disputed Grubb's assertions that a plane
mirror of large size was excessively difficult to make, that blanks were anyway
unobtainable and that such a mirror would be unmanageably heavy. Grubb
replied to these criticisms in detail (Grubb 1884b), endeavouring to show that
Loewy's arguments were full of mistakes and misunderstandings, and that his
design really did represent a superior approach.

When British astronomers attending the 1887 Astrographic Congress in
Paris had the opportunity to look at objects through Loewy's telescope they
were nevertheless uniform in their praise of it (Knobel *et al* 1887).

The largest siderostatic telescope that Grubb constructed was the Sheepshanks 32-cm instrument of 1898 (Ball 1899) in Cambridge. There exists a

[2]Maurice Loewy (1833–1907), Assistant Director of Paris Observatory, later (1896)
Director.

letter (Grubb 1895a) from Grubb to Ball concerning the design which, according to W.M. Smart, 'combined in a unique way the principal disadvantages of both the refracting and reflecting forms of telescope' (Dewhirst 1982).

"Dear Sir Robert Ball

I have now roughed out a design which I hope will be satisfactory for the new siderostatic telescope. By the way! I hope that this telescope will not be called a 'Coude'' telescope as otherwise it will certainly be put down as one of the French instruments and you may remember that when I first of all proposed this form of telescope, Monsieur Loewy ridiculed the idea of such an instrument ever being made. The Coude' of course has its advantages over this form but I think this also has it's advantages over the Coude', and I trust that the instrument we make for you will be a very serviceable and workable one.

I have prepared a small rough model which will be useful not only in giving you a general idea of the instrument I propose, but also for the laying out of the necessary piers and the building to form an observatory room, as well as the shutters and necessary arrangements for protection against the weather ...

I would like you to consider whether the arrangement at the upper end would be such as would be convenient for the observer. I have endeavoured to keep everything out of the reach of his person as far as possible, and I assume that the general position of the observer will be that of a sitting posture with the body slightly bent forward when the telescope is being used for visual observations, as in the case of microscopic work ...

The only point that I have not satisfied myself about is that of the Finder, and that seems rather a difficult problem ...

As to the question of cost:- It is not easy to estimate for a perfectly newly designed instrument. I find that hardly any of our existing models will work in for this with the exception of the clock work and some few portions of the gearing. I estimate that the work on this instrument will be quite as much if not more than on one of our ordinary Standard Stellar Instruments, while we will have to make totally new sets of working drawings, and models all through.

The mechanical part of one of our standard Stellar Photo instruments costs £900. I think that a fair price for this instrument considering what I have said above would be £1,100. If the piers are built by some local man the erection of this instrument would be quite a trivial matter as compared to the erection of a dome which was formerly proposed ..."

The objective of the Sheepshanks telescope was not made by Grubb but rather by T. Cooke & sons, apparently at the suggestion of Gill, as the following letter from H.D. Taylor [designer of the 'Cooke Triplet'] (1895) shows:

> "...I cannot but feel gratified by the expression of the kind interest which you take in my efforts to improve the achromatic telescope, & we feel much obliged to you for your reccommendation of our triple O.G. to Sir Robert Ball and the Cambridge committee ..."

The triplet was afterwards replaced by a photographic doublet. This telescope had a successful career and was used by *inter alia* H.N. Russell for stellar parallax determination (Dewhirst 1982).

9.3   Smithsonian Heliostat (1890)

On 15 January, 1890, Grubb read a paper before the Royal Dublin Society (Grubb 1890b) on a novel form of heliostat that he had constructed for the Smithsonian Institution in Washington D.C. according to the wishes of S.P. Langley[3]. The main mirror of this instrument was a flat of 46 cm diameter. Its basic layout is due to Foucault and the mechanical arrangement can be thought of as an analogue computer. The mirror is mounted on trunions and is freely movable in azimuth. A rod sticking out behind it is driven by a regular telescope right ascension mechanism through a short declination axis. The flat mirror then moves so that the image of the sun is reflected onto the slit of a spectrograph some 50 feet away.

In the Smithsonian instrument, the drive clock, requiring a 1000-lb weight, was of the massive pattern that had been used previously for the astrographic telescopes. Not only could the R.A. and declination positions be adjusted from the spectrograph by means of cords, but also the altitude and azimuth of the image could be adjusted by turning 50-feet long rods.

An interesting feature of the mounting of the heavy flat mirror was the use of a mercury flotation bath to take almost all its weight. In this way, friction was minimized and the bearings were not strained by the load, keeping their precision. Later telescope builders used the same principle quite extensively. Both the Mt Wilson 60-inch (1908) and 100-inch (1918) telescopes used mercury support systems for their polar axes.

In a later description of the heliostat, Langley (1900) says '...this substantial and accurate piece of apparatus ... is worthy of the maker's well-earned reputation, but in the course of its use many changes dictated by experience of local needs have been made from the writer's first design'. The main changes

---

[3]Samuel Pierpont Langley (1843–1906) was a largely self-educated astronomer whose work mainly concerned the investigation of solar radiation. He invented the *bolometer*, an instrument for measuring the total amount of radiation falling on it, independent of wavelength. He was also a pioneer in the field of aviation. He designed successful model aeroplanes, but a manned machine was flown only after the Wright brothers' achievement.

Figure 9.2: Heliostat provided for the Smithsonian Institution in Washington DC (Langley 1900).

seem to have been the substitution of a Warner and Swasey governor for the Grubb original and the use of small motors to give the R.A. and declination fine motions instead of the long cords and rods originally supplied. Details of the changes, including photographs, were given by Wadsworth (1894), who seems to have done the work.

9.4 28-inch Greenwich Refractor (1894)

In 1886, Stokes (Larmor 1907f) wrote two letters to Christie, the Astronomer Royal, about a new idea which would allow visual objective lenses to be used for photography. The following year, Grubb (1887a) mentioned this new design at the Royal Astronomical Society. As a result of the interest generated, a 28-inch visual refractor, convertible for photography, was ordered around 1888 by the Royal Observatory to replace their elderly 12.75-inch Merz instrument. The latter was supported by a very solid mounting, designed by Airy, that was judged capable of taking the new telescope. Grubb was asked to supply a new tube and a 28-inch lens which was destined to be the largest he ever made.

The turret at Greenwich, which had been built for the Merz, was too small for the new telescope, whose focal ratio was to be F12, and a new onion-shaped replacement, now a familiar feature of the old Royal Observatory at Greenwich, was made by Cooke of York to stand on the same walls that had supported the old dome.

The acquisition of suitable blanks for such a large lens took considerable time, as might be expected. In October 1888 Grubb reported to Christie that he had at last obtained satisfactory crown and flint discs from Chance Bros [17 October 1888, RGO 7/41].

> "They are of course not absolutely faultless, no large discs are, but the defects are very insignificant & cannot in my opinion affect the definition in any way. I believe that they are the finest pair of discs of their size which have ever been made & I have no doubt that I can make a very perfect Objective of them."

In 1890 the 28-inch lens was 'well under way'. Because the photographic field was expected to be limited to about one degree in diameter, it was intended to use the lens for spectroscopy and direct imaging of relatively small areas of sky, such as the Moon. 'There have been some delays in the early stages because the work has been largely experimental' (Christie, 1890).

In response to a demand in mid-1893 for a progress report, Grubb wrote to Christie to apologize as follows [11 July 1893, RGO 7/41]:

> "I have all along endeavoured to meet your views as far as possible nor did I even allow my own personal convenience to stand in the way, for instance, not feeling very strong since I had the influenza this spring, I had arranged to go to Biarritz for a few weeks in April or May, but seeing you were very anxious to have matters as forward as possible for the Visitation, I put off my trip ...the consequence was when I did get there I unfortunately came in for a great burst of heat which completely laid me up in Biarritz, and when I did get back I had ...to hurry home and practically lie by for 10 days before I was fit for much."

In September 1893 Grubb went with an employee named McDonagh to the Royal Observatory to set up the 28-inch lens and shorten its tube [F.W. Dyson to Grubb, 11 March 1913, RGO 7/37]. It was ready to use by October 1 and complete except for a few details such as the dew-cap.

Christie (1894) and Grubb talked about the first results obtained in the photographic mode to the Royal Astronomical Society. This required the reversal of the crown component and the alteration of the separation. Grubb, at the same meeting, described how he had been figuring the lens, but explained that he had not had suitable means of testing it in the photographic configuration.

In general, the photographic mode was not really successful, probably because of the limited field of good definition that it offered. The visual performance of the lens was, however, excellent.

In recent times the lens was tested again in its visual mode (Anon 1960) by the Hartmann method, following some doubts about its performance:

> "During the year the objective was tested by Hartmann's method, and was found to be slightly over-corrected. Hartmann's constant was satisfactorily small (0.3), but a detailed calculation of the diffraction image then showed that the central intensity was only 60 percent of that of the theoretical Airy disc. Ray-tracing indicated that the over-correction could be removed by a slight further separation of the lenses, and an additional 0.8 inch was adopted after further trials. The spherical aberration then virtually vanished except for a small zone of slightly longer focal length near the centre of the lens, and Hartmann's constant over thirteen zones was found to be 0.055 compared to 0.16 for the Yerkes 40-inch, the best object-glass for which information was available."

The telescope was moved to Herstmonceux from Greenwich after World War II. It was mainly used there for double-star observing. However, it was moved back to Greenwich again in 1980. It is kept in operating condition as part of the National Maritime Museum.

9.5   Heidelberg Twin Refractor

In 1889, Miss Catherine Wolf Bruce (?–1900), a New Yorker with a strong interest in astronomy, presented $50,000 for the construction of a 24-inch photographic refractor to Harvard College Observatory (Bailey 1931). Later she made donations of funds to purchase photographic instruments to Lick Observatory and the Grossherzoglichen [Grand Ducal] Observatory in Heidelberg (now Landessternwarte Heidelberg-Königstuhl). At that time the latter was under the direction of its founder, the energetic Max Wolf[4]. Twin 16-inch lenses were to be made by Brashear of Albany, New York.

On 6 Oct 1893, Grubb sent Wolf his catalogue, following a mention by Huggins of his interest. He wrote in the accompanying letter as follows [Heidelberg, 6 October 1896]:

> "I have made the construction of these large Equatorial instruments the study of my life, and it has been the opinion of most practical men that they are better constructed for really practical work than those of other makers.
>
> Professor Hale of Chicago, who had been visiting most of the Observatories in the world last year, told me that he preferred my design to any others, and were it not for the prejudice in the United States in obtaining instruments out of the country, he would have preferred to have got his instruments from me."

---

[4]Maximilian Franz Josef Cornelius Wolf (1863–1932)

Wolf later visited Grubb's factory and, in due course, commissioned a mounting from Grubb, even though the final properties of the lenses were not yet known. Wolf's instructions [Heid. 11 July 1896] were quite specific:

> "Now you know my intentions, to get a very strong and steady stand, very easy moving telescope, exceptionally good in following for a long time exactly the stars: no accuracy in reading circles, no mikrometers or such kind. No elegancy and polishing."

Grubb's quotation contained his usual flattery [Heid. 23 December 1896]:

> "... it is only because I know what good use you would make of any instrument I supply to you & the high esteem I have for you personally & your work, that I have quoted the exceptionally low prices mentioned ..."

At Wolf's insistence, this instrument incorporated for the first time a complete wormwheel instead of the usual sector that Grubb favoured. Although astronomers disliked having to rewind the sectors every few hours, Grubb (see Grubb 1894a) felt that they offered a very stable and rigid method of driving which took up much less space and offered a much more compact overall instrument than a full wormwheel would have allowed. He had also developed special equipment for cutting the teeth in sectors under a microscope. It is, of course, true that a continually (sidereally) driven worm wheel would wear much more evenly than a sector and would therefore last longer.

The clock was delivered before some of the other parts which depended on the focal length of the objectives, not determined until late in the project. On delivery, pieces of the instrument were found to be defective. Some of them were even rusty. Wolf was quite sarcastic [Heid. 13 January 1899]:

> "But there are other things, which your workmen have not made well, especially in the clock work. As a specimen you may regard the Crown wheel, which drives the heavy frictional governor. If you had examined it you would have seen, that it is a piece worthy of an international exhibition. Nothing is in good order on it. The prick-point [pivot] is eccentric regarding the shaft, and the wheel against the shaft and the prick ... but the clock and Russel-control[5] is made by a great artist, as we would say in our workshop; please say to him my congratulations and that I am fearing that this clock will cost us a large amount of labour and [?] before it will be in a good order ..."

This brought a typical grovelling reply [16 June 1899]:

---

[5]This seems to have been an alternative to Grubb's phase-locked loop system for controlling the worm drive. See also fig. 9.3.

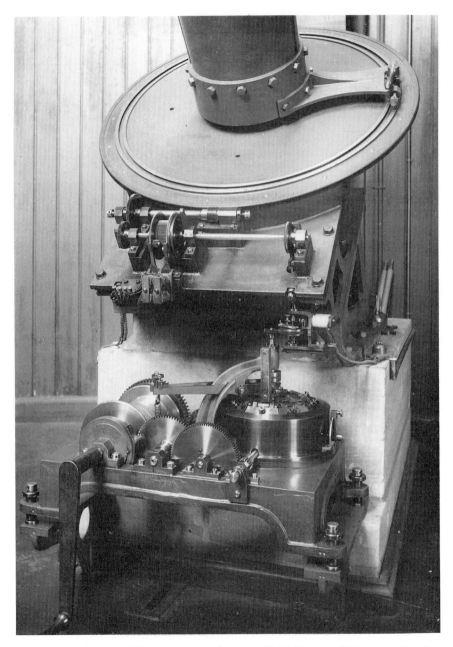

Figure 9.3: Drive of Bruce twin-refractor, Heidelberg. This was the first Grubb telescope with a full wormwheel. Much of the mechanism is typical of the drives that Grubb supplied for photographic telescopes from the astrographics onwards (Landessternwarte Heidelberg-Königstuhl).

"It is with extreme regret ... It is most incomprehensible to me, for this clock is the exact facsimile of those we have made for the stellar photographic telescopes and many others of the same size, and in no single instance has there been a complaint of a single pinion or wheel of one of the clocks we have sent out ...

The foreman of that department who re-cleaned and fitted up the clock, although very many years with me was not at the time acting satisfactorily, and I have since had to remove him to another department, and this is the only excuse I can make for the misfortune.

I must beg that you will not go to any trouble or expense about this but that you will kindly re-pack it and send it back to me here, as I am most particularly desirous myself to examine & see the nature of these faults and try & fix the responsibility on the right man, and I will of course pay all the expenses of carriage and packing both ways.

It would be a lasting regret to me if you should have any of my work which was not perfectly satisfactory to you."

Some dimensions, such as the length of the tube, had to await the completion of the lenses by Brashear. Wolf was anxious to show off his new telescope to the members of the *Astronomische Gesellschaft* and the many foreign astronomers expected to be present at their meeting in Heidelberg in the summer of 1900. When the final details became available, he pressed Grubb to complete the job as quickly as possible. He soon became quite desperate [13 June 1900]:

"You do not imagine in what difficulties and disagreeable situations you have brought me by the procrastination of my affairs!

There are now still six weeks and 3 days only from today to the beginning of the international astronomical congress, and today I have nothing here of all and nothing ready. And it seems regarding the slowness of the seafreight and transportation absolutely impossible to get all here over, to erect it, to bring the Dublets at their places, to mount them, to bore the holes ... nothing ready ...

It was the intention of our prime-Minister to show himself to the foreign astronomers this observatory, and to make parade of it ...

And now I myself have made this act impossible—was myself though innocent and brought only by your laziness in this position and I will feel the full consequences; I will hear not only the derision of my colleagues ... but I will never get more any assistance by his Excellency or by the State and it may be the beginning of the end of my career caused by your laziness only."

Grubb had, in fact, been away from mid-May to 5th June at the solar eclipse in Spain. There followed one of his 'righteous indignation' letters [15 June 1900]:

> "I am greatly distressed at your letter of the 13th which has just come to hand. I feel conscientiously that I do not deserve the strictures that you have expressed in that letter ...
>
> I have tried to do the best I could for you; I have not neglected your work for others, but I have been hampered & kept back by the necessity for continual alterations as the work went on, due in the main to lack of information from Mr Brashear as on his work my work also depended. I do not make this statement with any idea of arguing this point with you but I do expect that when you reflect calmly over the matter you will see that the remarks you have made (which are extremely hurtful to me) have not been justified by the facts; on the contrary the personal intercourse which we have had made me most wishful and anxious to do the best I could for you. I am very sorry that I failed to do so but I cannot see even now that I could have done any better."

Wolf felt he had to apologise in his next letter [18 June 1900]:

> "You are in error if you think that I am not content with your work or interest in our telescope ...
>
> Now I beg you to take my letter of last week how it is: an expression of my desperation!"

He ended by asking Grubb to use the 'urgent' method of sending at twice the usual price.

The instrument appears to have been assembled in time, though not without some damage to one of the bearings whilst in transit and some last-minute grinding of the surfaces to make the polar axis move freely.

The final appearance of the mounting bears considerable resemblance to many of those produced by the successor firm, Grubb Parsons. It was of an asymmetrical English type. The southern end of the polar axis was supported by a 3-tonne cast-iron 'tapered pillar' and the northern by a cast-iron block. The 5.5-metre polar axis was made of two riveted sheet-metal cones attached to a cast cube in the middle and having steel axial pins at the ends. The adjustable counterweight was attached to one side of the cube and a cradle on the other held the twin tubes of the telescope and another for the guider. The moving parts weighed ten tonnes and the weight for the clock 250 kg. The fine-motion in declination and RA followed Grubb's usual designs. The slow motions in RA could be controlled electrically from a handset. The main wormwheel had 1440 teeth, so that the worm had to turn at the rate of one revolution per minute of sidereal time (Wolf 1900, 1901).

9.6   Mississippi Refractor (1893)

According to Warner (1968), a replica of the famous Pulkovo Observatory near
St Petersburg, Russia, was built in Oxford, Mississippi in 1859. The President
of the University of Mississippi, F.A.P. Barnard, asked the Cambridgeport,
Massachusetts, firm of Alvan Clark to make them a refractor of 19 inches
aperture, which was to be the world's largest. The Clarks were prepared
to make an 18.5-inch, but regarded the project as risky and would not take
money until the instrument was finished. Unfortunately, though the lens
did get finished, the Civil War broke out and the Clarks were stuck with
it. It ended up in the original University of Chicago and later Northwestern
University.

Twenty years later, when the dust had settled, the University of Mississippi
was again in the market for a large telescope. Although a bid was received
from Clark, Grubb won the order. Thus the largest Grubb telescope in the
United States is the 15-inch made for the University of Mississippi in Oxford.
It is a visual refractor and has a 9-inch photographic objective mounted with
it (Dimitroff and Baker 1945).

9.7   Large Telescope Hopes

Grubb always hoped that he would be commissioned to make a large reflector.
In the first paper of the first volume of *Transactions of the Royal Dublin
Society*, in 1887, he wrote on his ideas for *Great Telescopes of the Future*. He
pointed out that eventually the sheer thickness of glass in refractors would
limit the transmission of light. He therefore advocated the use of reflectors
with the main mirror constructed of speculum metal, the medium he was used
to.

> "As regards silver on glass mirrors, it is hardly worth discussing
> their relative powers of permanence, as at the present date the art
> of glass-making has not arrived at that degree of perfection that
> will permit the makers to undertake discs of any kind of suitable
> glass of six feet in diameter; but I may mention, that this is perhaps
> not to be much regretted, as the difficulty of preserving a silvered
> glass surface of large size would be almost an impossibility, and
> the process of resilvering, when the mirror is of large dimensions,
> becomes most formidable ... "

The advantages of reflectors which he listed are: achromatism, ability
to reflect ultraviolet and infrared light, the ease of supporting giant mirrors
compared to giant lenses and the moderate length of the instrument. He
goes on to show how successful annealing of large speculum metal discs could
be accomplished by monitoring and controlling the temperatures within the

Figure 9.4: Grubb's scheme for a large reflector in a sphere supported by water flotation (SAAO collection).

annealing oven using thermocouples, a method not available to Lord Rosse some decades previously when he cast his 6-feet mirrors.

Grubb had his first opportunity to work on a large glass mirror in 1890 or 1891 when he was asked to re-figure one of the 36-inch primaries of the Crossley reflector. This and another mirror had been made by G. Calver[6], for a telescope being built by A.A. Common. When Common turned his attention to constructing a 60-inch, in 1885, the smaller instrument was sold to Edward Crossley, a wealthy textile manufacturer. Unfortunately, it soon became obvious that its mirrors had not been figured at all well. On expert advice, Grubb was asked to re-figure the worse of the two. However, the work he did was not at first satisfactory and the mirror had to be returned for a second effort. By the time the telescope was ready to use, Crossley's theological views had changed and he was no longer interested in astronomy. He eventually presented the telescope to Lick (Stone 1979), where it is still known as the 'Crossley'. Although the original Common telescope was a beast to use, the quality of the images was very good (Campbell 1902) and played a significant role in persuading US astronomers that reflectors were the way to go.

In an article in *Knowledge*, Grubb (1894b) described how the mass of a large telescope could be supported by a water-tank arrangement. The tele-

---

[6]A British telescope maker, usually supplying amateurs

scope tube would be surrounded by a ball-shaped float. All would be operated by electricity, air would be blown down the (insulated) tube and the mirror would be heated to avoid dewing and other problems arising from the high thermal content of the water.

Grubb's hopes that he would get to build a large telescope were raised by a letter from Gill on 2 October 1895:

> "Some of the millionaires here are said to be willing to go in for a big thing in telescopes but it must be the biggest thing that ever was. The matter is merely talked about after dinner, and therefore I don't want you to spend money or make plans till matters are 'forwarder'. But what is the biggest refractor that you would undertake to construct? What would be its approximate cost equatorially mounted. What the cost of dome. What is the cost of machinery for rising floor . . . I promised to ascertain these matters for the friend who is pushing this matter amongst rich people."

Grubb had just then been approached about a telescope for an exhibition to be held in Paris in 1900. The instrument was to be based on a giant fixed refractor with an steerable flat mirror of equal diameter placed in front of it. The idea had been to project images of celestial objects into a hall where members of the public could pay to see them. The syndicate hoped that an expenditure of £120,000 would cover the costs and that from 10 to 20 million visitors would pay a franc to see the telescope!

In a report to the Exhibition's directors, Grubb (1895b) pointed out the many problems of the project—bad weather, only the sun and moon really suitable, limited opening hours etc. He counter-proposed that a floating reflector to his design should be built instead and that about 50 people per hour could be charged a much larger fee to look through it. In the end, the instrument, in the construction of which Grubb played no part, was successful as an exhibit but was financially disastrous for the promoters (King 1955).

Grubb's reply to Gill's enquiry was sent on 24 October. At least there was no further mention of speculum-metal mirrors!

> "My dear Gill,
> In reply to yours about the proposed giant telescope for Capetown.
>   I have written to Mantois to ask him what is the largest size discs he will undertake and when I get the reply I will send you the information you require as to the cost &c; meanwhile as your mind may be running on such things, I think it may be no harm to send you confidentially a copy of a Report which I have made lately to a French Syndicate on a similar subject . . .
>   I received a letter from the Manager of the 'Nord Glass Co' asking me if I would undertake to put an optically plane surface on a mirror 2 metres in diameter. At first I thought the thing was not

probably bona fide, & I rather put them off, but seeing they were in earnest I corresponded with them, and on my way to Switzerland called on them, and found that they had actually in the oven at that time 4 discs of glass of 2 metres in diameter and about 14 inches thick, and I have practically completed arrangements with them to grind and polish an optical surface on one of these discs which have since been taken out of the oven and I believe three of them are good. At the same time I made the acquaintance of the Principal of the Syndicate, a Mons Francois Deloncle ...

You will see it is proposed to have a 4 foot O.G. so it is evident that Mantois has undertaken a pair of 48 inch discs. In order therefore to carry out the ambition of your friends at the Cape it would be necessary to have a Refracting telescope of something over 4 feet aperture or a Reflector telescope of something over 2 metres aperture. If a refractor be chosen, what would you think of adopting Elkin's plan that is halving the length of the telescope tube & putting a plane mirror at the lower end and reflecting the light back to the photo plate or eyepiece beside the O.G? If this form were adopted, it would be quite possible to mount the instrument on the flotation principle as the lower end of the tube would be closed, but even if the flotation principle be not adopted, the problem of mounting a 50 foot tube is very much less than that of mounting a 100 foot tube.

The point I would strongly urge in these monster mountings is, that if carried out, the motions should all be effected by some form of motor, and not attempted by hand. The Yerkes telescope is the first where this has been carried out to any extent, although I urged them to do it in the case of the Lick, and I do not think it would have been carried out in the case of the Yerkes either, only that I understand Hale's father is a great constructor of hydraulic lifts, while Yerkes is the King of the electrical tram roads system there, and consequently they naturally employed these adjuncts ..."

A full specification of a 2 metre reflector of 18 metres focal length, mounted on Grubb's flotation principle, was sent to Gill. However, the latter indicated that he preferred a reflector of 3 metres (10 feet) aperture and with a primary focal length of 60 feet so that it could be used for photography. There should also be a Cassegrain focus for spectroscopic and eye work. The flotation principle was rejected outright.

Grubb [2 January 1896, to Gill]

"... I note that you put aside altogether any idea of my floating scheme; you may be quite right in this, and I may be quite wrong, but it would have been more satisfactory if you had mentioned any one reason on which you have founded your opinion. This form of

mounting has been freely discussed both here and in America: it
has been almost universally approved of and any objections that
have been raised are easily to be combatted. You will therefore
surely not blame me if I still consider this the best form yet suggested for mounting large Reflectors, until at least I hear of some
objection that I cannot meet.

I have therefore made out two estimates, one for the ordinary
German form as per your request, and one for my floating form
. . .

I find the largest mirror I can get any glass Works to estimate
for at present is two metres. The estimate for the rough glass for
this is £4,000, and my price for working this, as supplied to the
Paris Syndicate is £4,000. Total £8,000 for optical work."

Rough Estimate for large Equatorial

Gill Form

Optical parts, 2 metre mirror &c	£8,000
Mechanical Parts, German form	£14,000
Lifting Floor, 80 feet diameter	£4,000
Dome of 80 feet diameter	£10,000

Floating Form

Optical Part 2 metre mirror &c	£8,000
Mechanical Part	£12,000
Sliding roof to cover instrument	£2,000

A full specification of the floating form, with a primary of eighteen metres
focal length, followed. Seven motors were to take care of the coarse and fine
motions, the ventilating fan, the clock weight and the observing platform.

Unfortunately, nothing further came of this project. In April 1896, Gill
went to England and stayed with McClean, during which time, as explained
in Chapter 8, he seems to have become convinced that McClean's grievances
were legitimate. His relations with Grubb became cool and formal for some
time.

In 1903 Grubb (1903) addressed the Royal Dublin Society on a 'Floating
Refracting Telescope' essentially similar in design to his floating reflector. In
this case, the telescope was folded using a plane mirror, so that the observer
sat near the objective lens, supported by a movable gantry.

9.8   The Eclipse of 1900

At the suggestion of Sir Howard Grubb, the Royal Irish Academy and the Royal Dublin Society decided to organize an expedition to observe the total eclipse due to occur on 28 May 1900 (Anon, 1904). The participants included Sir Howard himself, and other members of the small Irish astronomical community such as Rambaut (from 1897 Radcliffe Observer in Oxford), W.E. Wilson and C.J. Joly[7]. The site chosen was Plasencia, near where astronomers from Madrid had decided to set up their camp. George Rudolph Grubb, who had graduated Bachelor of Engineering at Trinity College in 1899, arrived in advance to assist in the setting up of the Spanish instruments and erect supports for the coelostats of the Irish expedition.

For the expedition, Grubb provided two coelostats with adjustment for latitude, so that they could be used on future eclipse expeditions also. An unusual instrument called a 'kinematograph' was constructed so that 12 plates could be exposed in 12 seconds without any lost time betwen them. The coelostats fed photographic cameras—one with a 6 inch objective of 7 ft $10\frac{1}{2}$ inches focal length, the other a 4-inch objective of 19 feet focus. The latter lens with an 8-inch Grubb coelostat was used on a much more famous eclipse expedition, that to Sobral in 1919, when Einstein's theory of general relativity was successfully put to the test (Dyson *et al* 1920).

---

[7]Charles Jasper Joly, FRS (1864–1906), Rambaut's successor at Dunsink, and a second cousin of the physicist John Joly.

Chapter 10

1905–1925; The Last Years of the Firm

10.1 Grubb's Later Years

As Grubb entered late middle age, his prosperity evidently increased. In the early years of the 20th century he lived in 'Rockdale', a large late Victorian house on Orwell Road, Rathgar, then a developing area of Dublin. In 1910, he moved to a similar house, 'Aberfoyle', next door. These two houses now constitute a hotel. He also still had a summer house in Wales called 'Inglewood', at Colwyn Bay. His personal notepaper bore a crest with the motto 'Strength is from Heaven'.

He was a member of several social clubs, the Hibernian, the United Services and the Royal Irish Yacht. Since 1889 he had held honorary office in the Royal Dublin Society, of which he was a leading member. On 16 April 1912, he received the Society's Boyle Medal from the Chairman, Professor John Joly[1], (Anon 1912c) (having been ineligible before that date owing to a provision which had prevented the Society from making an award to its own officers). In 1913 he was appointed Scientific Advisor to the Commissioners of Irish Lights in succession to Sir Robert Ball. The commissioners made a cruise around the coast each summer, inspecting the lighthouses. They were affiliated to Trinity House in England, and the members enjoyed a splendid dinner in London each year. Grubb was also at this period a Governor of the National Gallery of Ireland and an honorary member of the Royal Institute of Engineers of Ireland.

During these years, through no fault of its own, his firm had fewer chances to compete for the really exciting contracts. This was the result of the fundamental economic changes that were slowly but surely shifting economic power from England to the United States of America. There, the new century saw

---

[1] John Joly F.R.S., 1857–1933, physicist, geophysicist and inventor.

the emergence of astrophysicists with expansive ideas and the necessary financing for bigger and better instruments than the Europeans felt able even to wish for. The larger American telescopes, since the middle years of the Alvan Clark firm, were rarely the work of single companies, but were constructed by numerous sub-contractors. George Ellery Hale, at first of Chicago, and later of the California Institute of Technology, working together with the telescope designer and optician G.W. Ritchey, inaugurated a new era of astronomy with the construcion of the 60-inch reflector on Mount Wilson in the (at least in those days) fabulous climate of southern California. The British and colonial institutions, on the other hand, ordered very few instruments in the first 25 years of the 20th century. Grubb must have watched the American developments with envy, but nevertheless he continued to write about his ideas for large instruments in papers such as *On Floating Refracting Telescopes* (1903) and *The reflecting Telescope and its Suitability for Physical Research* (1908), the latter partly a series of reminiscences on his own work on reflectors and the difficulties he had faced in getting the professional astronomical community to accept them. Ironically, the instrument that did the most to convince the American astronomical community of their value was the 36-inch Crossley reflector of Lick Observatory, whose mirror had at one time been re-figured by Grubb himself. Grubb did quote for the 72-inch reflector of the Dominion Astrophysical Observatory in Canada, but the contract was awarded elsewhere.

On the continent, the very well organized firm of Zeiss in Jena, Germany, was coming to the fore. Unlike most contemporary optical firms elsewhere, Zeiss had a strong staff in the area of research and development and did not depend for its ideas on one or two men. They were well equipped to take advantage of new discoveries in science and engineering. The associated Schott glassworks was in close proximity and Zeiss lens designers were quick to make use of the new types of optical glass that they were turning out. They soon acquired a reputation for well-designed instruments in many fields besides astronomy. Most of the new telescopes that rapidly increasing wealth had made possible for German observatories were made by the Zeiss firm.

Whether because of declining business in large telescopes or a natural interest in such affairs, Grubb seems to have turned his thoughts in the early 1900s towards military and surveying instruments. Several curious inventions were described to the Royal Dublin Society at its meeting on 17 November, 1903, such as an attachment for taking bearings using a ship's compass and an improved 'dipleidoscope', a device for determining time from solar observations.

However, the telescope business had by no means come to an end and did continue, although at a less hectic pace than in the eighties and nineties of the previous century. Even if the very largest instruments were constructed by others, Grubb nevertheless was destined to work on several quite impressive projects before he eventually was forced to retire.

10.2   The Radcliffe Twin Telescope (Oxford)

The Radcliffe Twin telescope was the last of the large Grubb refractors constructed on the old pattern where the right ascension drive was provided by a sector that had to be re-wound every few hours, frequently interrupting long exposures.

When Arthur A. Rambaut (1859–1923) was appointed Radcliffe Observer, he inherited a very old-fashioned establishment whose chief telescope was a heliometer, an instrument which had been entirely outmoded by the advent of celestial photography. He persuaded the Radcliffe Trustees to allow him to get quotations for a large photographic telescope, and recommended in 1898 that they should purchase a 24-inch photographic refractor combined with an 18-inch visual instrument. The cost, including dome, rising floor and other parts of the building was estimated at £7500. The trustees met and awarded the contract to Sir Howard Grubb in February, 1899. He was soon able to write to Max Wolf [Heidelberg: 30 April 1899] that he was at work on the new 24-inch photographic telescope for the Radcliffe Observatory Oxford, which 'I hope to make the most complete thing in England'. The instrument was mechanically complete in the summer of 1902, but did not receive its lenses until 1903. The weather was so bad that season that Grubb had to wait some time until final tests had been carried out and he had the gall to say that he had never experienced such critical examination, pointing out that several astronomers for whom he had done similar work had given their approval after one or two nights' trial in the workshop!

One of the most interesting points of this installation was that Grubb finally got his chance to build a large rising floor. The floor itself was counterbalanced by weights on cables and a hydraulic ram provided the power to lift about six or eight people. The clock-weight of 940 lbs had originally to be wound by hand (Thackeray 1972), but was later raised by a hydraulic mechanism. As to the slow-motion drive, Grubb's usual pendulum-controlled system was installed, but with the addition of a 'Quick slow motion' or setting speed. As previously mentioned, this refinement was later added to the McClean Telescope in Cape Town.

The twin telescope was utilized fully for parallax and proper motion work. In 1935, when the Radcliffe Observatory moved to South Africa, the instrument was presented to the University College, London, Observatory at Mill Hill.

10.3   'Retirement' of Huggins

In 1908 Sir William Huggins was 84 years old and felt he could no longer observe. At his suggestion, the Royal Society arranged with Grubb to move the telescope they had provided for him so long before to the Department of Astrophysics at Cambridge.

Grubb (quoted by Ronan 1967) recalled the occasion in funereal style:

> "The Equatorial had been partially dismantled; all the numerous parts and attachments had been removed and were scattered all over the floor, which was encumbered and littered with axes and various parts of the instrument, some of which had already been placed in packing cases; and in the midst of this litter, wrapped in a large cape and seated on a packing case, was Sir William himself, and his faithful collaboratrice who was flitting about watching the packing with keen interest and loving care ... Lady Huggins had asked me to let her know when I was ready to close the box [which contained the large object-glass from the telescope], and when I intimated that I had it safely in the case, she took Sir William by the hand and brought him across the room to have a last look at their very old friend ... They gazed long and sadly before I closed the lid".

10.4 Submarine Periscopes

One important device amongst Grubb's new century inventions was a type of periscope for use in the gun-turrets of battleships, which combined the functions of a telescope and the simple two-mirror periscope in one instrument. This naturally led to similar devices for submarines. Unfortunately, submarine development was shrouded in secrecy, and it is rather difficult to find out very much about Grubb's work in this area.

The earliest British submarines, the first of which was launched on 2 October 1901, were the 'Holland' boats, called after their Irish-American designer. Holland[2], incidentally, was financed by American members of the Fenian movement who hoped to use them for their anti-British campaign in Ireland. However, he seems to have sought support wherever he could get it and was not particularly anti-British in principle. A serious disadvantage of these early vessels was that they had no means of seeing where they were going when underwater, and had to surface frequently to take bearings. Sir Reginald Bacon (1940), the first 'Inspecting Captain', or head, of the submarine section of the Navy, claimed to have invented the submarine periscope, though this is undoubtedly (Compton-Hall 1983) an exaggeration:

> "After considerable thought I hit on the idea of a tube long enough to reach from the boat to above the surface of the sea ... Naturally, it would be necessary to place a forty-five degrees reflecting prism on top of the tube so as to reflect from the horizontal vertically down the inside of the tube ... I copied the arrangement of one leg of a pair of binoculars; and in front of the prism, put a

---

[2]John Philip Holland, 1840–1914.

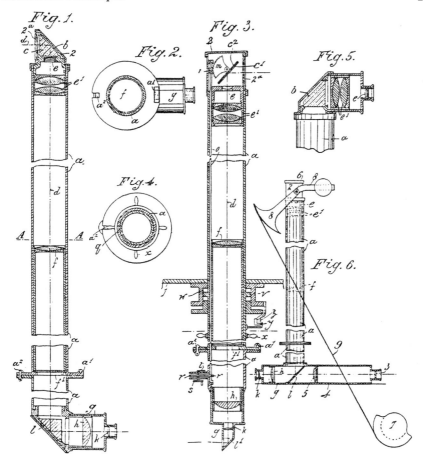

Figure 10.1: Early Grubb periscope designs, from a patent application (Grubb, 1901).

double concave lens. I then pushed an ordinary long-distance telescope up the tube and lay on my back and looked up the eyepiece ... found I had an excellent view of the dockyard and surrounding mud flats. Naturally it was inconvenient to lie on one's back, so I had a second forty-five degree prism mounted in the draw-tube of the eyepiece so that I could sit in a normal upright position ... This original tube was fitted on the first Holland boat, and it enabled all her trials, as well as those of the second boat, to be carried out in safety ...

After the tube had been installed I was introduced by Lieutenant Trevor Dawson, the Submarine representative of Messrs. Vickers, Sons & Maxim (as the firm was then called), to Sir Howard Grubb, the eminent Dublin optician. He naturally evolved a better optical arrangement; and, eventually, through a series of improvements, produced the present-day periscope.

The first periscopes made by Sir Howard Grubb gave a lot of trouble. First it was difficult to make the prism chamber at the top of the tube water-tight; and, secondly, if the air inside the tube was not bone dry, the cooling of the tube, owing to the cold water rushing past it when travelling submerged, caused moisture to condense on the lenses and blur the image. To cure this, dessication of the air had constantly to be resorted to."

The first successful use of a Grubb periscope to keep course accurately was reported to the Admiralty by Vickers by telegram in 1902 (Scott 1962).

The accompanying diagram from a patent application (figure 10.1) shows some of Grubb's early periscope designs (Grubb 1901). He referred to his invention as a 'Phyhydroscope' to distinguish it from the Cleptoscopios, Omniscopes and Storoscopes that already existed. The simple watertight stuffing box used to form a rotary seal in the roof of the submarine was not satisfactory because water pressure when the vessel was moving caused the tube to be pushed to one side. The periscope then became very difficult to rotate. Later versions were placed for most of their length so as to rotate inside a second tube which took care of the force exerted by the water (Talbot 1915).

Glazebrook (1923) mentions a Grubb system for getting two different magnifications in periscopes by moving two lenses simultaneously with a common mechanism.

According to Grubb's obituary in *Nature*, he supplied about 95% of the periscopes for British submarines during the First World War. A large number of photographs exist, in a series of photographic albums which formerly belonged to Miss Mary Grubb, showing Grubb at the ceremonial launching of submarines (Wayman, private communication).

10.5   Johannesburg Refractor

The last big refractors made by the company were ordered before the First World War but were not completed until long after its end.

R.T.A. Innes[3], Director of the newly-formed Transvaal Observatory, the only wholly South African observatory in that country, had started as early as 1905 to agitate for a large instrument. He obtained quotations from Grubb which indicated that about £10,000 would be necessary for a 24-inch refractor, or £12,000 for a 27-inch (Hers 1987). A petition signed by leading astronomers who attended the British Association meeting in South Africa in 1905 did not succeed, but just before the Union of South Africa was formed in 1910, the

---

[3] Robert Thorburn Ayton Innes, 1888–1933, noted double star observer. Scottish-born, he came to South Africa from Australia where he had been an amateur astronomer. He became a member of Gill's staff at the Royal Observatory, Cape, and was fist director of the Transvaal Observatory which later became the Union and then the Republic Observatory.

Figure 10.2: R.T.A. Innes, Director of the Union Observatory, Johannesburg (SAAO collection).

Transvaal government found itself with funds which it did not want to share with the other provinces in the new political arrangement and the Minister of Lands, Mr J.B. Rissik, authorized the purchase of a 26-inch refractor. It is related that Innes was asked to state his case at a meeting where both J.C. Smuts[4] and Rissik were present. Smuts wanted to know whether such a big telescope was really necessary and Innes replied 'Well, no Sir, but it will be such fun'. He was then asked what size would be needed and, thinking it would be best to aim rather high, asked for a 26-inch. To his great surprise, this was immediately agreed to. In a letter to Gill [15 July 1909] he relates:

> "Now that the telescope is authorized, I am like Clive, surprised at my moderation; the Minister ordered the biggest telescope I mentioned and I believe would have gone to a 30 or 33-inch just as easily, but I am satisfied!"

Smuts in later life was a keen supporter of astronomy and on one occasion

---

[4]Jan Christiaan Smuts, 1870–1950, South African Statesman and military leader. Smuts was an advocate of the 'holistic' movement in philosophy and one of the founders of the United Nations. His interests included astronomy and he was for many years a fee-paying member of the Astronomical Society of South Africa.

he surprised a meeting of the Astronomical Society of South Africa by his attendance in the middle of a political crisis.

The order for what actually became a 26.5-inch was placed on July 15, 1909, and Sir David Gill was appointed scientific adviser for the project. Gill had hoped to retire on income from investments, but as early as 31 May 1909 he had written confidentially to Innes

> "My investments at the Cape in mortgages on houses in Cape
> Town have been so disastrous, that I have had to add to my income
> by taking up remunerative work."

He went on to mention various projects for which he was acting as a consultant, his terms being $2\frac{1}{2}\%$ commission on the overall contract plus travel expenses. Gill was clearly worried about delays and warned Innes [4 August 1909]:

> "Grubb has his hands very full with navy contracts for pe-
> rioscopes [sic] for submarines, to the value of many thousands of
> pounds—and his mind is full of that work just now. So unless he
> is ready to bind himself very closely in the contract as to delivery
> &c, there is great fear of disappointment."

Again, on 25 November, Gill wrote (concerning an order for a micrometer), with unconscious humour:

> "Grubb is too big a bug now for these things. His mind is
> full of Admiralty work of which he has many thousands of pounds
> worth on hand—in the way of gun sights and perioscopes [sic]"

It was agreed that the mechanical parts of the instrument should be finished within 2 years of the signing and that they were to be examined and tested in every particular by Sir David.

The mechanical parts were indeed pretty well finished on time. By 1911, Grubb had erected a testing tower for lenses. Unfortunately, however, there were severe problems about the supply of the blanks for the lens. Although Parra & Mantois had been given the contract, it became evident that they were unable to do the work. Grubb wrote to Innes on 5 December 1913:

> "As regards Mantois:- The case seems absolutely hopeless. I
> correspond with him still, but every letter is a repetition of the one
> before and each letter commences with a set form of words, which
> as I said to Sir David Gill, he might as well have an india-rubber
> stamp made for ... "

Other problems were besetting Grubb, for the letter continued:

"We are greatly troubled and annoyed here at present with another matter and that is the great strike in Dublin which you have no doubt heard of. None of our own men are absolutely disaffected, but we cannot get materials to work upon and when instruments are complete we cannot get them away. Forty-five tons of cases containing all the work of the Dome constructed for Santiago have been lying in our yards for 32 months, and we are also held up for castings and materials as the port of Dublin is completely closed.

Up to the present we have been able to keep our men together and keep them working, but if it goes on much longer we will have to discharge men simply for want of materials to keep them working on. It is the most pitiable state of affairs, as there is really no dispute as regards wages, and the men could go to work to-morrow if they choose on wages which they would be quite satisfied to work with, but there are 18,000 men out."

Chance Bros then got the contract to supply the glass. However, they too had little success and the first World War had broken out without any discs having been supplied. Although Robbins (1923) states that Chance Bros. supplied the blanks eventually, it appears (Manville 1971) that the flint was actually made (paradoxically) by the Derby Crown Glass Co., owned by Sir Charles Parsons. A lecture by David Gill in 1912 had as illustrations several pictures which show that the mounting was virtually complete at that time. Gill regarded it as containing 'nearly all that experience has taught us in the matter of the modern equatorial mounting.'

Sir David Gill died in January 1914 as a consequence of pneumonia caught while on a shooting expedition. Innes thereafter had nobody to keep Grubb on his toes, and little progress was made before the World War broke out later that year.

10.6 Changes in Mechanical Design

The design of the Johannesburg instrument, and also that of the 24-inch ordered for Chile by the German astronomer Ristenpart, show that radical changes had taken place in Grubb's thinking about mountings. Perhaps Gill's strictures about the unsatisfactory nature of the sector drive had eventually hit home, for the new instruments had mountings with continuous circular worm wheels that did not have to be re-centered every few hours. Apart from the obvious advantage that observations no longer needed to be interrupted, the new design meant that wear on the gears would be much more uniform, unlike what was experienced with sectors whose centres were preferentially worn. Ball bearings were used in the friction relief system for the first time in a Grubb design, ensuring freer movement. At Gill's suggestion, these new

Figure 10.3: Parts of the Johannesburg 26.5-inch and Chilean 24-inch telescopes in the works in Dublin, probably just before the First World War
(SAAO collection).

instruments also included a clock-driven right ascension circle, an important
labour-saving measure (Grubb, 1912).

It may also be that these changes were due to the employment of Cyril
Young as engineer and designer to Sir Howard Grubb. Young (1875–1949),
a Devonshire man, had previously worked with Grubb's only British rival,
Cooke of York, and had also been for nine years Works Manager for the
Cambridge Scientific Instrument Company (Anon 1949). In 1910 he joined
the Dublin company and was responsible for the design and construction of
large astronomical instruments. It must be remembered that by this time
Grubb was 66 years old, and it is probable that he felt the need to hand
over some of his work to someone more up to date in engineering methods.
Young was to survive Grubb's control of the Company, and remained with its
successor, Grubb-Parsons, until his retirement in 1945.

10.7   The Move to St. Albans

No telescope work could be done during the War and, in fact, the Navy had Grubb's factory moved from Dublin to the Fleet Works, St. Albans, (Hertfordshire, England) in order to ensure continuity of supply of periscopes in the face of the 'Troubles' in Ireland and the German submarine threat to shipping in the Irish Sea. T.H. Mason, a well-known Dublin optician, visited the works in 1917 and remarked (Mason 1944):

> "[Sir Howard] piloted me round his works and showed me two large telescopes which had been finished sometime previously for the Russian Government, but the war and revolution had prevented shipment. I noticed also that the entire production then in hands was for the British Admiralty and this fact was responsible for the loss to Dublin of the works. The British Admiralty insisted, for three reasons, on the transfer to England. The reasons were:
> - (1) Transport delays and dangers—the 30 ft. steel tubes for the periscopes were made by Vickers' in the North of England; they were not really tubes, but steel rods that had been bored out in an immense lathe. (2) Proximity to headquarters for consultation and inspection and delivery of the finished periscopes, &c. (3) The growing political unrest in Ireland—an armed guard was placed at the works ... "

Some of Grubb's patent applications towards the end of the War were made in both his own name and that of Vickers Ltd, the submarine manufacturers. Whether this implies that he was in some way an employee of Vickers, or had merely used their facilities in the development work, is uncertain.

In his patent specification No 178,474 of 1920, concerning Cinematograph apparatus, Grubb described himself 'formerly of Rathmines, Dublin, Ireland, but now of Hurstlea, St. Albans, in the County of Herts, a British subject ... '

Contact between Grubb and Innes concerning the telescope for the Union Observatory was only resumed in March 1919. After several letters from Innes, Grubb finally wrote from 'Sir Howard Grubb & Sons, Branch Works, Charlemont Bridge, Dublin' as follows [27 March]:

> "In reply to your letter which we got at the beginning of this year. We delayed answering this letter hoping that every week things would be in a more settled condition and that we would be able to give you some news as to when we could resume progress with your work. Unfortunately things seem to be getting worse and worse here. Labour troubles are spreading everywhere. Our men are out on strike and our Works are picketed here so that we can neither send anything out or get anything in.
>
> The state of the labour market is most unsatisfactory, the wages the men have been geting during the War being from two

to three times what they got before and naturally they dont feel inclined to have these at all reduced, but until some satisfactory arrangement is come to it will be very difficult to resume work again.

In addition to all this the Government during the War considered it necessary that we should move our Works to England especially as regards the work for the Navy as there was sometimes great trouble in getting Periscopes and other instruments transported from Ireland to England, and the arrangements for this move had gone so far when the Armistice occurred that it was impossible to go back, the result is that we are all in the trouble now of moving some three hundred tons of machinery over to St. Albans in England where the Government have commandeered a factory for us, and at the same time our men being out on strike it is impossible to get transport of this machinery.

Again we do not know how we are situated as regards optical glass. On receipt of your letter we wrote to Messrs. Chance, twice, we think, respecting the discs for your object glass and we have as yet received no reply. We expect that they are very much in the same position as we are ourselves.

The whole labour market is in a most chaotic condition and until the Government take the matter firmly in hands it will be impossible to get to work."

In a hand-written enclosure Grubb also wrote:

"Our works have been completely in the hands of the Govt & still & for some months to come guarded by a strong military force as we are full up of Govt stores & will not be free for some time yet. We have not done any Astronomical Inst work or private work of any kind since August 1914— & we have suffered very much from damage to instrs & depreciation of stock & plant. Since the Armistice things are worse & we cannot get men to work. The Govt are paying them all for not working ...

It is possible that when peace is signed things may settle down but just at present all business is in a hopeless condition. The writer has just recovered from 2 months of illness but is at work again ...

[30 April 1919] We are in all the trouble and worry at present of moving our Works and I am hoping to-morrow morning to get across to London to see after many matters, amongst others, the possibility of getting discs for your Object Glass.

All our skilled men are on strike for the last ten weeks and are living very comfortably on the out of work donations that the Governmnent are providing so kindly, they dont feel as if there is any need for working any more. I am afraid we are in for a bad time."

10.8   Post-War Confusion and Financial Problems

Just how difficult things had become slowly emerged. On 2 March 1921 Cyril Young wrote in a note on behalf of Grubb:

> "The enormous wages that have to be paid to workmen now and the enormous overhead expenses for carrying on factories render it very difficult to get houses to carry out pre-war contracts, except at an enormously increased rate."

Again, Grubb to Innes, 26 May 1921:

> "I expect they [the glass manufacturers], like ourselves, have lost many of their most experienced hands.
> About a year ago negotiations were started to re-organise our business on a very much enlarged basis, and the arrangements included an intimate association with the house of Zeiss of Jena, and I thought this would give a good opportunity of getting the Jena house of Schott to try to mould the big discs and I had taken some preliminary steps in this direction, but owing to the state of trade and the money market here for the last year these negotiations fell through and I had to fall back on Messrs Chance.
> [19 August 1921] It is very difficult for an outsider to understand the state of things in this country just now. If we were a conquered and not a conquering country it could well be worse; factories closing or closed all round, everyone trying to realize, no one buying ... "

Even several years after the end of the War the firm remained in a state of confusion. Robbins (1923) related that 'there in the confused heaps of material, tools, patterns, periscopes, range-finders, and waste, lying on the new workshop floors, ... the famous [Johannesburg] telescope was lying dismembered and for the most part unrecognisable.'

By 1922, Innes was sufficiently aroused that he arranged to go to England to find out what was going on at Grubb & Sons. His report to the Secretary of the Interior, Pretoria [19 May 1923], to whom he was responsible, shows the sorry state of affairs that he found:

> "I have the honour to report concerning my recent visit to Europe for the purpose (mainly) of getting work on the 26-inch refracting telescope brought to completion:-

Immediately upon my arrival at Norwich, England, I made appointments with the Officers at the High Commissioner's Office in London [an official representing the Government of the Union of South Africa] and with Messrs. Howard Grubb and Sons ...

I had my first interview (in London) on the 9th October 1922 (a week after my arrival) and discussed generalities with Messrs. Grubb. They were not entirely frank or perhaps I was somewhat obtuse and missed the full import of their hints as to their financial position. I found out that since their removal from Dublin to St. Albans, the telescope which had necessarily to be dismantled had not been reassembled and it even appeared that they hardly knew what work had still to be done on it. I therefore directed them to re-assemble the telescope and to prepare a close estimate of the money required to complete the instrument (a) mechanically and (b) optically. This they promised to do and we fixed a date as to our next meeting in London (18th October) by which time they were to be ready with all particulars.

It was also necessary to consider the supply of optical glass and we have to remember that it was the failure to get this glass that led to the loss of time between 1910 and 1914. I had entered into negotiations with the Paris firm of Parra Mantois whilst Grubb's had continued negotiations with Chance Bros. of Birmingham and had opened negotiations with a third firm (Derby Glass Works, controlled by Sir Charles Parsons); it also seemed probable that we might have to find out the possibilities of getting the glass from Jena ...

At the second interview (18th October) Messrs. Grubb asked for a sum of money which I considered quite unreasonable and I told him so. They again dropped hints, the implications of which were not entirely lost upon me this time as to their financial position. They also agreed to 'revise' their figures and to receive me at St. Albans in about a fortnight when I could actually see the telescope.

I asked a friend in the City to make enquiries as to the financial status of Messrs. Grubb and in due course received two reports. These I handed in at the High Commissioner's Office, but it will suffice to say that the firm was weak financially and probably in the hands of their bankers (Barclay & Co.)

On the 30th October I went to St. Albans taking with me (at my expense) Mr. Frank Robbins[5] F.R.A.S. as a possible witness in case of dispute etc. I saw the telescope practically complete <u>in the raw</u>. Grubbs again asked for a reasonable sum and I told

---

[5] Frank Robbins, 1860–1945, was an employee of the City of London and an amateur astronomer. His friendship with Innes was lifelong, and he was appointed as the latter's agent in some of his dealings with Grubb.

them that I must ask them to adhere to paragraph 2 of the preamble of the original agreement, by which they had undertaken to deliver the mechanical part of the telescope for the payment already made. They acknowledged the justice of my request but pleaded their utter inability to accede to it—they had no money—and I daresay I had by then hinted that I was aware of their financial position, they offered to complete the work 'on time and line' and retired to get out a fresh estimate. At last they produced their bedrock price. I pressed them - said they must sacrifice some of the profit they expected to make on the optical side of the contract etc. etc., and at last, almost with tears in their eyes, they reduced the bedrock price by £200.

Previously I had asked Messrs. Cooke of York (the only other capable firm in Great Britain) for quotations and had received their figures. On Grubb's last figures, Cooke's showed but a trifling saving. Against it was the danger that after the telescope had been transferred from St. Albans to York, Messrs Cooke would have found some fault with the work already done by the other firm. All the pros and cons were fully discussed the next day (30th Oct) with Captain Bowden [of the High Commissioner's Office] and Mr. Cundy and they agreed (I concurring) that there was no hope of securing better terms from anywhere, and it was arranged that you should be cabled for authorization of the additional £1000 more or less which was required ...

The next interview took place on the 17th November at Captain Bowden's office, Mr. Romney Grubb being present. Captain Bowden stated the stringent conditions as to future payments and Mr. Grubb asked time to consider these—we to meet again on the following Monday (20th November). We met as arranged and Messrs. Grubb accepted Captain Bowden's conditions, an agreement was to be drawn up forthwith, the main principles being that (a) the work was to be paid for as the work was done, (b), the optical work—the discs to be paid for by the High Commissioner on account of Grubbs and 75% of the cost of the optical work to be paid as done, the balance to be paid on approval and after taking delivery.

Authorization was duly received, the new contract signed and work restarted.

I paid four visits to St. Albans to inspect the work done,
namely:- 11th December 1922
12th February 1923
19th March 1923
25th April 1923 (with Mr. Robbins)

On each occasion satisfactory progress had been made and on the last occasion I found the mechanical work all but completed, the telescope assembled and in working order. It appeared to be most satisfactory in every detail and is probably the finest instrument of its class ever made. I duly signed four out of the five certificates covering the cost of the work etc on the mechanical portion.

It will be noted that I visited St. Albans on the 25th ultimo and left Southampton on the 27th ultimo. There is no doubt but that Messrs. Grubb put heart and soul into the work so as to complete it ere I left England ...

Then Messrs. Chance invited the contractors and myself to inspect the discs at Birmingham and we (accompanied by Mr. Robbins) duly did so on the 21st March last. The contractors (Messrs. Grubb) were satisfied with the glass so far as the tests made there went, and Messrs. Chance assured me that the two discs were the best they had ever turned out—that in the past they were content if the strains caused dispersions of 5 wavelengths, and that with these two discs the dispersions were in one case $\frac{1}{8}$th of a wavelength, in the other case, nil ...

I am of opinion that a lot of the trouble we had in the past was due to lack of proper supervision over the contractors—Sir David Gill was not young and Dublin is a tiresome journey from London, and he died in 1913 [actually 1914]. I then thought that correspondence would hurry the producers of optical glass, and by the time that the weakness of this method became apparent to me, the Great War had started and all such work was abandoned, and could not be successfully renewed until last year, because of high costs and labour unrest ...

As to the time for completion of the object-glass (to be made from the two glass discs)—this is agreed upon at 12 months (1924 March 31) but the duration may be shortened. The tube of the telescope is to remain in St. Albans until the object-glass is approved—the remainder of the instrument is to be shipped to South Africa forthwith ... "

Late in 1924, Innes again went to England. His report to the Secretary of the Interior in South Africa, of 3rd February 1925, carries on the story:

"I learned on arrival that the financial position of Messrs. Grubb was more critical than ever and that the firm could only last whilst it was being supported by the Russian Government for whom it was making two large telescopes and an observatory.

Personally and through Mr. Robbins I kept in touch with the Russian scientist charged with the supervision of the work (Dr. Blumbach). I learned incidentally that Messrs. Grubb's position was such that they had to take orders form Dr. Blumbach and that he had informed them in writing that they were to do no work on our telescope. It was not however difficult to persuade Dr Blumbach that it was to his advantage to let Messrs. Grubb finish with us as the telescope and object glass would show their actual possibilities. He consented and allowed me the use of one of his telescopes with which to test the object glass. It should be added that Messrs. Grubb were most anxious to serve us and in the end, they went into liquidation well within one week of our taking over the object glass.

Soon after I got to England and work on the two discs progressed, it was discovered that the flint disk supplied through Sir Charles Parsons firm [it appears that the Chance flint turned out unsatisfactory] was not perfect and Sir Howard Grubb actually recommended me to decline it—his optician [John Armstrong] was however not so pessimistic and considered that a workable glass might result.

I consulted the Astronomer Royal (Sir F. Dyson) and Sir Charles Parsons.

If I rejected the disk, then we might feel sure that Messrs. Grubb would go into liquidation forthwith. Sir Charles Parsons in my presence instructed his manager to cast another flint disk forthwith and privately told me that if Grubb's went under 'he would see me through'—I asked him if he would mind putting that in writing but he declined, because he said that 'Grubbs' liquidator might use such a promise as an asset'. He explained more fully his intentions which I do not repeat now because they are hardly relevant—they were however most generous to us.

Under our original contract with Grubbs' they had to provide a star test to my satisfaction at St. Albans and if I was satisfied the transaction closed. I made indifferent tests under Dr. Blumbach's direction (on his telescope) and as far as they went they were satisfactory. [12th–14th October, 1924] Messrs. Grubb informed me verbally that they were not able to give me a test as per agreement because of their financial position—the cost of such a test would be from £300 to £400. In lieu thereof they agreed to allow me to make the tests here [Johannesburg] and such tests would be binding on them and that we should retain £900 until they delivered a satisfactory object-glass."

An informal letter from Innes to his assistant, H.E. Wood, in Johannesburg, dated 16 October, 1924, gives more detail of what was going on:

"They are now going to dismount the O.G. & give it some final touches which will take about a month—then a final test & accept or reject. Accept or reject. Only in theory—because the

firm is going into liquidation immediately. Dr. Blumbach will not
support them any longer—in other words he will not order the
41-inch O.G. from them.

On the 15th I saw Sir Chas Parsons with the Grubbs (R.
Grubb, Young & Armstrong) and the manager of the Glass Factory (Mr Rands). The arrangement stands as follows -

If at all passable I am to take delivery of the 26—in in 4 weeks
time but Messrs Grubb undertake to supply another flint disk
(furnished free by Sir C. Parsons) & to make a perfect O.G for us
if within 6 mos. after erecting the present O.G. at Jhbg we find it
not good enough—at a nominal charge.

Here I have no choice—they are finished & I must virtually
close the contract & that quickly. In return they give me a contract
which in law (as they go into liquidation) is worthless—but against
that— they have personally—this more particularly as regards
Romney Grubb & Armstrong the optician—engaged themselves to
Sir C. Parsons & myself to honor the agreement. I guess that when
they go into liquidation & desert St. Albans that they (or some of
them) will go to Sir C. Parsons Heaton Works Newcastle /T and
he will make telescopes. But he Sir C.P. cannot say anything or
write anything until the Fleet Works are finished with—the Fleet
Works are too vast & are really useless. Sir C.P. has plenty of
room at Newcastle ..."

All these arrangements were made not a moment too soon, because Innes'
letter of 3rd February continues:

"Acting on a hint, the High Commissioner sent suddenly to
St. Albans and removed all our property (on a Friday) and on the
following Wednesday the firm went into liquidation ..."

The completed telescope was found to be a very fine one and was used
for many years by some of the world's greatest double star observers until its
semi-retirement in 1971, on the closure of the Republic Observatory (successor
to the Transvaal, later Union, Observatory).

10.9   The Simeis Reflector

In 1912 the Imperial Russian Government ordered from Grubb three telescopes, a 32-inch refractor with 45-feet dome and rising floor, a solar spectrograph for Pulkovo, the great observatory near Petrograd, and a one-metre
silvered-glass reflector with a 32 feet dome for Simeis, the Crimean observing
station of Pulkovo.

The refractor was never, in fact, completed. After the takeover of Grubb's
firm by Sir Charles Parsons, it was agreed with the Soviet Russian government, which had in the meantime come to power, to increase its size to 41

Figure 10.4: The 26.5-inch refractor in Johannesburg (SAAO collection).

inches aperture, thus making it the largest equatorial refractor to have been attempted. Although the mounting and dome were, in fact, finished off and readied for shipment, the lens blanks were rejected and the project ground to a halt. It is thought that the finished parts were sold for scrap during World War II (Warner 1975).

The coelostat for the solar telescope was installed on the roof of one of the observatory buildings and the image was reflected down the outside of the building towards the 7-metre grating spectrograph proper which was located on the ground floor. It was completed in 1923 at St Albans and subsequently installed at Pulkovo (Anon 1924c). Presumably it perished at the time of the

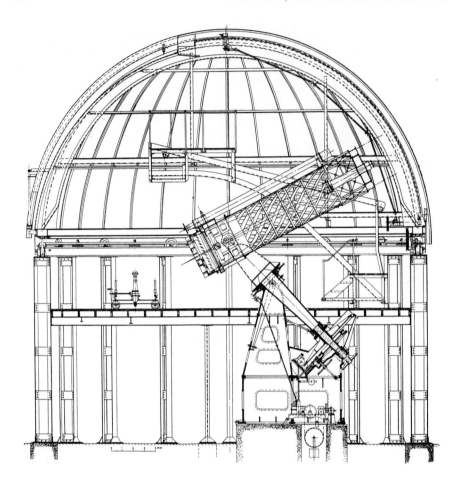

Figure 10.5: Sectional drawing of the 1-m telescope and dome for Simeis (Grubb Parsons Publication No 1, 1926).

destruction of Pulkovo during the Second World War.

The Simeis reflector was, like everything else, delayed by the First World War. In addition, the Russian revolution had taken place, and Grubb did not expect the new government to honour his contract, as is made clear in his letter to Innes of 27 March 1919:

> "With regard to a reflecting instrument about which you asked some questions. It occurs to us that we have here a very elaborate and carefully made Reflector intended for the Russian Government which we suppose will never now be required by them, and although this is made for a different latitude it would not cost very much to have it adapted for your latitude. If we could only find out definitely whether there is any possibility of this being

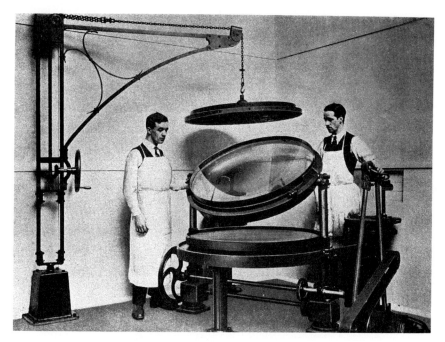

Figure 10.6: The polishing of the Simeis 1-m mirror. Armstrong, the optician, appears on the left side (Grubb Parsons Publication No 1, 1926).

> required in Russia or not we could then go into the question as
> to the possibility of adapting it for your latitude and give you an
> estimate of the cost as it would seem to be a very good opportu-
> nity of acquiring a fine instrument. We have a disc for the mirror
> that was made at the old St. Gobain Works now alas destroyed,
> and we were just commencing the figuring of this mirror when the
> War broke out."

However, in 1922, the Soviet Russian government gave instructions for its completion (Anon 1924a,b), and Prof Blumbach was put in charge of its completion, in circumstances described in the previous section. The designs had been carried out in consultation with the Poulkovo astronomers J.O. Backlund (1846–1916) and his successor as Director, A.A. Belopolsky[6], in collaboration with Gill. The layout owed a lot to the 60-inch on Mount Wilson, California. A fork mounting was used, and there were two focal stations which could be set up by changing the top end of the tube. One was a bent Cassegrain system to which a spectrograph could be attached, and the other was a regular Newtonian for photography. Friction relief for the upper end of the polar axis of the Simeis reflector was provided by roller bearings

---

[6]Belopolsky, Aristarch, 1854–1934

whereas the Mt Wilson instrument relied on a large mercury flotation tank to take most of the load.

G.A. Shajn (1892–1956) was placed in charge of the new instrument (Struve 1958). The mirror arrived at Simeis in March 1925 in a double crate weighing 850 kg in all. It was extensively tested by the Hartmann method in a laboratory and its figure was found to be exceptionally good (Shajn 1926). The Hartmann 'T' value was found to be 0.1, corresponding to an angular size for the image of a point source of only $0''.2$. Placed in the telescope in June, 1926, a figure of $0''.6$ was obtained, still exceptionally good.

With this telescope, Shajn carried out many fruitful spectroscopic programmes, such as stellar spectra, radial velocity determinations and determination of the orbits of spectroscopic binaries.

Sad to say, the 1-metre telescope, like so much else to do with Pulkovo, fell victim to the Nazi invasion of Russia during World War II. *Observatory* magazine (Shajn 1944) carried the following dismal report of the events surrounding its end, telegraphed by Shajn:

> "A week or two before the enemy occupied the southern part of the Crimea, the staff of the Simeiz Observatory was evacuated. The workers took with them the object glasses of two astrographs and part of the laboratory equipment.
>
> In May 1944, after the Crimea was liberated by the Red Army, the Academy of Sciences sent me to inspect the remains of the observatory. The following facts were established. During September and October 1943, German specialists dismantled all the observatory's instruments and moved them in thirty or more trucks to Simferopol, whence they were dispatched to Germany. The equipment stolen was the 40-in. reflecting telescope, the double astrograph, the new astrograph for zonal observations, a photoheliograph, three stellar spectrographs, a large coelostat, a long-screw measuring machine, a Repsold machine, a microphotometer and two astronomical clocks.
>
> In addition to this, much other laboratory equipment and the whole library collection of over nine thousand negatives, and the equipment of the power station and workshop were all taken away.
>
> On January 18, 1944, the main building of the observatory, where a Rumanian army unit was quartered, caught fire. It continued to burn for two days, but the commander of the unit did not call out the fire brigade nor did he take any steps to extinguish the flames. Only the framework of the building remains. Most of the trees in the observatory grounds were felled for firewood ..."

According to Dadaev (1972), the mounting was used by the Germans for scrap metal.

10.10   The End of the Grubb Firm

In January 1925, *Nature* (Anon 1925a) carried the report:

> "Every one familiar with astronomical and other optical in-
> struments will see with regret the announcement that the old-
> established firm of Sir Howard Grubb and Sons, Ltd., St. Albans,
> and formerly of Dublin, has gone into voluntary liquidation, and
> is for sale ... It is to be deplored that a firm with such a record of
> splendid work, and a reputation so high among optical instrument
> manufacturers, should have lacked sufficient support to keep it in
> existence as a profitable concern."

However, by April (Anon 1925b) the rescue had been effected:

> "We are glad now to learn from Sir Charles A. Parsons that a
> new company, trading as Sir Howard Grubb, Parsons and Co., has
> purchased from the liquidator the goodwill, drawings, and sundry
> plant and machinery of the firm, and that workshops of up-to-date
> design are being erected at Heaton, Newcastle-on-Tyne, especially
> suitable for the building of large telescopes and observatory equip-
> ment. The advice and experience of Sir Howard Grubb will be at
> the disposal of the new company ..."

Sir Charles Parsons (1854–1931) was the youngest of six sons of the third
Earl of Rosse, who so many years earlier had been associated with Thomas
Grubb. He was an active and interesting person in his own right, being noted
for the discovery and successful exploitation of the steam turbine. He was also
strongly interested in optical matters and the manufacture of optical glass,
having acquired the Derby Crown Glass Company in 1920 when it was on the
verge of collapse due to the lack of orders after the end of the war. He also
acquired control of Ross Ltd. of Clapham, makers of camera lenses, binoculars
and cinema projectors, and was its chairman (Manville 1971).

Only a few of the Grubb staff were retained in the new concern, these
including Cvril Young, who was appointed its general manager, and Romney
R. Grubb, the latter somewhat reluctantly on Parson's side. Others were John
A. Armstrong, optical manager, Robert Sinclair, engineering foreman, and Bill
Latimer of the optical department (Manville, 1964). The solar spectrograph
etc. for Pulkovo and the Simeis reflector were both completed in the new
works.

10.11   Sir Howard's Last Years

After the closure of the St Albans works, Sir Howard returned to Dublin where
he lived for a while at No 1 de Vesci Terrace, Kingstown (now Dun Laoghaire)

Later, he moved to No 13 Longford Terrace, Monkstown, where he spent the rest of his days. Both houses overlook the sea. Although he rented No 13, Grubb owned another house in the same terrace! This house was afterwards divided into flats and has only recently been restored to single-family occupancy. The dining room, however, remains unchanged from Grubb's time.

On his 82nd birthday, 28 July 1926, Sir Howard was presented with a touching congratulatory address, inscribed on vellum, by eighteen of the leading astronomers of Great Britain, which read as follows:

> "On the approach of the eighty-second anniversary of his birthday, we wish to convey to Sir Howard Grubb our hearty good wishes.
>
> We recall with admiration his devoted application of his resourcefulness and ingenuity to the development of the instrumental equipment of astronomers through more than sixty years, and we wish to record our grateful sense of the great services rendered by him and his celebrated firm to our science.
>
> Especially do we recall with pleasure his contribution to the undertaking of the Photographic Survey of the Heavens, in the provision of suitable object glasses, and of the refined clockwork needed for the accurate movement of the telescopes.
>
> It gives us great pleasure to note that his scientific interests are still maintained, and we hope that they will so continue for many years to come."

According to T.H. Mason (1944), Grubb had a small workshop at his home where he worked on various inventions such as anti-dazzle headlights for motor cars. As an old man, four children remained to him, but they were scattered far and wide and, except for the youngest, they saw little of their parents. His oldest daughter, Ethel, married Frank Carlisle in London in 1910 and seems to have stayed there. His second son, the oldest surviving one, George Rudolph, had gone to India after helping with the 1900 eclipse expedition. There he married Emily May Turnbull of Ootacamund, a well-known 'hill station'. He died in 1941. Romney Robinson, the third son, married Ada Margaret Pearson in 1910 and continued to work for the firm for some time after the Parsons takeover. He spent a few years in Newcastle but left in 1929 following his divorce and re-marriage for Montego Bay, Jamaica, where he had a plantation. According to his son, Rodney Brian Grubb (1989), 'He loved it, built his own house and made his own electricity'. He died in 1947. May or Mary, the youngest of the family, probably lived with her parents until their death. Mary eventually inherited her parents furniture and other effects. She had a farm called Ballyquirke in Co Tipperary and died in 1969.

The children that had died young had never been forgotten, for there exists a bill dated the year before Grubb's own death which shows that he had the stone above the grave of his sons Herman and Howard Jr. repaired.

Figure 10.7: Howard Grubb in old age (Photo: Mr R.B. Grubb).

One of Grubb's last remaining letters, dated 25th February, 1931, was written in a very shaky hand to J. Joly (Grubb 1931), and concerned Royal Dublin Society matters. It commenced rather pathetically:

"Excuse my not having answered yours of 23rd by return of
post but I have my good, and my bad days, & sometimes this
causes a little delay ..."

Lady Mary Hester Grubb died at the Grubb's last residence, 13 Longford
Terrace, Monkstown, Co. Dublin, on 12 April 1931. Her funeral service was
held at Monkstown Church and she was buried in Dean's Grange cemetery.

Sir Howard died only a few months later, on 16 September 1931, at the
age of 87 years.

10.12   Obituaries

Sir Howard was the subject of several obituaries, in *Observatory* (Anon 1931a),
Nature (Anon, 1931b), *Monthly Notices of the Royal Astronomical Society* by
his former employee, Cyril Young (Young 1931) and in *Proceedings of the
Royal Society* by 'S.S.C.' (presumably Sidney Chapman 1932), which is the
longest and most interesting. Some reminiscences from the latter read as
follows:

"Professor H.F. Newall of the Observatory, Cambridge, writes:
'He was a delightful companion, full of amusing stories. He had an
attractive way of quietly whistling to himself when he was faced
with a difficulty. It seemed to aid him in finding the solution. He
was endlessly patient in going into details of design and always
ready to listen to suggestions'.

Mr L.E. Steele, Vice-President of the Royal Dublin Society and
for many years a co-worker with Sir Howard Grubb in the work
of that Society, writes: 'Grubb was not a public man. He shrank
from debate and dialectics and confined his energies and interests
to societies which called for peaceful discussion. In one of these
he was particularly interested. He devoted many years of his life
to the welfare of the Royal Dublin Society and as a Member of its
Council and one of its Vice-Presidents his wise advice was much
sought after.'

To his friends he presented a most attractive personality. Gentle, courteous and warm-hearted, his modesty and the absence of
anything which suggested self-assertion, endeared him to a wide
circle of friends. He was eminently a sociable man and delighted
in hospitality which made his house the centre of pleasant inter-
course, and in this was much assisted by Lady Grubb who pre-
deceased him by a few months and from whose loss he never really recovered. With his keen sense of humour his stories, always
kindly, of the many distinguished men he had met in his career
and of the incidents of his life, were a source of much interest to
his friends. A talk with him was an intellectual treat. Had he

been more of a literary man he might have left behind him a volume of reminiscences which would have been of more than passing interest; but for him writing was an irksome effort. A man of simple piety and always ready to help those in need of assistance, his kindness was a marked characteristic. His knowledge was always at the disposal of his friends and he was ever pleased to talk about his scientific pursuits even with those whose scientific knowledge was of the scantiest."

Appendix A

Publications by T Grubb

A.1 Published Papers

A short account of the results of some experiments made with the view of ascertaining how far the Gregorian and Cassegrain forms of the reflecting telescope are suited to micrometrical purposes; with a description of a simple and effective mode of illuminating the wires of all kinds of telescopes, &c., *Mon. Not. R. Astron. Soc.*, **3**, 177–179, 1836.

Experiments suggest that the Cassegrain configuration of reflecting telescope is best for micrometrical purposes. Also describes a means of illuminating the field and cross-wires of a telescope, in which a small hole is made in the centre of the secondary and a 45° mirror is placed behind it, so that light from a lamp at the side of the tube can be allowed to enter the exit pupil.

On an improvement in the Illuminating of Objects in the Microscope, *Proc. R. Irish Acad.*, **5**, 296–297, 1853. (Delivered 10 May 1852.)

An informal account of a talk concerning an improved method for illuminating objects on a microscope stage.

A new method of determining, approximately, the spherical aberration of a combination of lenses for microscopic purposes, *Proc. R. Irish Acad.*, **6**, 59–63, 1853–57. (Read 27 February, 1854.)

Describes his use of ray-tracing, over 'several years', in lens design.

On the substitution of surface-printing (for copperplate) in the production of bank-notes; including an examination of a Paper on the subject by Alfred Smee, F.R.S., Surgeon to the Bank of England, published in the Journal of the Society of Arts, London, December, 1854, *Reports of Scientific Meetings*, Nov 24, 1848 to June 7, 1855, 267–283. Royal Dublin Society, 1855. (Read 26 January and 23 February, 1855.)

A defence, amusing in places, of engraving as a method for the production of banknotes. Surface printing is considered too expensive because of the cost of watermarked paper to afford protection against forgery. It is in any case too easy to imitate.

Report on the Improvement of Telescope and Equatorial Mountings, *Rep. British Assoc.*, 195–200, 1857.

Explains his preference for the Cassegrain form of telescope on a 'German' mount.

On Improvements in the Optical Details of Reflecting Telescopes and Equatoreal Instruments, *Trans. Sections, British Assoc.*, 8–9, 1857.

A condensed version of the preceding paper.

On Decimal Systems of Money etc., *J. R. Dublin Soc.*, **1**, 21–32, 1856. (Read 30 November 1855.)

Advocates a decimalisation of money based on 10 shillings as the main unit. However, all measures of weight, length etc. should be decimalised at the same time to make the change worthwhile.

On Lunar Photography, *J. Photogr. Soc.*, **3**, 279, 1857. (Read 6 May 1856.)

Advocates a clock-driven slide for counteracting Lunar motion in long exposures.

On some of the Optical Principles involved in the Construction of Photographic Lenses, *J. Photogr. Soc.*, **4**, 108–111, 172–174, 1858.

On a New Patent Compound View Lens for Photographic Cameras, *J. Roy. Dub. Soc.*, **2**, 27–29, 1858. (Read 26 March 1858.)

Description of his patent lens, designed to give a large field of view.

On a New Table Microscope, *J. R. Dublin Soc.*, **3**, 85–88, 1860. (Read 26 March 1858.)

Description and illustration of his "Compound Microscope" which included a number of improvements relating to the illumination of objects under examination.

On the Equivalent Focus of Photographic Lenses, and on the Angle of Subjects Included, *Brit. J. Photography*, **9**, 187–188, 205–206, 224–225, 248, 287–288, 1862.

(See von Rohr 1904)

Description of the banknote printing machine at the Bank of Ireland, *Proc. Inst. Mech. Eng.*, 166–178, 1865 (no volume number).

Concerning automatic machine for printing of banknotes by the copper-plate engraving process.

Description of the Great Melbourne Telescope, with R. Robinson. *Phil. Trans. R. Soc.*, **159**, 127–161, 1869. Abstract in 1868, *Proc. R. Soc. London*, **16**, 434–437.

A lengthy and interesting description of the design and construction of the 48-inch telescope and its accessories.

The Great Melbourne Telescope: An Examination of and Reply to the Official Reports from Melbourne Respecting the Instrument, Its Erection at Melbourne, &c., &c., Dublin, 23 March, 1870. 20pp. Printed (by Browne & Nolan, Nassau St.) for Private Circulation.

Replies to various printed reports attributing the telescope's problems to faults on his own part.

Improvement of the Spectroscope, *Proc. R. Soc.,* **22**, 308–310, 1874.

A discussion of a means for reducing the curvature of the spectral lines in a multi-prism spectrograph of high dispersion.

A.2 Patents

1854 No. 1477 'Improvements in Microscopes'. Deals with his improvements to the stage and its illumination. Provisional Specification only; patent not proceeded with.

1857 No. 2574. 'An Improved Photographic Lens'. Sealed 6 April 1858, Dated 8 October 1857. Deals with Grubb's meniscus-shaped 'view lens'.

Appendix B

Publications by H Grubb

Celestial Photography, *British J. Photographic Almanac*, Greenwood, London, 1869, p.78.

Describes the taking of Lunar photographs with the Great Melbourne Telescope and the problems of celestial photography in general.

On a Recently Observed Meteor, *J. R. Dublin Soc.*, **5**, 444–446, 1870. (Read 15 November 1869.)

About a bright meteor observed at several places in Ireland and England.

The Great Melbourne Telescope, *J. R. Dublin Soc.*, **5**, 460–474, 1870. (Read 29 May 1869.)

A popular account of the famous telescope, similar in outline to the more technical one by Robinson and T. Grubb (1868).

Automatic Spectroscope for Dr. Huggins' Sun Observations, *Mon. Not. R. Astron. Soc.*, **31**, 36–38, 1871.

Describes a multi-prism spectrograph whose collimator and observing telescope remain stationary. A complex system of levers and hinges move the prisms so that each line, when centered, is at the angle of minimum deviation.

On some new Points in the Mounting of Astronomical Telescopes, *British Assoc. Rep.*, **42**, 30–34, 1872 (Brighton).

Mainly to do with improved illumination of the field and the position angle circle in a micrometer.

On Clocks for Equatorial Telescopes, *J. R. Dublin Soc.*, **6**, 474–482, 1875. (Read 17 November 1873.)

Discusses governors for telescope drive clocks, especially the Grubbs' own 'frictional governor'. Also mentions Gill's feedback control system, invented while he was at Dun Echt.

Report of the Committee of Science of the Royal Dublin Society

on the Feasibility of Improving the Regularity of Public Clocks in Dublin. With G.J. Stoney and R.S. Ball. (Pamphlet, 13pp, Dublin, 1873.)

A proposal to distribute time by electrical means to eliminate discrepancies amongst the public clocks of Dublin, amounting to several minutes.

On a Method of Photographing the Defects in Optical Glass arising from want of Homogeneity, *Rep. British Assoc.*, 37–38, 1876 (Glasgow).

A sort of Foucault test is applied to a lens formed of the piece of glass to be tested.

On Recent Improvements in Equatorial Telescopes, *Rep. British Assoc.*, 37, 1876 (Glasgow).

A brief note on a talk which evidently was a summary of several other Grubb papers published around this time.

On the Testings (sic) of Large Objectives, *British Assoc. Rep.*, 36–37, 1876 (Glasgow).

A number of lenses were made to be placed between an objective to be tested and the eyepiece. These lenses introduced small quantities of positive or negative spherical or chromatic aberration and from their effects one could judge what had to be done to the tested O.G.

On Great Telescopes of the Future, *Trans. R. Dublin Soc.*, 1, 1–12, 1877. (Read 19 February 1877.)

Compares refractors and reflectors in relation to their suitability for large intruments. Discusses annealing furnaces, advocating the monitoring of temperatures by means of thermopiles to ensure proper control of cooling rate and uniformity of temperature.

On Babbage's System of Mechanical Notation as Applied to Automatic Machinery, *Proc. R. Dublin Soc.*, 1, 111–116, 1878. (Read 17 December 1877.)

On a New Form of Electrical Contact-maker for Astronomical and Other Clocks, *Proc. R. Dublin Soc.*, 2, 115–116, 1878. (Read 18 February 1878.)

Improvements in the Stereoscope, *Proc. R. Dublin Soc.*, 2, 179–190, 1879. (Read 20 January 1879.)

Solar Halo, *Nature*, 20, 628, 1879.

First and Second Reports of the Committee, consisting of Mr. DAVID GILL, Professor G. FORBES, Mr. HOWARD GRUBB and Mr. C.H. GIMINGHAM, appointed to consider the question of Improvements in Astronomical Clocks, *Rep. British Assoc.*, 56–61, 1880 (Swansea).

Concerns an attempt to make a perfect pendulum, driven by absolutely uniform pulses and 'read' without mechanical contact. A light-sensitive relay, reliant on radiation pressure, was to detect the position of the pendulum.

On the Equatorial Telescope, and on the New Observatory of the Queen's College, Cork, *Proc. R. Dublin Soc.*, **2**, 347–369, 1880. (Read 21 Apr 1879.)

An interesting paper which sets forth improvements to telescope clamps, illumination, and slow-motion movements. A mechanical means of controlling the telescope siderial drive from an accurate pendulum is explained. The dome and a roof for a transit instrument, as well as a number of accessories such as a micrometer and a spectroscope are described.

On a New Form of Ghost Micrometer, *Mon. Not. R. Astron. Soc.*, **41**, 59–63, 1880. With C.E. Burton.

A micrometer where the graticule is formed as an image rather than as a set of wires.

On a New Form of Ghost Micrometer for Use with Astronomical Telescopes. *Proc. R. Dublin Soc.*, (with C.E. Burton) **3**, 1–11, 1881–83. (Read 15 November 1880.)

The Equatorial Coudé of the Paris Observatory, *Nature*, **30**, 100–101, 123–124, 1884. (Letters to the Editor.)

On the Adjustment of Equatorial Telescopes, *J. Liverpool Astron. Soc.*, 1884 October. (Reprinted in *J. R. Astron. Soc. Canada*, **51**, 368–373, **52**, 15–26, 1921)

Note on the Effect of Flexure on the Performance of Telescope Objectives, *Proc. R. Dublin Soc.*, **4**, 149–151, 1882–1885. (Read 18 June 1883.)

Explains why the flexure of objective lenses, which are usually very thin in relation to their diameters, does not have such a serious effect on the images as does the flexure of primary mirrors in reflectors.

On a New Form of Equatorial Telescope, *Trans. R. Dublin Soc.*, **3**, 61–68, 1884. (Read 21 January 1884.)

Discusses a type of equatorial coude telescope incorporating a 'dialyte' optical design. In the latter, a single-element crown primary is used with a much smaller flint lens quite some way towards the eyepiece.

Notes on Some Points in the Construction of Turret Clocks, *Proc. R. Dublin Soc.*, **4**, 447–448, 1885. (Read 1 March 1885.)

Describes some details of a turret clock he had constructed for 'Farmley, on the far side of Phoenix Park' (the huge park to the NW of central Dublin).

On the Adjustment of Equatorial Telescopes, *Observatory*, **8**, 9, 43, 1885.

Design for Working the Equatorial and Dome of 'Lick' Observatory, California, by Hydraulic Power, *Rep. British Assoc.*, 553, 1886 (Birmingham).

Very brief summary of a lecture on this subject.

On a new System of Electrical Control for Uniform-motion Clocks, *Rep. British Assoc.*, 552, 1886 (Birmingham).

Note on Some Improvements in Equatorial Telescope Mountings *Proc. R. Dublin Soc.*, **5**, 107–111, 1886. (Read 20 January 1886.)

Describes a backlash-free declination fine-motion drive, a 'position finder', an improvement to his usual right-ascension slow-motion drive and a planetary gear system for accelerating or retarding the sidereal drive.

Telescope Objectives and Mirrors; their Preparation and Testing, *Proc. R. Inst.*, **11**, 413–432, 1887. Also *Nature*, **34**, 85–92, 1886. (Read 2 April 1886)

One of Grubb's most famous papers in which he reveals a great deal about his optical techniques, dealing with the futility of designing lenses in too much detail and explaining his empirical methods of figuring.

Instruments for Stellar Photography, *Rep. British Assoc.*, 580, 1887. 1p.

On the Choice of Instruments for Stellar Photography, *Mon. Not. R. Astron. Soc.*, **47**, 309–322, 1887. (Read 6 April 1887.)

Discusses the best choice of telescope for celestial photography. Points out superiority of reflectors for photographs of objects having low surface brightness (e.g. nebulae), on account of the 'faster' focal ratios they could attain. Describes his first electrical phase-locked loop system for precise sidereal drives, as well as other innovations that helped pave the way for the routine use of photography in astronomy.

Note on a Graphical Method of Solving Certain Optical Problems, *Proc. R. Dublin Soc.*, **5**, 482–483, 1887. (Read 16 February 1887.)

Describes a graphical method which can also form the basis of an analogue computer for solving the simple lens formulae.

New Arrangement of Electrical Control for Driving Clocks of Equatorials, *Mon. Not. R. Astron. Soc.*, **48**, 352–356, 1888. (Read 13 April, 1888). See also *Observatory*, **11**, 211 *et seq.*, which includes the discussion after the presentation of this paper.

Describes Grubb's final and most successful clock-drive system for telescopes, incorporating Gill's idea for detecting irregularity of motion and his own method for effecting the correction. All Grubb's photographic telescopes afterwards were fitted with this system.

On the Latest Improvements in the Clock-Driving Apparatus of Astronomical Telescopes, *Proc. Inst. Mech. Eng.*, 308–316, 1888.

A Photographic Objective, *Nature*, **37**, 439, 1888. (Letter to the Editor.)

Points out that a design described in a letter to *Nature* from Pickering about an objective adaptable to either photographic or visual work had been anticipated by Stokes and himself.

Telescopes for Stellar Photography, *Nature*, **40**, 441–444, 645–649, 1889. (See *J. R. Soc. Arts*, ca April 1888.) (Read 18 April 1888.)

A popular style review of the properties a telescope should have for stellar photography. Much of the article is devoted to Grubb's efforts to secure a really good sidereal drive.

On a Heliostat for the Smithsonian Institution, Washington, *Proc. R. Dublin Soc.*, **6**, 598–602, 1890. (Read 15 January 1890.)

Descriptive of a large heliostat.

The Construction of Telescopic Object-Glasses for the International Photographic Survey of the Heavens, *Trans. R. Dublin Soc.*, **4**, 475–480, 1891. (Read 19 November 1890.)

A bland, non-quantitative, account of the difficulties of designing an objective corrected not only for chromatic and spherical aberration, but which was also coma-free over a large field.

On an Improved Equatorial Telescope, *Proc. R. Dublin Soc.*, **7**, 492–495, 1891–92. (Read 20 January 1892.)

About a 4-inch telescope for the amateur market, with a means of reading the right ascension and declination circles from near the eyepiece.

Revolving Machinery for the Domes of Astronomical Observatories, *Proc. R. Dublin Soc.*, **7**, 484–491, 1892. (Read 22 May 1891.)

Discusses the various ways of mounting a dome in order to ensure ease of movement.

On the Mounting of Large Refracting Telescopes, *Knowledge*, **17**, 98–101, 1894.

A design for a large reflector where the weight of the instrument is supported by a water bath instead of resting on the bearings.

Presidential Address, *British J. Photography*, **41**, 438–439, 1894.

The Development of the Astronomical Telescope, *Proc. R. Inst.*, **14**, 304–320, 1896. (Delivered 25 May 1894.)

A review, mainly of his own ideas and successes.

On a New Form of Equatorial Mounting for Monster Reflecting Telescopes, *Proc. R. Dublin Soc.*, **8**, 252–257, 1894. (Read 21 February 1894.)

Notes on a Paper recently published in the Astrophysical Journal, by Professor E. Hale, of the Yerkes Observatory, Chicago, on 'The Comparative Values of Refracting and Reflecting Telescopes for Astrophysical Observations', *Proc. R. Dublin Soc.*, **8**, 523–526, 1897. (Read 19 May 1897.)

Proposal for the Utilization of the 'Marconi' System of Wireless Telegraphy for the Control of the Public and other Clocks, *Proc. R. Dublin Soc.*, **9**, 46–49, 1899. (Read 18 January 1899.)

Note on the Results that may be expected from the proposed Monster Telescope of the Paris Exhibition of 1900, *Proc. R. Dublin Soc.*, **9**, 55, 1899. (Read 18 January 1899.)

On the correction of Errors in the Distribution of Time Signals, *Proc. R. Dublin Soc.*, **9**, 37–45, 1899. (Read 16 November 1898.)

A new Collimating-Telescope Gun-Sight for Large and Small Ordnance, *Trans. R. Dublin Soc.*, **7**, 321–330, 1901. (Read 20 March 1901.)

Some new Forms of Geodetical Instruments, *Trans. R. Dublin Soc.*, **7**, 385–390, 1902. (Read 18 December 1901.)

A Circumferentor, *Proc. R. Dublin Soc.*, **10**, 143–145, 1903–1905. (Read 17 November 1903.)

Describes an instrument 'for rapidly observing horizontal and vertical angles for military purposes; but it is expected that it will also prove of use for many other purposes ....'

Floating Refracting Telescopes, *Proc. R. Dublin Soc.*, **10**, 133, 1903–1905. (Read 17 November 1903.)

Describes a monster folded refractor with a folded optical train, mounted in a floating sphere.

Registration of Star-Transits by Photography, *Proc. R. Dublin Soc.*, **10**, 138–140, 1904. (Read 17 November 1903.)

A rather casual paper about an instrument which simultaneously records on a photographic plate the transit of a star and the necessary timing information.

A new Form of Dipleidoscope, *Proc. R. Dublin Soc.*, **10**, 141–142, 1904. (Read 17 November 1903.)

Describes a superior type of sundial. 'Even in these days of rapid travelling and telegraphic communication there sometimes exists a difficulty in ascertaining true time in country places'

A new Form of Position-Finder for Adaptation to Ships' Compasses, *Proc. R. Dublin Soc.*, **10**, 146–148, 1904. (Read 17 November 1903.)

Describes a viewer which attaches to a compass and enables magnetic bearings to be taken very easily.

A Modified form of Electrical Control for Driving Clocks, *Proc. R. Dublin Soc.*, **11**, 34–36, 1905. (Read 17 January 1905.)

Describes the motorized slow-motion of the McClean telescope in Cape Town.

A new Form of Right-Ascension slow Motion, for Equatorial Telescopes, illustrated by the Driving-Gear of the Cape Town Equatorial *Proc. R. Dublin Soc.*, **11**, 37–38, 1905. (Read 17 January 1905.)

Describes the way in which a 'quick' slow motion was introduced into his standard slow-motion drive to aid in setting the telescope. The planetary gears, instead of merely being stopped as when guiding-speed movement is required, are driven by means of an electric motor so as to produce a much greater change of speed.

A new Form of Divided Object-Glass Telescope, *Rep. British Assoc.*, 603, 1908 (Dublin).

Describes an improvement to a telescope with divided object glass, where the pupils from each part are kept separate by means of baffles and allowed to form separate images side-by-side.

The New Spectroheliograph for Madrid Observatory, *Rep. British Assoc.*, 603–604, 1908 (Dublin).

A spectroheliograph (instrument for forming a photographic image of the sun in a narrow wavelength range) of special design is described.

The Reflecting Telescope and its Suitability for Physical Research, *Rep. British Assoc.*, 605, 1908 (Dublin).

Points out that his ideas of 31 years before about the advantages of reflectors have now been generally accepted and discusses the problems that still remain.

Clock-driving Mechanism of Equatorials, *Rep. British Assoc.*, 829, 1908. See also *Engineering*, September 18, 1908.

Describes a simplified version of his standard sidereal drive.

Improvements in Equatorial Telescope Mountings, *Proc. R. Dublin Soc.*, **13**, 223–228, 1912. (Read 28 November 1911.)

Describes improvements to the support systems for telescope axes, now consisting of a combination of roller bearings and V's. Only a small proportion of the weight rests on the latter, which are used to define the axis of motion rather than to give support. Also a new from of right ascension circle.

B.1 Anonymous Publications Probably Inspired by Grubb

The Great Vienna Telescope, *Nature*, **24**, 11–14, 1881.
Reflecting Telescope for Simeis Observatory, Crimea, *Nature*, **113**, 1924.
See also *J. Sci. Instrum.*, **2**, 1, 1924.

B.2 Articles in 'Engineering'

Grubb's Equatorial Telescope, *Engineering*, **28**, 278, 1879.
The Vienna Equatorial, *Engineering*, **29**, 114–116, 1880.
Vienna Equatorial, - No. II. *Engineering*, **29**, 199–202, 1880.
Vienna Equatorial, - No. III. *Engineering*, **29**, 309–311, 1880.

Vienna Telescope, - No. IV. *Engineering*, **29**, 391, 1880.
The Vienna Telescope, - No. V. *Engineering*, **29**, 409, 1880.
The Vienna Telescope, - No. VI. *Engineering*, **29**, 467–469, 1880.
The Vienna Telescope, - No. VII. *Engineering*, **30**, 314–315, 1880.
The Vienna Telescope, - No. VIII. *Engineering*, **30**, 424–428 1880.

This series of articles describes in great detail the Vienna telescope, at the time the World's largest refractor, and its dome, also constructed by Grubb.

Astronomical Telescopes at the Manchester Exhibition, *Engineering*, **44**, 626, 630–632, 1887.

Deals with Twin Equatorial similar to those supplied to Huggins and Roberts and includes a description of Grubb's first electrical sidereal drive correcting system.

Astronomical Telescopes at the Manchester Exhibition, *Engineering*, **44**, 667–668, 1887.

Deals with Clampless Equatorial, Micrometer, Star finder, Eyepiece for Binocular Telescopes.

Telescopes for Stellar Photography, *Engineering*, **45**, 402, 1888. (Preliminary design for *Carte du Ciel* telescopes)

Lists the requirements to be met by telescopes for the international Carte du Ciel project, describes Grubb's final electrically-controlled sidereal drive scheme and gives a preliminary design for his standard 'Astrographic' instrument.

Sir Howard Grubb's Works, Dublin, *Engineering*, **46**, 571–573, 1888.

Some historical about the works and machinery. Partly based on Royal Institution lecture of 1886.

Photographic Equatorial Telescope, *Engineering*, **50**, 720–722, 1890. (Final design, Carte du Ciel telescopes.)

Gives a description of the 'Astrographic' telescope as finally evolved by Grubb.

Equatorial Twin Telescope at the Radcliffe Observatory, Oxford, *Engineering*, **82**, 819–822, 1906.

Describes the complete installation, which includes a rising floor.

B.3   Patent Applications

Note: The Patent Office, London, has provided a list of abbreviated titles of Grubb patents. Most of these I have seen, but those without quotation marks I have not.

'Photographic Lenses', No 1968, 1871
'Stereoscopes', No 164, 1879
Taking and Projecting Photographs, No 4906, 1897

Acetylene and Gas, No 8254, 1897

'Improvements in Apparatus for the Generation of Acetylene Gas', No 28,264, 1897

'Improvements in Sighting Devices for Guns', No 12,108, 1900

Sighting Guns, No 20,813, 1900

'Improvements in Apparatus for Facilitating the Sighting of Distant Objects from Submarine Boats, Barbettes, and other Protected Positions', No. 10373, 1901

'Improvements in Sighting Devices for Guns', No 22,127, 1900

'Improvements in or relating to Geodetical Instruments', No 5806, 1901

'Improvements in Geodetical Instruuments', No 8735, 1901

'Improvements in Sight Mountings for Guns', No 9738, 1901

Range Finders, No 14,269, 1901

Photographic Pictures, No 20,477, 1901

'Improvements in or relating to Sight Mountings and Sighting Devices for Guns', No 5218, 1902

Range Finders, No28,179, 1902

'Improvements in and Means for Signaling and Indicating Position of Objects', No 21,856, 1903

'Improvements in Range Finders', No 25,682, 1903

Sighting Objects, No 13,438, 1909

'Improvements in Telescopic Apparatus', No 4005, 1911. (Convertible telescope/periscope)

'Improvements in or relating to Optical Instruments, more particularly for Gun Sighting Purposes', No 25,476, 1912. (Uses cemented components to reduce refractive losses)

'Improvements in or relatin to Optical Instruments specially suitable for use as Gun Sighting Telescopes', No 1511, 1913, withh C. Beck and H.C. Beck. (Periscope with wide-angle facility)

'Improvements in, and in Means for, Communicating Between Positions Alterable in Relation One to Another', No 3766, 1913, with Hon. Stuart Bouverie (Vickers Co). (Signalling to fast-moving aeroplanes etc)

Optical Eyepieces, No 16996, 1913

'Improvements in Periscopes', No 22,319, 1914, with Conrad Beck. (Variable-magnification periscope)

Range Finders, No 3778, 1915

Range Finders, No 14,966, 1915

'Improvements in or relating to Sighting Devices', No 15,552, 1915

'Means for Enabling an Outlook to be Obtained with Safety, suitable for use in Warfare', No 103,178, 1916. (Simple prismatic periscope)

'Improvements in or relating to Optical Observing Means, with special reference to Range Finding', No 124,497, 1916. (Long-distance rangefinding)

'Improvements in or relating to Vehicle Headlights and the like', No 157,478, 1919. (Anti-glare system)

'Improvements in or relating to Telescopes and the like', No 161,214, Appl. 1919

'Improvements in or relating to Cinematograph Apparatus, No 178,474, 1922. (Uses a projector where the film moves continuously, together with a rotating multi-facetted mirror, to cause images to dissolve into one another continuously, so avoiding the flickering associated with conventional projectors)

B.4   Catalogues

'Descriptive Catalogue of Astronomical Instruments, &c., Manufactured by Mr. Howard Grubb', Astronomical Works, Rathmines, Dublin, 1877.

'An Illustrated Catalogue of Astronomical Instruments, Observatories, &c., Manufactured by Howard Grubb', Astronomical Instrument Works, Rathmines, Dublin. 1885.

'An Illustrated Catalogue of Astronomical Instruments, Observatories, Etc. Manufactured by Sir Howard Grubb, F.R.S., F.R.A.S., Etc. Astronomical Instrument Works: Rathmines, Dublin. 1899'.

Apart from pictures of the various instruments available, this catalogue includes photographs of the inside of the factory, taken from the Fitzgerald (1896) article in *Strand Magazine*.

'An Illustrated Catalogue of Astronomical Instruments, Observatories, &c., Manufactured by Sir Howard Grubb, F.R.S., F.R.A.S., Etc.,' Astronomical Instrument Works, Rathmines, Dublin. 1903.

Catalogues were also published in 1888 and 1907 (Bennett and Morrison-Low, 1989).

Appendix C

List of Grubb Telescopes Etc

(This list is intended to be as comprehensive as possible for the Grubbs' larger telescopes. The reference lists are representative rather than complete.)

48-in reflector, Melbourne, Australia, 1869
Reference
Robinson T R and Grubb T 1869 *Phil. Trans. R. Soc.* **159** 127

41-in refractor, Nicholaieff (Pulkovo), Russia
Mechanical, but not optical, parts completed under Grubb–Parsons. Never installed. Included dome and rising floor.
References
Warner B 1975 *Sky & Telescope* **50** 370
1926 *Grubb–Parsons Publs* Nos. 1 & 4

40-in reflector, Simeis, Crimea, 1925
With 32-ft dome. Finishing touches possibly by Grubb–Parsons.
References
1924 *J. Sci. Instrum.* **2** 1
1924 *Nature* **113** 550
Shajn G 1926 *Bull. Obs. Central de Russie à Poulkovo* **10** 450

36-in refractor, Lick, USA (Designs only)
Reference
1886 *The Engineer* **42** 21

36-in reflector, Lick, USA (Crossley). (Refiguring of mirror only)
This was the mirror used from 1896 on. 17.5 ft f.l.
References
1899 *Observatory* **22** 135

1900 *Observatory* **23** 355
Campbell W W 1902 *Astrophys. J.* **16** 121
1926 *Grubb–Parsons Publ. No. 1*
Stone R P S 1979 *Sky & Telescope* **58** 307

30-in reflector/26-in refractor, Greenwich, England, 1897 (Thompson)

Photograph in album 'Miscellaneous Telescopes', Tyne & Wear Archives—with 30-inch grating. Mirror by Common. Refractor of 22.5 ft f.l.
Reference
1897 *Observatory* **20** 439

28-in refractor, Greenwich, England, 1893

On old mounting designed by Airy. Lens convertible for photography.
Reference
1893 *Observatory* **16** 401

27-in refractor, Vienna, Austria, 1878

For a time, world's largest refractor. With 45-ft dome and 3 others of 27 ft.
Reference
1880 *Engineering* **29** 114 (Start of a series)

26.5-in refractor, Johannesburg, South Africa, 1925 (Union, now Republic, Observatory)

References
Robbins F 1923 *Nature* **112** 104
Hers J 1987 *Mon. Not. Astron. Soc. Sthn. Africa* **46** 75

24-in reflector, Daramona, Ireland, 1881

10.5 ft f.l. Observatory of W.E. Wilson. Mounted originally on the stand of Wilson's 12-in reflector. New mount purchased 1892. In use after 1929 at Mill Hill Observatory (University College, London). Now in Merseyside County Museum, Liverpool (1996).
References
McNally D and Hoskin M 1988 *J. Hist. Astron.* **19** 146
Astronomical and Physical Researches Made at Mr Wilson's Observatory, Daramona, Westmeath. Privately printed, 1900.

24-in photographic refractor/18-in visual refractor, Royal Observatory, Cape, South Africa, 1900

22.5 ft f.l.
Reference
Gill D 1913 *A History and Description of the Royal Observatory, Cape of Good Hope* London, H.M.S.O.

24-in Newtonian reflector, Royal Observatory, Edinburgh, Scotland, 1872

Originally at Calton Hill Observatory. Later moved to Blackford Hill.
References
1898 *Publ. Astron. Soc. Pacific.* **10** 69 1898. (incl. illustr.)
Bruck, H.A. & Bruck, M.T 1988. *The Peripatetic Astronomer—the Life of Charles Piazzi Smyth* Hilger.

24-in photographic refractor/18-in visual refractor Radcliffe Observatory, Oxford, England, 1902
With 32-ft dome and rising floor.
Reference
1906 *Engineering* **82** 819

24-in refractor, Santiago, Chile, (Chilean National Astron. Obsy.) 1925
Ordered 1909. With 45-ft dome and rising floor. Dome finished ca. 1913 (Grubb-Innes correspondence). Illustrated under construction in *Grubb–Parsons Publ. No. 4* (1926). Moved from Santiago to Cerro Calan, 1956.
References
Rutllant F 1963 *Inf. Bull. S. Hem.* No. 4
Rutllant F 1957 *Sky and Telescope* **16** 474
1926 *Grubb–Parsons Publ. No. 4* p 29

20-in reflector (8.2 ft focal length)/7-in refractor, Roberts, Magull, England
Moved to Crowborough 1885. Moved to Norwich 1930.
References
1930 *Observatory* **53** 311
Hollis H P 1914 *Observatory* **27** 245

20-in reflector, Glasgow, Scotland, ca 1851
Perhaps only the speculum-metal mirror was made by Thomas Grubb, although Howard Grubb in his correspondence showed that he believed the whole instrument to be due to his father. Still in use, 1912.
References
1912 *Mon. Not. R. Astron. Soc.* **72** 278

20-in reflector, Poona, India, ca. 1887
F/33.5 Cassegrain. Started life as a 16.5-in Newtonian (q.v.). Became a Cassegrain in 1894. In 1896 became a 20-inch with mirror by A.A. Common. Moved to Kodaikanal 1912 but installed only in 1951. Now in Leh, North India (1989).
References
Hollis H P 1914 *Observatory* **27** 245
Kochar R K 1990 *Indian Inst. Ap. Newsletter* **5** 6
Salwi D M 1988 *J. British Astron. Assoc.* **98** 189
1888 *Observatory* **11** 438

19-in Heliostat, Smithsonian Astrophysical Observatory, Washington, DC, USA

The governor of the clock was soon replaced by one due to Warner & Swasey.
References
Grubb H 1890 *Proc. R. Dublin Soc.* **6** 598
Langley S P and Abbot C G 1900 *Ann. Astrophys. Obs. Smithsonian Inst.* **1** 45

18-in reflector/15-in refractor Tulse Hill (Huggins's Observatory) England, 1870

Property of Royal Society, loaned to Huggins. Originally the telescopes were interchangeable; they were placed on the same mount in 1882. With drum-type roof. Given by Royal Society to Cambridge University Observatory in 1909. In Cambridge until 1954
References
King H C 1955 *The History of the Telescope* (High Wycombe: Charles Griffin & Co)
Stratton F J M 1949 *Ann. Sol. Phys. Obsy Cambridge* vol 1

17-in reflector/8-in refractor, Manchester Exhibition, ca 1887

Possibly made up only for the exhibition. Reflector could be that of the 16.5-inch Poona telescope mentioned below.
Reference
1887 *Engineering* **44** 630

16.5-in reflector/4-in refractor, Poona College of Sci. Observatory, India

See 20-in reflector, Poona.
Reference
1888 *Observatory* **11** 438

16-in refractor, Madrid, Spain, 1920

With spectrograph and bifilar micrometer. Illustrated in album *Miscellaneous Telescopes* Tyne & Wear Archives, with a mfrs. plate marked 1912.

16-in twin photographic refractor, Heidelberg, Germany

Lenses by Brashear.
Reference
1900 *Vierteljahrsschrift der Astron. Gesell.* **35** 121

15.1-in refractor, Dun Echt, Scotland, 1873

Later at Royal Observatory Edinburgh.
Reference
1898 *Publ. Astron. Soc. Pacific* **10** 69 (incl. illustr.)

15-in refractor, Stonyhurst Coll. Obsy England

Memorial to Father Perry. Erected 6 Nov 1894.

References
1894 *Observatory* **17** 116

15-in reflector, Dunsink, Ireland (Roberts)

Originally a With mirror on a mounting by Cooke (probably the original mount of Roberts's 7-in Cooke refractor which became the guide telescope of his 20-in photographic reflector), this telescope was renovated by Grubb for presentation to Trinity College Dublin (Dunsink Observatory). Later it was remounted by Grubb. Mounting later carried a 28-inch reflector.

Reference

Wayman P A 1987 *Dunsink Observatory 1785–1985* (Dublin Inst. Adv. Stud. & R. Dublin Soc.)

15-in refractor, Nizamiah Observatory, Hyderabad, India, 1903

Donated by Nawab Zafer Jung to the Nizamiah Observatory. Now part of Osmania University. Photograph in album *Miscellaneous Telescopes* Tyne & Wear Archives, Grubb–Parsons collection.

Reference

Nizamiah Observatory, Platinum Jubilee Souvenir 1908-1983.

15-in refractor, Tacubaya, Mexico, 1880

15 ft f.l. With 24-ft dome.

Reference

Puga G B Y 1893 *Descripcion del Observatorio Astronomico N. de Tacubaya, Mexico* Secretaria de Fomento

15-in refractor, Mississippi, USA, 1893

15 ft f.l. According to Holden, with a 9-inch photographic refractor.

Reference

Holden E S 1892 *Publ. Astron. Soc. Pacific* **4** 155

15-in refractor, Dunn's Observatory, Maidenhead, England

There was a f/12 visual refractor. of 1893 and a photographic one of 1894. The latter telescope is the 'portrait lens' of 15 inches aperture and 89 inches focal length referred to in *Observatory* (1897). Grubb also supplied a hand-operated rising floor. Later at Wilfrid Hall's observatory in Hepple Woodside, Northumberland. A photograph exists in the album 'Miscellaneous Telescopes', Tyne & Wear Archives (Grubb–Parsons collection). Now known as the Wilfrid Hall telescope and located at the Alston Observatory of the University of Central Lancashire. Owned by the Royal Astronomical Society.

References

1897 *Observatory* **20** 155

1926 *Grubb–Parsons Publ. No. 1* p 45

Mentioned in Grubb-Gill correspondence.

Further information supplied by Prof G. Brommage, Univ. Central Lancs.

15-in reflector, Armagh, N. Ireland, 1835

Reflector barrel and primary missing. The remains constitute the oldest surviving Grubb telescope parts.

References

Moore P 1967 *Armagh Observatory 1790-1967* (Armagh Observatory)

McFarland J 1990 *Vistas in Astronomy* **33** 149 (Illustr.)

15-in Coelostat Kobe Marine Observatory, Japan

Reference

1926 *Grubb–Parsons Publ. No. 4* p 24 (Illustr).

13.3-in refractor, Markree, Ireland, 1834

Lens by Cauchoix, Paris. 25.5 ft f.l. For a time, the world's largest refractor.

Reference

Doberck W 1884 *Observatory* **7** 283, 329

13-inch reflector, Dun Echt, Scotland, 1874

Parts now in Royal Museum of Scotland.

Reference

Burnett J & Morrison-Low A 1990 *Vulgar and Mechanick* (R. Dublin Soc.)

13-in photographic refractor (Astrographic) Tacubaya, Mexico 1889

With 18-ft dome. Mounting used for 'twin Einstein cameras' during solar eclipse of March 2, 1970.

References

1888 *Engineering* **46** 571

1970 *Sky & Telescope* **39** 280

13-in photographic refractor, (Astrographic) Greenwich, England, 1890

Later moved to Herstmonceux. Later still, re-mounted by Grubb Parsons.

13-in photographic refractor, (Astrographic) Melbourne, Australia, 1890

13-in photographic refractor, (Astrographic) Sydney, Australia, 1890

Lens only.

Reference

1892 *Description of the Star Camera, at the Sydney Observatory* (Sydney Observatory)

13-in photographic refractor, (Astrographic) Royal Obsy, Cape, South Africa, 1891

With dome. No longer possesses original drive clock.

Reference

Gill D 1913 *A History and Description of the Royal Observatory, Cape of Good Hope* London, H.M.S.O.

13-in photographic refractor, (Astrographic) Perth, Australia, 1897

13-in refractor, Cork, Ireland
With dome. Added to 8-inch refractor. Mentioned in *Engineering* in 1888 as being under construction.
Reference
1888 *Engineering* **46** 573

12.5-in refr, (siderostatic coudé) Cambridge, England, (Sheepshanks Telescope) 1898
Lens was a triple apochromat by Cooke, later replaced by a photographic doublet. Used by H.N. Russell to determine some of the stellar parallaxes included in his first Colour-Magnitude diagram.
References
Ball Sir R 1899 *Observatory* **59** 152
Stratton F J M 1949 *Ann. Sol. Phys. Obsy Cambridge* vol 1
Dewhirst D W 1982 *J. Hist. Astron.* **13** 119

12.5-in refractor, Mecca, 1898
Photograph in album *Miscellaneous Telescopes* Grubb–Parsons Collection, Tyne & Wear Archives.
Reference
Grubb Catalogue (1899).

12.2-in refractor, Oxford, England, 1875
14.7 ft f.l.
Reference
1874 *Astron. Reg.* **12** 4

12-in reflector Melbourne, 1870.
Parts and a mount for a 12-inch speculum-metal reflector were sent to Melbourne so that local astronomers could practice polishing techniques for the 48-in reflector (see chap. 2). History uncertain, but at least mirror may still exist (Orchiston, 1990, private communication).

12-in refractor, Dresden, Germany, (von Englehardt's Observatory) 1879
Replaced an 8-in refractor. by Grubb (q.v.). Micrometer by Grubb had unsatisfactory lighting and was replaced in 1882 by a Repsold one. Given in 1897 to Imperial Russian Observatory, Kasan. Mentioned in Astronomcal Almanac for 1982 as being at Kazan R.S.F.S.R. The illustrations in von Englehart (1886) show a well-appointed private observatory of the time.
References
1891 *Observatory* **14** 353
1897 *Observatory* **20** 429
von Englehardt 1886 *Observations Astronomiques* (Dresden: G Baensch)

12-in reflector, Wilson, Daramona, Ireland, 1871
Used for lunar photography and 'experiments on solar radiation with thermo piles'. Mount used 1881–1892 for a 24-inch reflector by Grubb.
Reference
Astronomical and Physical Researches Made at Mr Wilson's Observatory, Daramona, Westmeath. Privately printed, 1900.

12-in photographic refractor/10.5-in visual refractor McLean, Tunbridge Wells, England, 1895
f.l. 11.25 ft. Photograph in album *Miscellaneous Telescopes* Grubb–Parsons Collection, Tyne & Wear Archives. Later (1913) presented to Norman Lockyer Observatory.
References
1894 *Observatory* **17** 344
1895 *Observatory* **18** 320
Hutchings A R 1982 *J. British Astron. Assoc.* **93** 25 (history)

12-in refractor, Dunsink, Ireland, 1868
Lens by Cauchoix. 19 ft f.l. The lens was that of the telescope made by Troughton and destroyed by South. Dome designed by Thomas Grubb. Altered by Howard Grubb, 1909.
Reference
Wayman P A 1987 *Dunsink Observatory 1785-1985* (Dublin Inst. Adv. Stud. & R. Dublin Soc.)

12-in lens Hyderabad, India, ca 1913
3.4m focal length. Guide telescope of astrograph at Nizamiah Observatory, Hyderabad. Dome and photo-telescope by Cooke.
Reference
Srinivasan S R 1986 *J. British Astron. Assoc.* **96** 339

12-in reflector with 8-in refractor, Manchester Technical School, England, 1899
Probably that illustrated on p.17 of 1903 Grubb Catalogue. (Newtonian reflector). Photograph in album *Miscellaneous Telescopes* Grubb–Parsons Collection, Tyne & Wear Archives.

11-in polar siderostat, Kodaikanal, India, 1897
With 6-in lens, 40′ f.l.
Reference
Report on the Madras Observatory for the Year 1897-98

10-in refractor, Armagh, N. Ireland, 1885 (Robinson Memorial)
Included dome—similar to Natal Observatory. Micrometer presented by Grubb as his contribution. Extant (1996).
Reference

Moore P 1967 *Armagh Observatory 1790-1967* (Armagh Observatory)
McFarland J 1990 *Vistas in Astronomy* **33** 149 (Illustr.)

10-inch refractor, Coats Observatory, Paisley, Scotland, 1897
With 10-ft dome.
References
Grubb Catalogs 1899, 1903.

9-in reflector, T Grubb's private observatory, Dublin, Ireland, 1830-1840
Reference
FitzGerald W G 1896 *Strand Magazine* **12** 369

9-inch refractor, Ballarat, Australia, (Col. Oddie), 1888
Photograph in album *Miscellaneous Telescopes* Grubb–Parsons Collection, Tyne & Wear Archives. Given on death of Oddie to what is now Mt. Stromlo Obsy.
Reference
Allen C W 1978 *Records of Austr. Acad. Sci.* **4** 27
Orchiston W 1989.*Search* **20** 198

9-in refractor Transvaal, South Africa, (later Union, later still Republic) Observatory 1907
On Grubb mount of 1879 [originally for a Repsold heliometer] donated by Sir David Gill. Lens re-worked, 1908.
References
Hers J 1987 *Mon. Not. Astron. Soc. Sthn. Africa* **46** 39
Innes R T A 1911 *Observatory* **71** 315

9-in photographic refractor, Royal Obsy Cape, South Africa, (Nasmyth lens), ca 1886
Mounted on the Grubb stand of 1879 owned by Gill and now carrying a 9-inch refractor at Republic Observatory. The lens still exists at SAAO (1996).
Reference
Glass I S 1989 *Mon. Not. Astron. Soc. Sthn. Africa* **48** 29

9-in photographic refractor, Sir H Thompson's Observatory, Hampton, England, ca 1888
Reference
1888 *Engineering* **46** 571

9-in refractor, 'Escobar', 1909
Photograph in *Miscellaneous Telescopes* Grubb–Parsons Collection, Tyne & Wear Archives.

9-in refractor, Castro-Urdiales, Spain (de Ocharan)
Reference

1926 *Grubb–Parsons Publ. No. 1* p 18 (Illustr.)

8-in photographic refractor with 6-in photographic doublet and 6-inch visual refractor, Madrid, Spain, 1891

Photograph in album *Miscellaneous Telescopes* Grubb–Parsons Collection, Tyne & Wear Archives.
References
Grubb Catalogue, 1903 p 5 (Photograph)
1926 *Grubb–Parsons Publ. No. 4* p 21

8-in refractor, Crawford Obsy, Cork, Ireland, ca 1878

Awarded Gold Medal at Paris Exhibition of 1878. Illustrated in most of Grubb's Catalogues as 'Standard Equatorial'. With 15-ft dome and spectroscope.
References
Grubb H 1880 *Proc. R. Dublin Soc.* **2** 347
1899 *Engineering* **28** 277

8-in refractor Castlemaine, Victoria, Australia (W Bone's Observatory), 1882

Later (1886) purchased by Tebbutt, Windsor, NSW, from Bone's estate.
References
1888 *Observatory* **11** 162
Orchiston W 1982 *Southern Stars* **29** 215; 1987, **32** 11
1985 *Sky & Telescope* **69** 160

8-in lens on Cooke 12-in Siderostat, Poona, India

Reference
1895 *Observatory* **18** 339

8-in refractor, Durban, South Africa, 1882

With dome and transit room. Observatory closed, 1913.
References
1913 *Mon. Not. R. Astron. Soc.* **73** 263 (closure)
History of Natal Obsy. (unpublished ms by M A Gray)

8-in refractor, Yale, New Haven, Ct USA, 1882

With two 15-ft domes.
References
1884 *Astron. Reg.* **22** 235
1881–1882 *Ann. Rep. Yale Coll. Obsy.*

8-in visual refractor, Madrid, Spain

References
1982 *Astron. Almanac*
Grubb Catalogue 1903 p 5 Photograph

8-in refractor Dresden, Germany, 1877 (von Englehardt)
Later exchanged for 12-in model (q.v.). 3.3 m f.l. Located at original observatory, Leibnitz Str 2.

8-in refractor, Caracas, Venezuela, ca 1888.
With 15-ft dome
Reference
1888 *Engineering* **46** 571

8-inch refractor, Louvain, Belgium, (private observatory of Terby), 1885
Mentioned in letter to Gill, 13 September, 1885

8-in refractor, São Paulo, Brazil, (Instituto Astronomico e Geofisico de São Paulo)
Reference
1967 *Inf. Bull. S. Hem.* No. 11

8-in coelostat (Royal Irish Academy), 1900
Was made for a joint eclipse expedition of the Royal Dublin Society and the Royal Irish Academy to Spain in 1900. Later, in 1919, it was used on the famous eclipse expedition to Sobral, Brazil, when Dyson, Eddington and Davidson verified Einstein's theory of general relativity by measuring the deflection of starlight due to the gravitational field of the sun.
References
1904 *Sci. Trans. R. Dublin Soc.* (2nd Ser.) **8** 65
Royal Dublin Society Bi-Centenary Celebrations 1931 Official Handbook.
Dyson F W *et al* 1920 *Phil. Trans. R. Soc.* **220** 291

8-in Coelostat, Ebro, Spain, ca 1900
Reference
Puig P I 1928 *El Observatorio del Ebro*

8-in Solar Telescope (Coelostat) Pulkovo, Russia, 1923
Ordered before WW I. Designed in collaboration with Dr Belopolsky. With a complete 7-metre solar spectrograph.
References
1924 *Engineering* July 18
Grubb–Parsons Publication No. 2

7.25-in refractor, Armagh, N Ireland, 1861
48 in f.l. Attached to Jones mural circle. An unusual refractor with two cemented doublets.
References
Robinson T R and Dreyer J L E 1886 *Second Armagh Catalogue ....* (Dublin: Thom)
McFarland J 1990 *Vistas in Astronomy* **33** 149 (Illustr.)

7.5-in refractor, Potsdam, Germany, 1877
References
1877 *Astron. Reg.* **15** 189
1882 *Astron. Reg.* **20** 209

7-in Woolwich, England, Royal Artillery Institute, 1872

> 'I came over here [London] to erect an Equatorial for the Artillery
> Institute at Woolwich but have come to a complete standstill the
> pier they have built being about 25°!!! out of the meridian & the
> stones cracked so badly that it would be absolutely dangerous to
> mount the instrument on them.' (H Grubb to G G Stokes, 21 Aug
> 1872. G482, Stokes Correspondence, Cambridge Univ. Lib.)

Reference
1872 *Report British Assoc.* p 30

7-in 'Panjab' 1913
Photograph in album *Miscellaneous Telescopes* Grubb–Parsons Collection,
Tyne & Wear Archives.

6.7-in Greenwich, England (Sheepshanks Refr) 1838
Objective of 8′ 2″ f.l. by Cauchoix, Paris. Currently (1990) in storage.
(Howse, private comm.) Reference
Airy G B 1847 *Greenwich Observations, 1845*

6.5-inch Sofia, Bulgaria. Before 1899
Photograph in album *Miscellaneous Telescopes* Grubb–Parsons Collection,
Tyne & Wear Archives.
Reference
Grubb Catalogue, 1899

6-in refractor, West Point, New York, USA, 1840
8-ft f.l. Objective by Lerebours, Paris
References
Bartlett W H C 1846 *Trans. Am. Phil. Soc.* new ser. **9** 191
André C. & Angot, A *L'Astronomie Practique et Les Observatoires en Europe
et en Amerique* .... Paris, Gauthier-Villars, 1877.

6-in reflector, Dublin, Ireland, 1836 or before
Primary of 3-ft f.l. Cassegrain, Gregorian and Newtonian. Referred to in a
discussion on the suitability of reflectors for micrometrical work.
Reference
Grubb T 1836 *Mon. Not. R. Astron. Soc.* **3** 177

6-in refractor, Port Macquarie, Australia (W.J. Macdonnell), 1870s or 1880s

Reference
1911 *Observatory* **71** 271
Orchiston W 1990, Private communication

6-in refractor, Tacubaya, 1882
Transit of Venus type.
Reference
Puga G B Y 1893 *Descripcion del Observatorio Astronomico N. de Tacubaya*
Mexico, Secretaria de Fomento

6-in refractor, Brisbane, F D G Stanley, before 1895
Reference
Orchiston W 1990 Private communication

6-in refractor, Science Museum, London, England, 1884
Purchased 1985. (J Darius, private communication)

6-in New Zealand, 1885
Referred to in Gill-Grubb correspondence. Probably Wellington instrument
mentioned in Grubb's catalogues.

6-in refractor San Fernando (near Cadiz), Spain
Probably before 1885.
Reference
1907 *Anales del Instituto y Observatorio de Marina de San Fernando*

**6-in refractor, Denver, Colorado, USA, Chamberlain Observatory
1894(?)**
(Mounting only, lens by Brashear). Dismantled 1944.
Reference
Bartlett T J 1950 *Sky & Telescope* **9** 51

**6-in refractor, Eastbourne, England, (Northfield Grange Observa-
tory, Mr Chambers)**
7′ 6″ f.l.
Reference
Chambers G F 1890 *Handbook of Astronomy* 4th edn, vol 2, Plate X, Oxford

6-in refractor, Barcelona, Spain
With dome (illustrated in 1926 *Grubb–Parsons Publ. No. 4*)
Reference
1919 *Boletin del Observatorio Fabra I Section Astronomica, No. 1*

6-in refractor, Cartuja, Spain, 1887
2.2 m f.l.
Appears to antedate the observatory. Possibly obtained second-hand.
References

Observatorio de Cartuja 1902-1927, Recuerdo del XXV Aniversario SAAO
Pamphlet Collection **104** No. 19

6-in refractor, Valencia, Spain, 1909 (Tyne & Wear Archives)

6-in visual refractor, Castro-Urdiales, Spain (de Ocharan)
With two photographic telescopes attached. $4\frac{3}{4}''$ camera, 24" focus. $4\frac{3}{4}''$
camera, 39" focus. Photograph in album 'Miscellaneous Telescopes' in Tyne
& Wear Archives, marked 1912.
References
1926 *Grubb–Parsons Publ. No. 1* p 2, p 18

6-in Constantinople [Istanbul], Turkey, 1884
Mentioned in a letter from Grubb to Gill 17 December, 1884. With dome.
Reference
Grubb Catalogue, 1885 p 21

6-in refractor, Royal Obsy, Cape, South Africa, 1882
Originally a 'Transit of Venus' telescope. Mounting replaced in 1886 by an-
other designed for an 8-in telescope. Lens broken during 1970s and replaced.
Drive electrified, 1980s. Clockwork in SAAO museum.

6-in refractor, 'Sykes' 1924
Photograph in album *Miscellaneous Telescopes* Grubb–Parsons Collection,
Tyne & Wear Archives.

**ca 6-in refractor, Springfield Observatory, Gomersal, England (Mr
Cooke)**
Before 1885. With 15-ft dome.
Reference
Grubb Catalogue, 1885

6-in Tokio Nautical College. Before 1903.

Reference
Tyne & Wear Archives

**5.6-in heliometers (refractors) Royal Observatory, Brussels, Bel-
gium**
Special heliometers for transit of Venus observations. Lens by Cauchoix.
Reference
Houzeau J C 1884 *Ann. Obs. R. de Bruxelles* NS 5

5.5-in Wellington, NZ
Pre-1890; first recorded owner T King; Still at Thomas King Observatory,
Wellington, 1996. Same instrument as 6-in, New Zealand, 1885?
Reference

Orchiston W 1990 Private communication

5.25-in refractor (J M Offord) 1885
Reference
1885 *Observatory* **8** 78

5-in binoculars, (D W Edgecombe, Newington, CT) before 1895
Reference
1895 *Popular Astronomy* **2** 370

5-in refractor, University of Northern Iowa
Now owned by J W Briggs, Chicago.

5-in refractor, Royal College of Science, England, ca 1911
Equipped with prism. Lens by Zeiss.
Reference
1911 *Mon. Not. R. Astron. Soc.* **71** 303

5-in portrait lens, Kodaikanal, India, ca 1898
36″ focal length. Mounted on Lerebours equatorial of 1850.
Reference
Kodaikanal and Madras Obsy. Report for 1903

5-in 'Astrographic', Coimbra Observatory, Portugal
Illustrated in album *Miscellaneous Telescopes* Grubb–Parsons Collection, Tyne & Wear Archives, as 6-inch photographic equatorial with 6-inch prism.
Reference
1926 *Grubb–Parsons Publ. No. 4* p 21

5-in Transit Circle, Cork, Ireland, (Crawford Observatory) ca 1880
With unusual roof shutter and glass circles.
Reference
1880 *Proc. R. Dublin Soc.* **2** 347

5-in refractor, Sydney, pre-1899
Earliest recorded owner C W Darley. At Physics Building, Univ. of Sydney.
Reference
Orchiston W 1990, Private Communication

5-in refractor, Mr and Mrs A Bourke, Ballina
Mounted on offset alt-azimuth head with tripod.
Reference
Illustrated in Mollan C *Mind & Hand, Instruments of Science 1685–1932*
Catalog of an exhibition held at Trinity College Dublin in 1995.

4.5-in photographic refractor, Liverpool Astron. Soc., England
Reference
Espin T E 1884 *Observatory* **7** 247

4-in siderostatic tel., Cork, Ireland, (Crawford Observatory), ca 1879.
References
1880 *Proc. R. Dublin Soc.* **2** 347
1883 *Trans. R. Dublin Soc.* **3** 61

4-in siderostatic telescope. Coats Observatory, Paisley, Scotland
Reference
Grubb Catalogue 1899

4-in refractor
Reference
Gould J A 1976 *J. British Astron. Assoc.* **87** 63

4-in lens, 19-ft f.l.
Used with 8-in coelostat (q.v.) of Royal Irish Academy in the famous 1919 eclipse expedition.

4-in refractor, San Fernando, Spain
Reference
1907 *Anales del Instituto y Observatorio de Marina de San Fernando*

4-in refractor, Sydney; pre-1913
Earliest recorded owner J Nangle.
Reference
Orchiston W 1990, Private communication

3-in speculum, 6-ft f.l.
Used in connection with an attempt to photograph the solar corona from a mountain site in Switzerland.
References
Woods C R 1884 *Observatory* **7** 376

3-in refractor, Kilgrew, Kimberley, South Africa, ca 1881
Ordered by Gill in a letter to Grubb, 12 July 1881.

3-in (?) Coronagraph, Royal Obsy Cape, South Africa, 1885
Mentioned in Gill-Grubb correspondence. With a wooden tube and a speculum mirror. Size uncertain. C R Woods was involved in the design. (See 3-in speculum, above)

C.1   Untraced and Miscellaneous, Mentioned in Catalogues

Transvaal. Untraced

Sicily

Collurania-Teramo has a Grubb filar micrometer and some sort of camera which attached to a Cooke telescope.

Havana 6–10 in. Untraced

Coelostat Spanish Govt
Illustrated in Grubb Catalogue, 1903. Size not mentioned.

Moscow. Untraced. 'Clock arrangements for Moscow' mentioned in letter from Grubb to Gill 20 January, 1886.

Rome. Untraced

Pekin
Small Equatorials for Peking.
Reference
Engineering **46** 571.

Naples. Untraced
Aci Reale (Sicily: Catania?)
Turin. Untraced
Tenerife. Untraced

Transit instrument of 46-in focal length, before 1836
In T Grubb's Private Observatory, Dublin, Ireland.
Reference
Grubb T 1836 *Mon. Not. R. Astron. Soc.* **3** 177

Spectro-heliograph, Madrid, Spain. Presumably with coelostat (before 1903
Reference
1926 *Grubb–Parsons Publication No. 4*

C.2   Domes (not Mentioned with Telescopes)

15-ft dome for Wind Tower, Royal Obsy Cape, South Africa, 1882.
  With gutter having lion-head outlets! Mentioned in Grubb-Gill correspondence. Tower demolished 1966. Dome sold to an amateur.

18-ft dome and dodecagonal iron observatory, Royal Obsy Cape, South Africa, 1886
Mentioned in Grubb-Gill correspondence, with drawings etc. Extant, 1997. Was built for a Repsold heliometer. Has openable sides to allow air circulation. Now used for a 49 cm reflector.

20-ft Gottingen, Germany, Royal Observatory
Reference
1888 *Engineering* **46** 571

38-ft turret Edinburgh, Scotland, (Blackford Hill, Royal Observatory)
Reference
Grubb Catalogue 1899

37-ft dome, Calton Hill, Edinburgh, Scotland, ca 1903
Reference
Grubb Catalogue 1903, p 22

Barcelona University Dome. No size given.
Reference
1926 *Grubb–Parsons Publ. No. 4*

C.3   Notes

Besides telescopes and domes, the Grubbs constructed many other instruments. Astronomical accessories included chronographs (a means for noting the precise time at which an event occurred), eyepiece micrometers (devices for measuring small angular distances such as the separation and position angle of double stars), spectroscopes, and clocks.

A 6-prism spectroscope made for Huggins is in the Whipple Museum of the History of Science, Cambridge (Burnett & Morrison-Low, (1989).

A 6-prism spectroscope of a different pattern to the above is in the National Museum of American History, Smithsonian, Washington. It was used by C A Young at Princeton.

The Royal Dublin Society possesses a 3-prism laboratory spectroscope.

Miscellaneous instruments, other than the magnetic equipment mentioned in Chapter 1, included base-line measures for surveying, microscopes, photographic lenses and a special heavy-duty precision balance from Thomas Grubb's time, now in the chemistry department of Trinity College, Dublin. The Museum of the History of Science in Oxford has a Thomas Grubb microscope.

Military equipment, about which little is known, included periscopes for submarines and, probably, gunsights and rangefinders.

A listing of Grubb instruments can be found in Mollan (1995).

The Grubb-Gill correspondence is in the SAAO archives, Cape Town.
The Grubb-Innes correspondence is in the CSIR archives, Pretoria.

Bibliography

Airy G B 1838, 1839, 1840 *Report of the Astronomer Royal to the Board of Visitors* 1839, 1840, 1841

—— 1847 *Greenwich Observations 1845*

Ambronn L 1899 *Handbuch der Astronomischen Instrumentenkunde* vol 2 (Berlin: Springer)

André C and Rayet A 1874 *L'Astronomie Practique et les Observatoires en Europe et en Amerique ....* part 2 (Paris: Gauthier-Villars)

André C and Angot A 1877 *L'Astronomie Practique et les Observatoires en Europe et en Amerique ....* part 3 (Paris: Gauthier-Villars)

Anon 1834 *Short Description of the Equatorial Mounting of Mr Cooper's great Achromatic Telescope* Trin. Coll. Camb. Ms. R.614 Dated from astronomical information contained therein

—— 1855 *R. Dublin Soc., Rep. Sci. Mtgs.* p 36

—— 1870 *Astron. Reg.* **8** 215

—— 1876 *Nature* **14** 418

—— 1877 *Astronomical and Meteorological Observations Made During 1874 at the United States Naval Observatory* (Washington, DC: US Government Printing Office)

—— 1878 *Nature* **18** 570

—— 1881 *Nature* **24** 11

—— 1887 *Engineering* **44** 626, 630, 667

—— 1888 *Engineering* **46** 571

—— 1904 *Sci. Trans. R. Dublin Soc.* 2nd ser. **8** 65

—— 1905 *Observatory* **65** 347

—— 1912a *Mon. Not. R. Astron. Soc.* **72** 278

—— 1912b *Dublin University Calendar Special Supplementary Volume* 1912–13 (Dublin: Hodges Figgis)

—— 1912c *Proc. R. Dublin Soc.* **13** 288

—— 1913 *Catalogo Astrophotografico, 1900 Tacubaya Zone* vol 1, Tacubaya, Mexico

—— 1924a *Nature* **113**

—— 1924b *J. Sci. Instrum.* **2** 1

—— 1924c *Engineering* Jul 18, 1924

—— 1925a *Nature* **115** 96

—— 1925b *Nature* **115** 581

—— 1931a *Observatory* **54** 274

—— 1931b *Nature* **128** 609

—— 1949 *Heaton Works J.* **5** 362 (C A Parsons & Co.)

—— 1960 *Quart. J. R. Astron. Soc.* **1** 76

Armagh, 1837, Armagh Observatory ms M442, M1565 (accounts)

Bacon, Sir R 1940 *From 1900 Onward* (London: Hutchinson)

Bailey S I 1931 *The History and Work of Harvard Observatory, 1839 to 1927* (New York: McGraw-Hill)

Ball, Sir R S 1892 *Story of the Heavens* (London: Cassell & Co.)

—— 1899 *Mon. Not. R. Astron. Soc.* **59** 152

Ball W V 1915 *Reminiscences and Letters of Sir Robert Ball* (London: Cassell & Co) p 112

Bartlett W H C 1841 *Report on the Observatories, Etc. of Europe* (ms) in Special Collections Division, Library of the United States Military Academy, West Point

—— 1846 *Trans. Am. Phil. Soc.* new ser. **9** p 191

—— 1854 *Astron. J.* **4** 33

Bennett J C 1990 *Church, State and Astronomy in Ireland, 200 Years of Armagh Observatory* Armagh Observatory, Armagh

Brück M T and Brück H A 1988 *The Peripatetic Astronomer: the Life of Charles Piazzi Smyth* (Bristol: Hilger)

Burnett J E and Morrison-Low A D 1989 *Vulgar and Mechanick, The Scientific Instrument Trade in Ireland 1650-1921* National Museums of Scotland and Royal Dublin Society

Butler C J and Elliott I 1992 *Stellar Photometry—Current Techniques and Future Developments (Proc. IAU Colloquium 136)* (Cambridge: Cambridge University Press)

Campbell W W 1902 *Astrophys. J.* **16** 121

Cauchoix R A 1831 *Astron. Nachr* **9** 350 (Letter to the Editor)

Chance W H S 1937 *Proc. Phys. Soc.* **49** 433

Chapman S S 1932 *Proc. R. Soc.* **135** iv

Christie W H M 1890 *Observatory* **13** 41

—— 1894 *Observatory* **17** 129

Clerke A M 1893 *A History of Astronomy in the Nineteenth Century* 3rd edn (London: Adam and Charles Black)

Compton-Hall R 1983 *Submarine Boats: the Beginnings of Underwater Warfare* (London: Conway Maritime Press)

CSIR: Correspondence concerning the Johannesburg 26-inch refractor is located in the Republic Observatory section of the CSIR Archives in Pretoria

Dadaev A N 1972 *Poulkova Observatory* Nauka, Leningrad (Transl. and abr. K Krisciunas) (NASA-Ames)

Danjon A and Couder A 1935 *Lunettes et Télescopes* Éditions de la Revue D'Optique Théorique et Instrumentale, Paris

Dewhirst D W 1982 *J. Hist. Astron.* **13** 119

Dimitroff G Z and Baker J G 1945 *Telescopes and Accessories* (Philadelphia, PA: Blakiston Co)

DNB 1890 *Dictionary of National Biography* **23** 301 (London: Smith Elder)

Doberck W 1884 *Observatory* **7** 283, 329

Dreyer J L E pamphlet *Robinson Memorial Fund* issued Nov 1882, Armagh Observatory

—— 1884 Armagh Observatory ms M88

Dyson F W, Eddington A S and Davidson C 1920 *Phil. Trans. R. Soc.* **220** 291

Ellery R L J 1885 *Observations of the Southern Nebulae made with the Great Melbourne Telescope from 1869 to 1885, Part 1* Government Printer, Melbourne

FitzGerald W G 1896 *Strand Magazine* **12** 369

Forbes G 1916 *David Gill: Man and Astronomer* (London: John Murray)

Foucault J B L 1857 *Rep. British Assoc., Trans. Sections* 6

—— 1859 *Ann. Obs. Imp. de Paris, Res. Astronomiques* **5** 197

Gascoigne S C B 1995 *Hist. Recs. of Austral. Sci.* **10** 223 (Reprinted in Gascoigne S C B 1996 *Quart. J. R. Astron. Soc.* **37** 101)

Gavine D 1982 Astronomy in Scotland 1745–1900 *PhD Thesis* Open University, Milton Keynes

Gill D 1892 *Bull. Com. Int. .... de la Carte du Ciel* vol 1, p 23

—— 1896 *Cape Photographic Durchmusterung* vol 1, p ix

—— 1912 *The Construction of Optical Instruments* (London: The Optical Society) (pamphlet)

—— 1913 *Cape Astrographic Zones* vol I (London: H.M.S.O.)

Glass I S 1989 *Mon. Not. Astron. Soc. Sthn. Africa* **48** 29

—— 1991 *Mon. Not. Astron. Soc. Sthn. Africa* **50** 131

Glazebrook, Sir R 1923 *Dictionary of Applied Physics* **4** (London: Methuen)

Grubb G W 1972 *The Grubbs of Tipperary* (Cork: Mercier Press)

Grubb H 1876 *Rep. British Assoc* 36

—— 1877 *Trans. R. Dublin Soc.* **1** 1

—— 1880 *Proc. R. Dublin Soc.,* **2** 347

—— 1884a *Trans. R. Dublin Soc.* **3** 61

—— 1884b *Nature* **30** 100, 123

—— 1886a *Proc R. Inst. of Great Britain* **11** 413

—— 1886b *Nature* **34** 85

—— 1886c *The Engineer* **42** 21

—— 1887a *Observatory* **10** 253

—— 1887b *Mon. Not. R. Astron. Soc.* **47** 309

—— 1888 *Mon. Not. R. Astron. Soc.* **48** 352

—— 1889 *Nature* **40** 441, 645

—— 1890b *Proc. R. Dublin Soc.* **6** 598

—— 1890a *Trans. R. Dublin Soc* **4** 475

—— 1901 Patent No. 10373

—— 1894a *Proc. R. Inst. of Great Britain* **14** 304

—— 1894b *Knowledge* **17** 98

—— 1895a Letter to Sir Robert Ball, 19 July 1895, Cambridge University Observatory Archives

—— 1895b Ms In R General Astronomy 1891–1895, SAAO archives

—— 1903 *Proc. R. Dublin Soc.* **10** 133

—— 1905 *Proc. R. Dublin Soc.* **11** 34

—— 1908 *Rep. British Assoc.* 605

—— 1912 *Proc. R. Dublin Soc.* **13** 223

—— 1931 Trinity College Dublin Library ms 2314/94, Joly papers

Grubb R B 1989 Letter to I S Glass

Grubb T 1853 *Proc. R. Irish Acad.* **5** 296

—— 1854 *Proc. R. Irish Acad.* **6** 59

—— 1857 *British Assoc. Report* p 195

—— 1858 *J. R. Dublin Soc.* **1** 21

—— 1860 *J. R. Dublin Soc.* **2** 27

—— 1862a *J. R. Dublin Soc.* **3** 85

—— 1862b *Brit. J. Photography* pp 187, 205, 224, 248, 287

—— 1865 *Proc. Inst. Mech. Engrs.* 166 (volumes unnumbered)

—— 1870 *The Great Melbourne Telescope: An Examination of and Reply to the Official Reports from Melbourne Respecting the Instrument, Its erection at Melbourne, &c., &c.* Privately Printed

Hart J *et al* 1996 *Publ. Astron. Soc. Pacific* **108** 220

Heid: Ms Heidelberg.Hs.3695 in Universitätsbibliotek Heidelberg. Incoming letters E, outgoing D2

Hers J 1987 *Mon. Not. Astron. Soc. Sthn. Africa* **46** 39, 75

Hogg A R 1958 *Austral. J. Sci.* **21** 2

Holden E S 1911 *Biographical Memoirs* National Academy of Sciences, Washington, DC, USA

Hoskin M 1982 *J. Hist. Astron.* **13** 146

Hyde W L 1987 *Proc. Astron. Soc. Austral.* **7** 227

Jones D H P 1988 in *Mapping the Sky* ed S Debarbat *et al* (Dordrecht: Kluwer) p 33

King H C 1955 *The History of the Telescope* (High Wycombe: Charles Griffin & Co Ltd) (reissued 1979 New York: Dover)

Knobel E B 1887 *The Observatory* **10** 210 (and following reports by Common, Christie and Gill)

Kochar R K 1990 *Indian Inst. Astrophys. Newsletter* **5** 6

Langley S P 1900 *Ann. Astrophys. Obsy. of the Smithsonian Institution* **1** 45

Larmor J 1907a (ed) *Memoir and Scientific Correspondence of the late Sir G G Stokes* vol 2, p 92

—— 1907b *ibid* vol 1, p 205

—— 1907c *ibid* vol 1, p 346

—— 1907d *ibid* vol 2, p 90

—— 1907e *ibid* vol 1, p 409

—— 1907f *ibid* vol 2, p 193

Le Sueur A 1870 *Proc. R. Soc* **18** 216

Lindsay, Lord and Gill, David jr 1873 *Mon. Not. R. Astron. Soc.* **34** 35

Lloyd H 1842 *Account of the Magnetical Observatory of Dublin, and of the Instruments and Mathods of Observations Employed There* (Dublin: Dublin University Press)

Loewy M 1884 *Nature* **30** 4, 52

Lyons F S L 1971 *Ireland Since the Famine* (London: Weidenfeld & Nicolson)

Lummer O 1900 *Contributions to Photographic Optics* (transl. and augm. by S P Thompson) (London: Macmillan)

Mantois M 1894 *Observatory* **17** 323

Manville G E 1964 Letter dated 10 November to Miss May Grubb

—— 1971 *Two Fathers and Two Sons* (Newcastle Upon Tyne: Reyrolle Parsons Group)

Mason T H 1944 *Dublin Historical Record* **6** 133

Mollan R C 1995 *Irish National Inventory of Historic Scientific Instruments* (Dublin: Samton Ltd)

Moore P 1967 *Armagh Observatory 1790–1967* (Armagh Observatory)

Naegamvala K D 1888 *Observatory* **11** 438

Newcomb S 1875 *Newcomb Papers* Library of Congress, Washington, DC

—— 1884 *Report to the Secretary of the Navy on Recent Improvements in Astronomical Instruments* (Washington, DC: US Government Printing Office)

—— 1903 *Reminiscences of an Astronomer* (London: Harper & Brothers)

Nichol J P 1857 *A Cyclopaedia of the Physical Sciences* (London: Richard Griffin and Co.)

O'Hora N J P 1988 *Mapping the Sky* ed S Debarbat *et al* (Dordrecht: Kluwer) p 135

Oxmantown, Lord 1840 *Phil. Trans. R. Soc.* p 503

Perdrix J 1992 *Austral. J. Astron.* **4** 149

Pershey E J 1984 *Sky & Telescope* **67** 309

Poggendorff J C 1863 *Biographisch-Literarisches Handwörterbuch* (Leipzig: Barth)

Pritchard A 1897 *Charles Pritchard: Memoirs of his Life* (London: Seeley & Co.)

Pritchard C 1874 *Astron. Reg.* **12** 4

Ritchey G W 1905 *Smithsonian Contributions to Knowledge* part of **34** 47

RGO: Royal Greenwich Observatory Archives, Cambridge University Library

Robbins F 1923 *Nature* **112** 104

Robinson T R 1840 *Proc. R. Irish Acad.* **2** 2

—— 1862 Unsigned Article 'Astronomical Instruments and Glass for Optical Purposes' *Mallett's Mechanics Journal* (Date Unknown. In a volume of cuttings. Armagh Observatory Archives.)

—— 1878 *Proc. R. Soc.* **169** 777

Robinson T R and Grubb T 1869 *Phil. Trans. R. Soc.* **159** 127

ROE: Royal Observatory Edinburgh archival collections

Ronan C A 1967 *Their Majesties' Astronomers* (London: Bodley Head) p 184

SAAO: Gill Correspondence, SAAO Archives. 'R Instruments Grubb 1879–1890'; 'R General Astronomy 1891–1895'; 'McClean Telescope Correspondence' 6 volumes

Sabine, Sir E 1869 *Proc. R. Soc.* **18** 105

Scott J D 1962 *Vickers, A History* (London: Weidenfeld & Nicolson)

Shajn G 1926 *Bull. Obs. Centrale de Russie à Poulkovo* **10** 450

—— 1944 *Observatory* **65** 250

Shane: Mary Lea Shane Archives, Lick Observatory

Smiles S 1884 *Men of Invention and Industry* (London: Murray)

STC: *Correspondence of the Southern Telescope Committee (later: Correspondence Concerning the Great Melbourne Telescope)* 1871 (In 3 parts. London, Printed for private circulation only, by order of the Council of the Royal Society)

Stokes: Add.ms.7656 George Gabriel Stokes papers, Cambridge University Library

Stone R P S *Sky and Telescope* **58** 307

Stoney G J and Ball R S 1884 Armagh Observatory ms M88

Struve F G W 1826 *Mem. R. Astron. Soc.* **2** 93

Struve O 1958 *Sky & Telescope* 17 272

Talbot F A 1915 *Submarines, their mechanism and operation* (London: Heinemann)

Taylor H D 1895 Letter to Gill dated 27 Nov 1895 *R. General Astronomy 1891–1895* SAAO archives

Tobin W 1987 *Vistas in Astron.* **30** 153

Thackeray D 1972 *The Radcliffe Observatory 1772–1972* Trustees of Dr John Radcliffe, London

von Rohr M 1904 *Die Bilderzeugung in Optischen Instrumenten* (Berlin: Springer)

Wadsworth F L O 1894 *Astron. Astrophys.* **13** 265

Warner B 1975 *Sky and Telescope* **50** 370

—— 1979 *Astronomers at the Royal Observatory, Cape of Good Hope* Balkema, Cape Town

—— 1982 *Quart. J. R. Astron. Soc.* **23** 505

Warner D J 1968 *Alvan Clark and Sons, Artists in Optics* (Washington: Smithsonian)

Wayman P A 1988 *Technology Ireland* September, p 53

Wilson W E 1900 *Astronomical and Physical Researches Made at Mr Wilson's Observatory, Daramona, Westmeath* Privately printed

Wilson W P *et al* 1870 *Sixth Report of the Board of Visitors to the Observatory* Govt. Printer, Melbourne

Wolf M 1900 *Vierteljahrschrift d. Astron. Gesell* **35** 121

—— 1901 *Vierteljahrschrift d. Astron. Gesell* **36** 106

Young C 1931 *Mon. Not. R. Astron. Soc.* **92** 252

Index